New Zealand Society of Animal Production Conference (NZSAP 2020)

Proceedings of the New Zealand Society of Animal Production
Volume 80

Online
2 July 2020

ISBN: 978-1-7138-3230-0

Printed from e-media with permission by:

Curran Associates, Inc.
57 Morehouse Lane
Red Hook, NY 12571

CURRAN ASSOCIATES INC. proceedings .com

Some format issues inherent in the e-media version may also appear in this print version.

Printed with permission by Curran Associates, Inc. (2021)

For permission requests, please contact New Zealand Society of Animal Production (Inc.) (NZSAP) at the address below.

New Zealand Society of Animal Production (Inc.) (NZSAP)
c/o Kate Crookston
PO Box 955
Cambridge, New Zealand

www.nzsap.org.nz

Additional copies of this publication are available from:

Curran Associates, Inc.
57 Morehouse Lane
Red Hook, NY 12571 USA
Phone: 845-758-0400
Fax: 845-758-2633
Email: curran@proceedings.com
Web: www.proceedings.com

TABLE OF CONTENTS

Miniature horses in New Zealand: demographics and feeding management

SY Goh[a*], EK Gee[a], DG Thomas[b], PJ Back[ab] and CW Rogers[ab]

[a]*School of Veterinary Science, Massey University, Private Bag 11-222, 4442, Palmerston North, New Zealand;*
[b]*School of Agriculture and Environment, Massey University, Private Bag 11-222, 4442, Palmerston North, New Zealand*

**Corresponding author:* Email: s.y.goh@massey.ac.nz

Abstract

An online survey on demographics and feeding management of Miniature horses in New Zealand was conducted using the Qualtrics Survey Software. There were 232 valid responses from respondents who kept 1183 Miniature horses, representing ~ ⅓rd of the New Zealand Miniature horse population. Miniature horses were kept for leisure and companionship (56%), competition (35%) and for breeding (7%). The majority (79%) of Miniature horses were kept at pasture on low (< 1000 kg DM/ha) to moderate (~ 2000 kg DM/ha) pasture masses across seasons. Pasture access was more commonly restricted by respondents during spring (60%), summer (60%), and autumn (55%) than in winter (43%). Most respondents (87%) practiced pasture-restriction strategies such as strip grazing, use of a paddock with little grass, and stabling/yarding. Respondents indicated the mode daily number of hours of stabling was 7-12 hours (n=57/195, 29%). The median stocking density was 10 horses/ha, (~1100 kg live weight/ha). The stocking density appeared high, however, on a live weight basis, it was comparable to the reported values in other classes of equine livestock.

Keywords: horse, Miniature horse; demographics; feeding; pasture

Introduction

The Miniature horse is phenotypically classified by its small stature (Petersen et al. 2013). The genetic basis of the New Zealand Miniature horses is the American Miniature horse, and in some cases Shetland and Timor ponies (Rogers et al. 2006). Miniature horses present a unique management challenge due to their small body size and a thrifty phenotype. These small equines can develop obesity, insulin resistance (equine metabolic syndrome, EMS) and laminitis; excess body weight developed as a result of ration mis-estimation, overfeeding or a lack of knowledge on the total amount of feed required (Scherer-Hoock et al. 2011).

Based on published New Zealand pasture energy content of 10 MJ DE/kg DM, an adult Miniature horse weighing 110 kg would only require 2 kg (or 1.8% of body weight) of pasture DM per day to meet maintenance energy requirement of 20.2 MJ [DE_m= 5.9 + 0.13 BW] (Hoskin & Gee 2004; National Research Council (U.S.) Committee 2007). However, little is known about the actual voluntary feed intake (VFI) of Miniature horses when fed *ad libitum*. Non-obese Welsh Mountain ponies were able to consume a complete, commercially manufactured chaff-based diet, comparable in nutrient profile to moderate quality hay, at 3.5 ± 0.1% (winter) or 4.6 ± 0.3% (summer) of body weight as dry matter when fed *ad libitum*, which was above maintenance requirements (Dugdale et al. 2010; 2011). As a result, their body weight increased rapidly (0.6-0.9 kg/day) (Dugdale et al. 2011). Therefore, feed intake must be restricted in ponies or small-sized horses to prevent increased body weight.

Restricting feed intake can be achieved by limiting the amount of time horses are kept on pasture (Glunk et al. 2013), or selective grazing on poor-quality pasture (Fleurance et al. 2009). Although pony breeds appear to have a better utilisation of less-nutritious feed (Cuddeford et al. 1995), with restriction of feed intake, suitable supplementary feeding and/or supplements may be required to ensure that their nutritional requirements are met.

In New Zealand, Miniature horses represent a fast-growing sector of the equine industry. Recent estimates suggest there are 3000 registered Miniature horses in New Zealand, making up ~3% of the entire horse population in New Zealand, or ~7% of horses involved in other equestrian, leisure or recreational activities (Rogers et al. 2017). Only one survey on New Zealand Miniature horses (a preliminary study on congenital and reproductive disorders) has been carried out (Rogers et al. 2006). At present the demographics and feeding management of New Zealand Miniature horses have not been well described. Thus, the aim of this study is to describe the demographics and feeding management of Miniature horses in New Zealand. The information gathered will be a useful reference in identifying the unique challenges in feeding and management of Miniature horses.

Materials and methods

An online survey was created using the Qualtrics Survey Software (https://massey.qualtrics.com/) and was published between 4th July 2019 and 26th November 2019. Recruitment of respondents was achieved via the snowball sampling technique. The link to the survey was published on social media pages of Miniature horse special-interest and breeder groups within New Zealand. In addition, key industry participants known to the authors were involved in disseminating the link of the survey via social media.

The survey consisted of eighty-five succinctly crafted questions, which were a combination of closed and open-text responses. The questions addressed four main subject areas; demographics, feeding, management practices and health care practices for Miniature horses in New Zealand. The survey was approved by the Massey University

Human Ethics committee as low risk (notification number: 4000021167).

The dataset from the survey was subsequently coded and cleaned for analysis within Microsoft Excel. Continuous data were examined for normality using histograms and the Shapiro-Wilk test. If data were non-parametric, the median, 1st quartile, 3rd quartile or mode frequency of the data series were reported. Differences between groups for non-parametric data were examined using Kruskal-Wallis test one-way analysis of variance, significant differences between the groups were further tested using a pairwise Mann-Whitney test. Differences in distribution between groups were tested using the Chi-square test. All statistical tests were performed, and significance was accepted at $P < 0.05$ using the SPSS Statistics 26.0 (IBM Corp., Armonk, N.Y., USA).

Results

Demographics

Of the 247 survey attempts, 232 resulted in valid responses, of which 153 had a 100% question completion rate and a further 41 responses had 97-99% question completion rate (n=194/232). Most respondents were female (n=226/232, 97%) aged 35-64 years (n=152/232, 66%), with the highest number of respondents in the 45-54 age bracket (n=65). Most Miniature horse owners had at least five years' experience of keeping Miniature horses (n=176/232, 76%), and kept their Miniature horses on a lifestyle block: land area ~4 hectares (ha) or ~10 acres (n=172, 74%). Responses were obtained from all regions in New Zealand: Canterbury (n=37), Waikato (n=29), Taranaki (n=28), Auckland (n=28), Manawatu-Whanganui (n=23), Northland (n=18), Wellington (n=15), Bay of Plenty (n=13), Hawke's Bay (n=11), Otago (n=9), Nelson-Marlborough (n=6), Tasman (n=6), West Coast (n=3), Southland (n=3) and Wairarapa (n=3).

Most respondents (n=164/232, 71%) registered their Miniature horses (n=1137) with the New Zealand Miniature Horse Association (NZMHA) registry. As Miniature horses can be registered with multiple breed registries or

Table 1 Data from the survey on demographics and feeding management of Miniature horses in New Zealand: the number of Miniature horses per respondent, the number of Miniature horses according to age, and the stocking density of Miniature horses, categorized according to primary use.

Primary purpose of Miniature horse ownership	Leisure and companionship	Competition	Breeding *	Total	P
Number of responders (%)	130 (56%)	82 (35%)	17 (7%)	232[§] (100%)	-
Total number of Miniature horses	459 (data from 126 respondents)	589 (data from 79 respondents)	135 (data from 13 respondents)	1183 (data from 218 respondents)	-
Median(IQR) Miniature horses per respondent	2 (1-4)[b] (data from 126 respondents)	6 (3-11)[a] (data from 79 respondents)	10 (4-16)[a] (data from 13 respondents)	3 (2-7) (data from 218 respondents)	P <0.05
Age distribution of Miniature horses (number of horses, n)	<3 yrs (n=28) 3-5 yrs (n=57) 6-15 yrs (n=280) >15 yrs (n=94)	<3 yrs (n=117) 3-5 yrs (n=120) 6-15 yrs (n=267) >15 yrs (n=85)	6-12 yrs (n=30) 13-15 yrs (n=81) >15 yrs (n=24)	1183 (data from 218 respondents)	P <0.05
Median (IQR) stocking density or the number of Miniature horses per hectare, ha	10 (5-17)[a]	13 (7-22)[b]	12 (4-13)[a]	10 (5-20)	P<0.05
Number of hours, h of stabling (number of respondents, n)	0 h (n=29) 1-6 h (n=17) 7-12 h (n=30) 13-18 h (n=14) 19-24 h (n=22) (data from 112 respondents)	0 h (n=13) 1-6 h (n=18) 7-12 h (n=24) 13-18 h (n=8) 19-24 h (n=10) (data from 73 respondents)	0 h (n=6) 1-6 h (n=1) 7-12 h (n=2) 13-18 h (n=0) 19-24 h (n=0) (data from 9 respondents)	0 h (n=48) 1-6 h (n=36) 7-12 h (n=57^) 13-18 h (n=22) 19-24 h (n=32) (data from 195 respondents)	ns
Subset data: number of hours, h of stabling for the purpose of restricting pasture access (number of respondents, n)	0 h (n=3) 1-6 h (n=10) 7-12 h (n=23) 13-18 h (n=11) 19-24 h (n=8) (data from 55/112 respondents)	0 h (n=0) 1-6 h (n=7) 7-12 h (n=16) 13-18 h (n=6) 19-24 h (n=4) (data from 33/73 respondents)	0 h (n=1) 1-6 h (n=1) 7-12 h (n=2) 13-18 h (n=0) 19-24 h (n=0) (data from 4/9 respondents)	0 h (n=4) 1-6 h (n=18) 7-12 h (n=42^) 13-18 h (n=17) 19-24 h (n=12) (data from 93/195 respondents)	

[*] refers to broodmares only.

[§] includes data from three respondents with unknown primary purpose of Miniature horse ownership

[^] includes data from one respondent with unknown primary purpose of Miniature horse ownership

[a,b] denotes significant difference within row ($p<0.05$) using the Mann-Whitney pairwise comparison between three different data series.

societies, 131 respondents indicated that their horses had more than one registration. There were 23% of respondents (n=54/232) who did not register their horses with any breed society.

Respondents were provided with multiple options to describe the reasons for keeping Miniature horses: as pets (n=143), for showing (n=135), as a companion for other horses (n=81), for leisure driving (n=71), for breeding (n=64), for competitive driving (n=57), to be ridden by children (n=41), and as a therapy horse (n=25). Miniature horses were grouped into three categories i.e., leisure and companionship, competition, and breeding, according to owner's primary purpose of horse-keeping (Table 1). Some respondents who used Miniature horses primarily for competition (45%, n=37/82) or leisure and companionship (8%, n=11/130), were also involved in breeding Miniature horses.

A total of 1183 Miniature horses were kept by 218 respondents (Table 1). Over half of the Miniature horses were between 6-15 years of age (n=658, 56%), with the remainder evenly divided between the other age categories listed in Table 1. Few respondents (n=81/223, 36%) kept Miniature horses exclusively, with the majority (n=134/223, 60%) also kept horses of other breeds. The overall median number of Miniature horses kept per respondent was 3 (IQR 2-7).

Feeding and management practices

The overall median stocking density of Miniature horses was 10 (IQR 5-20) horses per hectare. The stocking density differed according to the horse's primary uses (Table 1). The majority (n=919/1119, 82%) of Miniature horses were kept at pasture; few horses had no, or limited access to pasture (n=153/1119, 14%) (Table 2). In terms of percentages, Miniature horses used for breeding (71%) were more likely to be kept exclusively at pasture across seasons, compared with horses used for leisure (28%) and competition (37%) (Table 2). The majority (n=815/1036, 79%) of Miniature horses were kept on low (< 1000 kg DM/ha) to moderate (~ 2000 kg DM/ha) pasture masses across seasons (Table 3).

Pasture access was more commonly restricted during spring (n=125/208, 60% of respondents, n=625/1119 horses, 56%), summer (n=125/208, 60% of respondents, n=632/1119 horses, 56%), and autumn (n=115/208, 55% of respondents, n=567/1119 horses, 51%) compared to winter (n=89/208, 43% of respondents, n=403/1119 horses, 36%). Approximately half (n=105/208, 50%) of the respondents kept their Miniature horses (n=656/1119, 59%) exclusively at pasture during winter.

The majority (n=173/198, 87%) of respondents practiced pasture-restriction strategies such as strip grazing (n=118), the temporary use of a paddock with little grass (n=99), confinement for part of a day in a stable or yard (n=94), turning out horses to graze in the early morning only (n=42), or fitting a grazing muzzle (n=24). Another pasture restriction strategy cited by respondents (n=15) was provision of a track system (where fencing is placed around the centre of the paddock in order that the horse(s) walk on the outside of the fences during grazing). Strategies

Table 2 Data from the survey on demographics and feeding management of Miniature horses in New Zealand: total number of Miniature horses managed with different types of pasture management strategies across seasons, subcategorised according to primary use of Miniature horses.

Pasture-management strategies	Total number of respondents (N)	Primary use of Miniature horses			Total
		Leisure and companionship	Competition	Breeding	
	(Data from 208 respondents)	(Data from 445 horses)	(Data from 580 horses)	(Data from 94 horses)	(Data from 1119 horses)
		Number of horses, n (%)	Number of horses, n (%)	Number of horses, n (%)	Number of horses, n (%)
Always on pasture all seasons	59	124 (28%)	212 (37%)	67 (71%)	403 (36%)
Have variable access to pasture in spring, summer and autumn, but always on pasture in winter	45	86 (19%)	165 (28%)	0 (0)	251 (22%)
Mostly on pasture all seasons	37	92 (21%)	117 (20%)	22 (23%)	231 (21%)
Either mostly on pasture or mostly stabled/ yarded all seasons	12	22 (5%)	12 (2%)	0 (0)	34 (3%)
Mostly stabled/yarded all seasons	33	51 (11%)	58 (10%)	5 (5%)	114 (10%)
Always stabled/yarded all seasons	8	37 (8%)	2 (0.3%)	0 (0)	39 (3%)
Other strategies	14	33 (7%)	14 (2%)	0 (0)	47 (4%)
Total	208	445 (~100%)	580 (~100%)	94 (~100%)	1119 (~100%)
Unknown strategies	24	-	-	-	64
Grand total	232	-	-	-	1183

Table 3 Data from the survey on demographics and feeding management of Miniature horses in New Zealand: seasonal pasture mass or seasonal pasture availability for three groups of Miniature horses.

Seasonal pasture mass or seasonal pasture availability				Total number of respondents (N)	Primary use of Miniature horses			
Spring	Summer	Autumn	Winter	(Data from 196 respondents)	Leisure and companionship (Data from 381 horses) Number of horses, n (%)	Competition (Data from 555 horses) Number of horses, n (%)	Breeding (Data from 100 horses) Number of horses, n (%)	Total (Data from 1036 horses) Number of horses, n (%)
Low	Low	Low	Low	35	49 (13%)	65 (12%)	0 (0)	114 (11%)
Moderate	Moderate	Moderate	Moderate	20	20 (5%)	82 (15%)	18 (18%)	120 (12%)
Mostly low	Mostly low	Mostly low	Mostly low	35	101 (27%)	81 (15%)	13 (13%)	195 (19%)
Mostly moderate	Mostly moderate	Mostly moderate	Mostly moderate	22	55 (14%)	99 (18%)	16 (16%)	170 (16%)
Low or moderate	Low or moderate	Low or moderate	Low or moderate	19	70 (18%)	33 (6%)	5 (5%)	108 (10%)
Low or moderate	Low or moderate	Low or moderate	High	11	16 (4%)	44 (8%)	0 (0)	60 (6%)
High	Low or moderate	Low or moderate	Low or moderate	5	3 (0.8%)	8 (1%)	4 (4%)	15 (1%)
Low or moderate	Low or moderate	High	Low or moderate	3	2 (0.5%)	11 (2%)	0 (0)	13 (1%)
Low	No pasture (barren) or low	Moderate	Low or moderate	3	1 (0.3%)	19 (3%)	0 (0)	20 (2%)
Other pasture masses combination across seasons				19	19 (5%)	85 (15%)	4 (4%)	108 (10%)
Incomplete information on seasonal pasture masses, respondents kept their horses on pasture at certain seasons only (their horses were not kept on pasture all seasons)				24	45 (12%)	28 (5%)	40 (40%)	113 (11%)
Total				196	381 (~100%)	555 (~100%)	100 (~100%)	1036 (~100%)
Unknown pasture availability				36	-	-	-	147
Grand total				232	-	-	-	1183

used for pasture maintenance included picking up horse manure from pasture (n=138/198, 70%), rotational grazing (n=125/198, 63%) or mixed grazing (n=92/198, 46%), harrowing pasture (n=77/198, 39%) or topping or mowing pasture (n=57/198, 29%).

Respondents that stabled their horses used varying hours of confinement per day (1-6 hours, 7-12 hours, 13-18 hours and 19-24 hours), with the highest number of respondents stabling their Miniature horses for 7-12 hours/day (n=57/195, 29%) (Table 1).

In addition to pasture, most owners provided the horses with additional feed (n=194/232, 84%). Additional feedstuffs were hay (n=180), chaff (n=130), premixed concentrates (n=117), fermented forages (n=51), and other types of feed (n=33) such as oats, copra, soy, molasses, sugar beet pulp. Respondents (n=131) would offer up to six different types of supplements to their Miniature horses, however, respondents (n=38, 37) usually offered either one or two different types of supplements. The most common categories of supplements reportedly fed were vitamin and mineral supplements (n=114) and hoof and coat supplements (n=55).

Most respondents did not objectively assess their horse's weight using either a weighbridge (n=198/213, 93%) or a weight tape (n=170/214, 79%). A few respondents (n=15/213, 7%) used the weighbridge at least once annually to monitor their Miniature horses' weight, and almost one-fifth of respondents (n=44/214, 21%) used a weight tape once or twice annually to monitor their Miniature horses' weight. Half (n=102/202, 50%) of the respondents indicated they observed body condition of their horses frequently but may not have used a formal quantification process.

Discussion

The respondents to this survey were mostly women, which is in agreement with other studies that have shown they tend to be over-represented in both equestrian sport and breeding (Fernandes et al. 2014; Agar et al. 2016; Burbage

& Cameron 2018). Additionally, most respondents were semi-experienced, or experienced, horse owners who have also kept horses of other breeds. This was similar to the profile described in other surveys, where the majority of the survey respondents and their families had many years of experience working with horses in general (Fernandes et al. 2014; Agar et al. 2016). The highest number of responses was gathered from respondents residing in the upper North Island (Waikato and Auckland), in the Central-West of the North Island (Taranaki), and in Central-East of the South Island (Canterbury). The greater number of responses received from these regions reflected the estimates of the distribution and density of horses in New Zealand (Rosanowski et al. 2012; Bolwell et al. 2017).

The majority (97%) of Miniature horses were kept at pasture (Table 2), with owners generally utilising some form of confinement as a method to restrict pasture access. Pasture restriction is seen as necessary; pony breeds had been reported to consume between 2.6 to 4.9% of BW as DM/day (Ralston et al. 1979; Dugdale et al. 2011), which is greater than their nutritional requirements. Assuming a moderate pasture-energy content (10 MJ DE/Kg DM), a typical Miniature horse requiring only 20.2 MJ of digestible energy for maintenance could consume their ration requirement of ~2 kg DM of pasture (~1.8% of BW as DM/day) in as little as six hours of grazing (Dugdale et al. 2011).

From the survey results, respondents have incorporated a variety of ingredients as supplementary feeds into the diet of their Miniature horses. Data on quantities fed were not collected, and the assumption from the answers was that supplementary feeds were provided in a manner like that reported by Fernandes et al. (2014) where concentrates and premixes were provided at low levels to "balance the ration" or to provide additional energy. Approximately half the respondents provided mineral or vitamin supplements to their Miniature horses. This level was similar to a report for sport horses in New Zealand (Verhaar et al. 2014). Data on quantities of minerals supplements provided were not collected; nevertheless, care must be taken by horse owners to avoid excess mineral supplementation. An online survey on the mineral supplementation for horses reported that the calculated intake of minerals was higher than the intake recommended by the National Research Council (NRC) (Grimwood et al. 2016)

The median stocking density for Miniature horses from this study was ten (IQR 5-20) horses per hectare, with the assumption of a mature weight of 110 kg ± 21 kg (Catalano et al. 2019) equating to approximately 1100 kg LWT/ha. This value is similar to the typical stocking density of full-sized horses (~500 kg each): ~1000 kg LWT/ha or ~2 horses per hectare, ha (or 0.8 horses per acre) (Singer et al. 2001; Cohen et al. 2005; Rogers et al. 2007; Bengtsson et al. 2018). As the majority of horses were kept on pasture with low (< 1000 kg DM/ha) to moderate (~2000 kg DM/ha) pasture masses, pasture growth of 20 kg DM/ha/day would meet maintenance requirement for ten Miniature horses (2 kg DM/horse) kept on a hectare of land (Baars' et al. 1990).

A high proportion of respondents from this survey indicated that they have undertaken mixed grazing as a pasture-management practice. This is not surprising as Thoroughbred and Standardbred breeding farms in New Zealand commonly utilise mixed-grazing practice with cattle and/or sheep (Bolwell et al. 2015). Most likely, Miniature horses were mixed-grazed with small-sized ruminants and other livestock. Mixed grazing of horses with sheep or cattle has recently been reported to have benefits in controlling strongylosis in horses (Eysker et al. 1986; Forteau et al. 2019).

Although weight monitoring was regularly practiced, very few Miniature horse owners used weight scales to monitor their horses' body weight; body condition scoring and weight tape were used more frequently, similar to data reported by Murray et al. (2015). Instead, respondents preferred a non-structured, daily "visual appraisal" to gauge their Miniature horses' body condition or described estimating their Miniature horses' body weight by experience. Both methods lack the precision of the formal body condition scoring. However, even on commercial farms there is often limited use of formal body condition scoring or weighing to monitor growth and body weight. The lack of body weight monitoring may be a risk factor for obesity, over-conditioning or severe clinical diseases such as equine metabolic syndrome (EMS) and laminitis.

There are several limitations with online surveys, one of the main ones being the non-response bias and the social-desirable bias from this survey. Respondents were gathered using the snowball sampling technique, a reflection of the "convenience sampling" technique where samples are drawn from a pool that is close at hand. As the responses were mostly gathered from respondents actively involved in social media pages for Miniature horses, there is a small risk that the data gathered in this survey are skewed towards respondents who are cognizant of the suitable/appropriate management practices or strategies for their Miniature horses. However, this sampling methodology provided an efficient method of targeting the population of owners/keepers of Miniature horses in a timely and cost-effective manner.

Across the non-commercial equine sector there is limited documentation of feeding and management practises. This lack of information makes it difficult for regional councils to understand land management use and for Veterinarians and industry consultants to provide targeted advice on feeding and management practices. The information gathered from this survey provides a useful reference point for further investigations on the inter-relationship between feeding management practices and the body weight of Miniature horses in New Zealand.

Acknowledgements

The authors would like to thank Ms Emma Kimberley, Massey University Equine Veterinary Clinic for her active support in research on Miniature horses and for sharing the link to the survey via the Miniature horse webpages on social media.

References

Agar C, Gemmill R, Hollands T, Freeman SL 2016. The use of nutritional supplements in dressage and eventing horses. Veterinary Record Open 3: e000154.

Baars' JA, Radcliffe JE, Rollo MD. Climatic change effects on seasonal patterns of pasture production in New Zealand. Proceedings of the New Zealand Grassland Association, 1990. 43-46.

Bengtsson J, Rogers CW, Back PJ, Emanuelson U, Roca J, Gee EK, Bolwell CF 2018. Characteristics of the grazing and farm management of broodmares on commercial Thoroughbred stud farms during spring. New Zealand Journal of Animal Science and Production 78: 88-91.

Bolwell CF, Rogers CW, Gee EK, Rosanowski SM 2017. Commercial equine production in New Zealand. 3. The racing and sport industries. Animal Production Science.

Bolwell CF, Rosanowski SM, Scott I, Sells PD, Rogers CW 2015. Questionnaire study on parasite control practices on Thoroughbred and Standardbred breeding farms in New Zealand. Veterinary Parasitology 209: 62-69.

Burbage J, Cameron LJ 2018. An investigation of bra concerns and barriers to participation in horse riding. Comparative Exercise Physiology 14: 1-9.

Catalano DN, Coleman RJ, Hathaway MR, Neu AE, Wagner EL, Tyler PJ, Mccue ME, Martinson KL 2019. Estimation of actual and ideal bodyweight using morphometric measurements of Miniature, saddle-type, and Thoroughbred horses. Journal of Equine Veterinary Science 78: 117-122.

Cohen ND, O'conor MS, Chaffin MK, Martens RJ 2005. Farm characteristics and management practices associated with development of Rhodococcus equi pneumonia in foals. Journal of the American Veterinary Medical Association 226: 404-413.

Cuddeford D, Pearson RA, Archibald RF, Muirhead RH 1995. Digestibility and gastro-intestinal transit time of diets containing different proportions of alfalfa and oat straw given to Thoroughbreds, Shetland ponies, Highland ponies and donkeys. Animal Science 61: 407-417.

Dugdale AH, Curtis GC, Cripps PJ, Harris PA, Argo CM 2011. Effects of season and body condition on appetite, body mass and body composition in ad libitum fed pony mares. The Veterinary Journal 190: 329-337.

Dugdale AHA, Curtis GC, Cripps P, Harris PA, Argo CM 2010. Effect of dietary restriction on body condition, composition and welfare of overweight and obese pony mares. Equine Veterinary Journal 42: 600-610.

Eysker M, Jansen J, Mirck MH 1986. Control of strongylosis in horses by alternate grazing of horses and sheep and some other aspects of the epidemiology of strongylidae infections. Veterinary Parasitology 19: 103-115.

Fernandes KA, Rogers CW, Gee EK, Bolwell CF, Thomas DG 2014. A cross-sectional survey of rider and horse demographics, and the feeding, health and management of Pony Club horses in New Zealand. Proceedings of the New Zealand Society of Animal Production 74: 11-16.

Fleurance G, Fritz H, Duncan P, Gordon IJ, Edouard N, Vial C 2009. Instantaneous intake rate in horses of different body sizes: Influence of sward biomass and fibrousness. Applied Animal Behaviour Science 117: 84-92.

Forteau L, Dumont B, Sallé G, Bigot G, Fleurance G 2019. Horses grazing with cattle have reduced strongyle egg count due to the dilution effect and increased reliance on macrocyclic lactones in mixed farms. Animal 1-7.

Glunk EC, Pratt-Phillips SE, Siciliano PD 2013. Effect of restricted pasture access on pasture dry matter intake rate, dietary energy intake, and fecal pH in horses. Journal of Equine Veterinary Science 33: 421-426.

Grimwood K, Penaluna L-A, Brown H 2016. A preliminary investigation into the mineral intake of horses in the UK. Journal of Equine Veterinary Science 36: 44-48.

Hoskin SO, Gee EK 2004. Feeding value of pastures for horses. New Zealand Veterinary Journal 52: 332-341.

Murray J-A, Bloxham C, Kulifay J, Stevenson A, Roberts J 2015. Equine nutrition: A survey of perceptions and practices of horse owners undertaking a massive open online course in equine nutrition. Journal of Equine Veterinary Science 35: 510-517.

National Research Council (U.S.) Committee 2007. Nutrient requirements of horses [Electronic Resource], Washington, D.C., National Academies Press.

Petersen JL, Mickelson JR, Cothran EG, Andersson LS, Axelsson J, Bailey E, Bannasch D, Binns MM, Borges AS, Brama P, Da Câmara Machado A, Distl O, Felicetti M, Fox-Clipsham L, Graves KT, Guérin G, Haase B, Hasegawa T, Hemmann K, Hill EW, Leeb T, Lindgren G, Lohi H, Lopes MS, Mcgivney BA, Mikko S, Orr N, Penedo MCT, Piercy RJ, Raekallio M, Rieder S, Røed KH, Silvestrelli M, Swinburne J, Tozaki T, Vaudin M, Wade CM, Mccue ME 2013. Genetic diversity in the modern horse illustrated from genome-wide SNP data. Plos One 8: e54997.

Ralston SL, Vandenbroek G, Baile CA 1979. Feed-intake patterns and associated blood-glucose, free fatty-acid and insulin changes in ponies. Journal of Animal Science 49: 838-845.

Rogers CW, Gee EK, Bolwell CF 2017. Horse production. In: Stafford, K (ed.) Livestock Production in New Zealand. 1st Edition. New Zealand: Massey University Press.

Rogers CW, Gee EK, Firth EC 2007. A cross-sectional survey of Thoroughbred stud farm management in the North Island of New Zealand. New Zealand Veterinary Journal 55: 302-307.

Rogers CW, Gee EK, Hangoor E, Firth EC 2006. Preliminary survey of congenital and reproductive disorders in the New Zealand Miniature horse population. Proceedings of the New Zealand Society of Animal Production 66: 274-278.

Rosanowski SM, Cogger N, Rogers CW, Benschop J, Stevenson MA 2012. A description of the demographic characteristics of the New Zealand non-commercial horse population with data collected using a generalised random-tessellation stratified sampling design. Preventive Veterinary Medicine 107: 242-252.

Scherer-Hoock AL, Greene EA, Lennox M, Brown-Douglas C 2011. A comparison of actual and suggested digestible energy intakes of Miniature horses derived from different feeding recommendations. Journal of Equine Veterinary Science 31: 180-184.

Singer JW, Bobsin N, Kluchinski D, Bamka WJ 2001. Equine stocking density effect on soil chemical properties, botanical composition, and species density. Communications in Soil Science and Plant Analysis 32: 2549-2559.

Verhaar N, Rogers CW, Gee EK, Bolwell CF, Rosanowski SM 2014. The feeding practices and estimated workload in a cohort of New Zealand competition horses. Journal of Equine Veterinary Science 34: 1257-1262.

Technical note: A comparison of editing criteria for lying-behaviour data derived from three-dimensional accelerometer devices on grazing dairy cows

SJ Hendriks[a]*, CVC Phyn[b], S-A Turner[b,c], KR Mueller[d], B Kuhn-Sherlock[b], DJ Donaghy[a], JM Huzzey[e] and JR Roche[b,f,g]

[a]School of Agriculture and Environment, Massey University, Palmerston North 4410, New Zealand; [b]DairyNZ Ltd., Hamilton 3240, New Zealand; [c]Current address: Dairy Goat Co-operative, PO Box 1398, Hamilton 3240, New Zealand; [d]School of Veterinary Sciences, Massey University, Palmerston North 4410, New Zealand; [e]California Polytechnic State University, Department of Animal Science, San Luis Obispo, CA 93407; [f]School of Biological Sciences, University of Auckland, Private Bag 92019, Auckland 1142, New Zealand; [g]Current address: Ministry for Primary Industries, Wellington 6140, New Zealand

**Corresponding author:* Email: s.hendriks@massey.ac.nz

Abstract

Shorter, more-frequent lying bouts (LB) could be used to predict calving and as an indicator of animal discomfort and ill-health. In this technical study, we reviewed the literature to describe criteria for removing false short LB, caused by minor movements, from accelerometer data using IceRobotics technology. Using an existing dataset of grazing cows, we compared unedited with edited accelerometer data after applying three different LB thresholds (LB <33 s, ≤2 min, and <4 min were removed) within IceQube and IceTag accelerometers. Daily lying time, LB (no./d) and LB duration were derived from either IceQube or IceTag devices for 146 and 159 multiparous cows, respectively. Very-short LB were more common in IceTag than IceQube data. Applying a shorter LB criterion (<33 s) to the IceQube dataset produced minimal differences between unedited (8.8±3.6 no./d; n=64,512 lying records) and edited data (8.3±3.4 no./d; n=60,463). In contrast, we observed large differences between unedited (307±293 no./d; n=2,305,693) and edited data (8.8±4.1 no./d; n=66,139) when a longer LB criterion (≤2 min) was applied to the IceTag dataset. Removing short LB that are unlikely to represent true behaviour will improve the interpretation of lying behaviour data; however, prospective studies are needed to determine the most-suitable LB criterion.

Keywords: lying behaviour; grazing cows; accelerometer

Introduction

Activity monitoring devices that measure cow behaviour may allow remote and individualised management of animals and improved dairy cow health and welfare. However, it is important that the methodology chosen to edit behaviour data is supported by an appropriate and robust validation study, where a high level of accuracy is reported (Charlton et al. 2017). Several studies indicate that unedited data from IceTag and IceQube accelerometer devices (IceRobotics Ltd., Edinburgh, Scotland) provide accurate records of daily lying time in cattle across a range of systems (Mattachini et al. 2013; McGowan et al. 2007; Ungar et al. 2018), but there is inconsistency in the literature regarding the appropriateness of editing criteria for lying bouts (LB), which are a potentially valuable indicator of cow health, welfare and comfort.

Lying bouts can be defined as the period of lying between two standing events and can be short in duration; therefore, a high sampling frequency is required to capture LB accurately. However, this creates a dichotomy because a high sampling frequency will also detect minor movements, such as kicking or scratching, which generate short LB (e.g., <4 min) in the dataset that are not reflective of true lying behaviour (Mattachini et al. 2013). These short LB are a systematic error and should be discarded to improve data accuracy. However, there is no consensus for a LB editing protocol that researchers can follow when analysing and interpreting lying-behaviour data from IceRobotics accelerometer devices.

We are interested in examining lying behaviours in grazing dairy cows during the transition period from late gestation to early lactation when animals are at greatest risk of adverse health events. To our knowledge, no researchers validating IceRobotics devices in grazing cows have recommended the removal of false LB from the dataset. We expect that data derived from IceRobotics devices will contain short LB that are unlikely to be representative of true behaviour, as reported in housed cows, and will need to be discarded (Kok et al. 2015). Therefore, our first objective was to review published experiments that have validated IceRobotics devices to assess criteria used for editing behavioural data prior to analysis. Our second objective was to use an existing dataset from transition dairy cows grazing pasture to retrospectively examine descriptive lying behaviour data before and after applying editing criteria, and to justify the selection of the final criteria for subsequent research.

Literature review

We reviewed the published literature for studies that used either the IceQube or IceTag device manufactured by IceRobotics Ltd. (Edinburgh, Scotland). The IceQube and IceTag should be considered separately when determining an appropriate experimental methodology due to their different sampling frequencies (4 and 16 Hz, respectively). We first reviewed studies that have used either device in grazing cows to evaluate editing criteria applied. Second, we reviewed studies validating either device to evaluate the experimental design and editing methodologies. Due to our interest in using both lying time and LB behaviour derived from IceQube and IceTag devices, we focused specifically on studies that validated both behaviours.

Few studies undertaken in grazing cows or in cows with access to pasture have examined both lying time and LB using IceTag devices and our literature search returned no studies using IceQube devices. One study in grazing cows (Umstatter et al. 2015) and two studies in which cows had access to pasture (Black & Krawczel 2016; Rice et al. 2017) determined lying time and LB; however, there was no single preferred method for managing the data. For example, Umstatter et al. (2015) discarded LB <4 min as recommended by Tolkamp et al. (2010), while others discarded LB ≤2 min, as recommended by Munksgaard et al. (2006), Endres & Barberg (2007), and Bewley et al. (2010). While most researchers removed LB ≤2 min, the justification for this editing criteria was not based on validation studies (e.g., Endres & Barberg 2007, Bewley et al. 2010) or the study did not provide a detailed description of the experimental design (e.g., Munksgaard et al. 2006).

Variation in the time animals spend engaged in certain lying and standing behaviours under different systems can affect the outcome of the validation study; therefore, validation studies undertaken under similar conditions are preferred when determining the most appropriate editing methodology for subsequent research (Kok et al. 2015; Ledgerwood et al. 2010). Only one study, however, has validated both lying time and LB behaviour derived from IceTag devices in dairy cows grazing pasture (McGowan et al. 2007). Others have validated both behaviours from IceQube (Charlton et al. 2017) and IceTag devices in cows housed indoors and taken out to pasture between morning and afternoon milking (Rutter et al. 2014); but these studies have limitations. McGowan et al. (2007) reported that the unedited dataset recorded by the IceTag provided accurate lying time and LB values; however, the short data collection period (3 d; ~9.3 h recorded data in total), the timing of the study (during the dry period), and small sample size (n=15) may have limited the variation within the test dataset and, in particular, its applicability to the lactating cow. In comparison, according to Rutter et al. (2014), LB behaviour derived from the IceTag was grossly overestimated; however, the gold standard measure of manual behaviour records used to validate the IceTag was inadequate due to the low recording resolution (5-min intervals). Furthermore, Charlton et al. (2017) validated the IceQube, but did not report appropriate accuracy measures suggested by others (e.g., sensitivity and specificity estimates or Lin's concordance correlation; Watson & Petrie 2010). Contradictory reports exist, where Rutter et al. (2014) advised caution when interpreting the number of LB derived from unedited data from IceTag devices in cows at pasture, but authors of two other studies concluded that the original unedited data from the devices gave accurate lying time and LB records (McGowan et al. 2007; Charlton et al. 2017).

Due to these contrasting recommendations and the limitations of studies in pastured cows, we then considered validation studies undertaken in housed cows, which have more robust methodologies (e.g., Ledgerwood et al. 2010; Mattachini et al. 2013). Mattachini et al. (2013) and Tolkamp et al. (2010) both reported good correspondence between the IceTag device and continuous video observations for lying time and LB, but differed in their editing criteria, recommending the removal of LB ≤2 min and <4 min, respectively. For the IceQube device, to our knowledge, only one validation study has reported lying time and LB measures, with authors recommending the removal of LB <33 s from the original data (Kok et al. 2015).

Based on our assessment of the literature, we chose LB editing criteria of <33 s, ≤2 min, and <4 min from previous validation studies to conduct our next phase of this study. We visually inspected our existing accelerometer dataset of transition dairy cows grazing pasture before and after applying the three different editing criteria to examine the within-device variability for IceQube and IceTag devices when short LB are removed.

Comparison of three editing criteria
Materials and methods

Description of dataset. A database, described in detail by Hendriks et al. (2019) was compiled from four separate parent experiments that investigated various management- and cow-related factors during the transition period in clinically-healthy grazing cows. Of 380 cows available from the four experiments, data from 311 multiparous mixed-age and breed (Holstein-Friesian, n=216; Holstein-Friesian x Jersey, n=93; and Jersey, n=1) cows were selected for analysis. In total, 69 cows were removed from the analysis due to incomplete data [>10 d of data missing between –5 to +10 d relative to the day of calving (d 0)], inaccessible files, the device fell off during the experimental period, or the cow was removed from the study.

Behaviour data collection and editing. Each cow was fitted with one device, either an IceQube (n=146) or IceTag (n=159) on the lateral side of a hind leg. No effect of hind limb choice for sensor attachment on lying behaviour has been reported (Munksgaard et al. 2006). IceQube and IceTag devices were equally spread across treatments within parent experiment. Both devices were contained within plastic housing secured by a leg bracelet (IceRobotics Ltd.) and captured data at a frequency of 4 Hz (IceQube) and 16 Hz (IceTag).

Through the position of the three axes of the devices, behavioural parameters were characterised. Lying behaviour was recorded when the orientation of the hind leg was horizontal and LB were defined as periods between the device changing from vertical to horizontal and back to vertical. These data were stored on the device (60 d on-board storage capacity) with data granularity at a sampling interval of one second. Data were removed and downloaded using the IceManager 2010 software (IceRobotics Ltd.) to generate a summary file containing all recorded LB, with a start date, start time (hh:mm:ss), and duration (s) and this was used to calculate daily LB (no./d) and mean LB duration (min/d). From the output dataset, the sampling dates for each individual cow were assigned an experimental day (expday) relative to d 0. Each cow's recording period began at 00:00 on the day following attachment, as recommended by Bewley et al. (2010). This transformed dataset was the basis of subsequent analyses.

Statistical analysis. Statistical analyses were undertaken using SAS version 9.4 (SAS Institute Inc., Cary, NC). Recorded data ranged from –40 to +162 d (mean ± standard deviation (SD); start expday = –19 ± 13 d and end expday = 43 ± 35 d). Using PROC FREQ, the number of daily behaviour records per cow was determined and expday were discarded where data from fewer than 100 cows and two studies were available. The remaining data included 14,891 records from 305 cows during the period –21 to +35 d. Lying time was calculated within expday by summation of LB durations for individual cows using PROC SUMMARY. Daily LB were calculated using the number of observations (n) output for individual cows within expday using PROC SUMMARY and mean LB duration was calculated using the means statement in PROC SUMMARY to average the durations of all LB for individual cows within expday.

Based on the literature review, three different LB criteria were applied to this organised dataset where LB <33 s, ≤2 min, and <4 min were discarded. To compare behaviour values from the original data and the edited data, mean, SD, and 95% confidence intervals (CI) were calculated for daily lying time, LB, and LB duration using PROC SUMMARY for the period –21 to +35 d for the two devices (Table 1). Confidence intervals were examined to determine differences at P <0.05 between editing criteria.

Results and discussion

Activity devices, such as those manufactured by IceRobotics Ltd., generate useful data that can be used to monitor cow behaviour; however, short false LB may overstate the lying behaviour recorded by these devices (Kok et al. 2015). As such, data editing may be necessary to improve the accuracy of the data (Mattachini et al. 2010). Mean daily lying time and LB number and duration before and after applying different LB criteria to our dataset are presented in Table 1. In the unedited data, the IceTag had 36 times more lying records than did the IceQube, indicating a very large number of short LB. Consequently, the mean daily lying time was 0.43 h greater in the IceTag than in the IceQube device; however, both devices had mean values within the range (7.50 to 10.3 h/d) of lying times previously reported for healthy grazing dairy cows (Sepúlveda-Varas et al. 2014) and cows on pasture and fed total mixed ration (Black & Krawczel 2016; Rice et al. 2017). There was no change in mean, SD, and 95% CI for daily lying time after the removal of short LB from the IceQube dataset using the three editing criteria, but mean daily lying time was reduced (by between 0.58 and 0.82 h/d) in the IceTag dataset after editing. Mean daily lying time for the IceTag dataset was shortest when LB ≤2 or <4 min were removed. False LB typically make up a small proportion of total lying time; for example, in the study by Ungar et al. (2018) removing LB ≤1 min eliminated 95% of the LB from the original data, however, LB ≤1 min only accounted for 3% of total lying time. Our results are consistent with reports that discrepancies between unedited data recorded by IceQube devices and direct observations are small when summarising daily totals for lying time (Ledgerwood et al.

Table 1 Number of records (n), mean, standard deviation (SD) and lower and upper 95% confidence limits for the daily lying time (h/d), lying bouts (LB; no./d), and LB duration (min) in grazing dairy cows for the period –21 to +35 d relative to the day of calving (d 0) wearing either IceQube or IceTag accelerometers (IceRobotics Ltd., Edinburgh, Scotland). Data are presented as original unedited data and as three subsets of edited data where different criteria were applied to the original dataset to remove LB <33 s, ≤2, and <4 min.

	IceQube					IceTag				
				95% Confidence Limits					95% Confidence Limits	
	n	mean	SD	Lower	Upper	n	mean	SD	Lower	Upper
Unedited data										
Lying time (h/d)	64,512	8.52	2.41	8.48	8.57	2,305,693	8.95	2.60	8.90	9.00
LB (no./d)	64,512	8.80	3.62	8.74	8.87	2,305,693	304	293	299	310
LB duration (min)	64,512	58.1	51.2	57.7	58.4	2,305,693	1.76	12.9	1.75	1.78
LB <33 s discarded										
Lying time (h/d)	60,463	8.52	2.41	8.48	8.57	157,200	8.37	2.41	8.32	8.41
LB (no./d)	60,463	8.25	3.39	8.19	8.32	157,200	20.8	21.5	20.4	21.2
LB duration (min)	60,463	62.0	50.6	61.6	62.3	157,200	24.1	43.5	24.0	24.3
LB ≤2 min discarded										
Lying time (h/d)	58,739	8.52	2.41	8.47	8.56	66,139	8.19	2.40	8.14	8.23
LB (no./d)	58,739	8.02	3.02	7.96	8.08	66,139	8.75	4.05	8.67	8.82
LB duration (min)	58,739	63.7	50.2	63.4	64.1	66,139	56.2	52.2	55.8	56.5
LB <4 min discarded										
Lying time (h/d)	56,887	8.50	2.41	8.46	8.55	56,866	8.13	2.40	8.09	8.18
LB (no./d)	56,887	7.77	2.72	7.71	7.82	56,866	7.52	2.77	7.47	7.57
LB duration (min)	56,887	65.7	49.8	65.4	66.1	56,866	64.9	51.3	64.5	65.2

Figure 1 Frequency (logarithmic scale) of lying bouts (LB) within a range of bout durations (between ≤10 s to >18,000 s) from unedited and edited data from IceQube (a) and IceTag (b) devices attached to transition dairy cows grazing pasture. To generate the edited datasets, LB <33 s and LB ≤120 s were removed from IceQube and IceTag datasets, respectively. Each cow was fitted with one device, either an IceQube or IceTag.

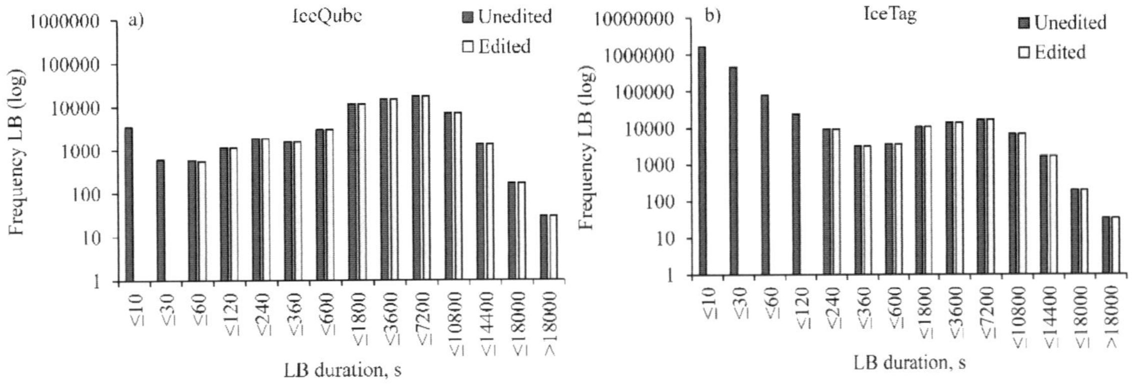

2010), and therefore, applying LB criteria has little to no effect on daily lying time as reported previously (Kok et al. 2015). Larger discrepancies in the daily lying times in the IceTag datasets after editing indicates that short LB make up a larger proportion of total lying time, which may lead to overestimation in unedited data.

In contrast, data editing using LB thresholds can substantially improve accuracy when estimating daily LB number and duration (Kok et al. 2015; Ledgerwood et al. 2010). Mean daily LB number decreased and duration increased for the IceQube dataset when each successive LB criterion was applied; however, these changes were small compared with the large differences obtained when editing IceTag data (Table 1). In total, 11.8% of the LB records from the IceQube had a duration <4 min (Fig. 1a). When LB <33 s were discarded from the IceQube data, 5.6% more LB were retained compared with the LB criteria of <4 min. Kok et al. (2015) validated the IceQube by comparing sensors on each hind limb and reported that despite relatively few LB records with a duration <4 min (7.2%), about half of those were assumed to be true LB and a LB criteria of <33 s retained 2.5% more records than a LB criteria of <4 min. Removal of LB <33 s improved combined sensitivity and specificity estimates (Se=99.3%; Sp=97.7%) relative to removing LB <4 min (Se=96.7%; Sp=100%) due to the underestimation of up to 10 LB per d using a LB criteria of <4 min (Kok et al. 2015). Therefore, based on the interpretation of our data and the recommendation of Kok et al. (2015), the use of the <33-s LB criterion in the IceQube device is our preferred option.

The frequency distribution of IceTag data was comprised of two peaks, with a left-skewed distribution of very large numbers of LB ≤240 s (≤4 min; Fig. 1b). The removal of LB <33 s, ≤2 min, and <4 min eliminated 93%, 97%, and 97.5% of LB records, respectively (Table 1). Hence, short LB made up a considerable number of the LB records in the unedited IceTag data, and although we cannot be certain from our data, it is unlikely that all of these records represented true LB (Tolkamp et al. 2010). Large numbers of erroneous short LB recorded by the IceTag may be explained, in part, by its high sampling frequency resulting in the detection of rapid behaviours and minor movements such as scratching and stepping.

It is more realistic to choose a LB criterion that is likely to represent true behaviour; therefore, we have justified our selected criteria based on LB values reported in literature. Discarding LB <33 s from our IceTag dataset (Table 1) still resulted in mean daily LB well outside of previously reported ranges of 9.5 to 13.1 no./d (Borchers et al. 2017; Calderon & Cook 2011), indicating that a higher threshold was required. Removing LB ≤2 min or <4 min in the IceTag dataset resulted in 58 and 64% fewer total lying records, respectively, compared with removing LB <33 s (Table 1). Although, when a criterion of removing LB ≤2 min was used relative to <4 min, the mean and SD for daily LB number and durations were different between these editing criteria. A validation study of IceTag devices indicated that removing LB <4 min increased accuracy, where only 2% of the LB in the final data were false (Tolkamp et al. 2010); however, that study was undertaken in housed beef cows during late pregnancy, so care should be taken when extrapolating these results to transition dairy cows grazing pasture. The authors did not recommend a shorter LB criterion because they did not record LB <4 min through video observation. However, others have reported that lactating dairy cows can spend <4 min lying in a single bout (Kok et al. 2015; Mattachini et al. 2013). Furthermore, studies undertaken in housed lactating cows using IceTag (Mattachini et al. 2013) and HOBO devices (Onset Computer Corporation, Pocasset, MA; Ledgerwood et al. 2010), which have a similar sampling frequency, support the removal of LB ≤2 min. A suitable

Figure 2 Profile of mean daily lying bouts (LB; no./d) in grazing dairy cows during the period –21 to +35 d relative to the day of calving (d 0) where LB <33 s and ≤2 min were removed from the IceQube (a) and IceTag (b) datasets, respectively. Each cow was fitted with one device, either an IceQube or IceTag. Error bars represent ± 1 standard deviation and grey shaded areas represent 95% confidence intervals around the mean.

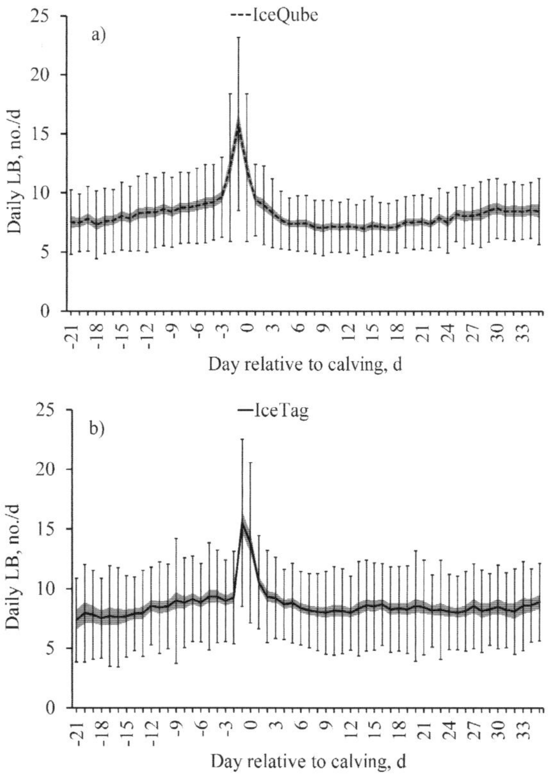

editing criterion should maximise the true records retained as well as minimise false records to ensure data accurately reflects lying behaviour (Kok et al. 2015). It is possible for our data to contain true short LB <4 min, particularly during calving; therefore, the removal of LB ≤2 min is our preferred criterion for the IceTag dataset, to limit the risk of excluding true short LB durations.

Visual comparison of the temporal profile of daily LB number over the transition period between IceQube and IceTag devices with LB <33 s and ≤2 min removed, respectively, indicates a similar number of LB were achieved across the two devices (Fig. 2a and b). It is evident from our data that the use of different LB editing criteria can have considerable effects on the output data of these devices (Fig. 1). Based on our study, we cannot determine whether the editing criteria chosen, represented cow lying behaviour at the same level of accuracy that has been reported in validation studies and the application of these editing criteria under different conditions to which they were tested is a limitation of our study; however, the final editing criteria chosen produced descriptive data that were consistent with previous literature and were biologically plausible.

Further investigations are required to determine inter-device agreement and the precision of accelerometer-derived data relative to true lying behaviours. Therefore, we recommend that future validation studies use an appropriate and robust experimental protocol, which considers potentially false LB, to test the accuracy, sensitivity and specificity of IceTag and IceQube devices for recording lying behaviour in grazing cows.

Conclusions

Short LB that are unlikely to represent true behaviour in the original data recorded by IceQube and IceTag devices biases the number and duration of daily LB derived, but without materially affecting daily mean lying time for IceQube devices. Using previous reports validating IceQube and IceTag devices, along with an assessment of our own dataset from transition cows grazing pasture, we chose from three editing criteria where LB <33 s, ≤2 min, and <4 min were discarded from the original data recorded by IceRobotics devices. Removing LB <33 s and ≤2 min from the data recorded by the IceQube and IceTag devices, respectively, was our preferred option. The removal of LB using these criteria reduced the within-device variation of LB. Future work is needed to validate a suitable LB criterion against a gold standard measure (e.g., visual or video observations) for IceQube and IceTag devices in grazing dairy cows.

Acknowledgements

This work was funded by New Zealand dairy farmers through DairyNZ Inc. and by the Ministry of Business, Innovation and Employment (contract numbers DRCX1302 and DRCX1201). S. Hendriks is also supported by the Colin Holmes Dairy Scholarship and the Ministry for Primary Industries Postgraduate Scholarship.

References

Bewley JM, Boyce RE, Hockin J, Munksgaard L, Eicher SD, Einstein ME, Schutz MM 2010. Influence of milk yield, stage of lactation, and body condition on dairy cattle lying behaviour measured using an automated activity monitoring sensor. Journal of Dairy Research 77: 1-6.

Black RA, Krawczel PD 2016. A case study of behaviour and performance of confined or pastured cows during the dry period. Animals 6: 41-57.

Borchers MR, Chang YM, Proudfoot KL, Wadsworth BA, Stone AE, Bewley JM 2017. Machine-learning-based calving prediction from activity, lying, and ruminating behaviours in dairy cattle. Journal of Dairy Science 100: 5664-5674.

Calderon DF, Cook NB 2011. The effect of lameness on the resting behavior and metabolic status of dairy cattle during the transition period in a freestall-housed dairy herd. Journal of Dairy Science 94: 2883-2894.

Charlton GL, Gauld C, Bleach E, Rutter SM 2017. The accuracy of accelerometer-based, legmounted sensors for measuring dairy cow locomotion and lying behaviour at pasture. Proceedings of the International Society of Applied Ethology, Aarhus, Denmark. Pg. 129.

Endres MI, Barberg AE 2007. Behavior of dairy cows in an alternative bedded-pack housing system. Journal of Dairy Science 90: 4192-4200.

Hendriks, S. J., C. V. C. Phyn, S-A. Turner, K. M. Mueller, B. Kuhn-Sherlock, D. J. Donaghy, J. M. Huzzey, and J. R. Roche. 2019. Lying behavior and activity during the transition period of clinically healthy grazing dairy cows. Journal of Dairy Science 102: 7371-7384.

Ledgerwood DN, Winckler C, Tucker CB 2010. Evaluation of data loggers, sampling intervals, and editing techniques for measuring the lying behavior of dairy cattle. Journal of Dairy Science 93: 5129-5139.

Kok A, van Knegsel ATM, van Middelaar CE, Hogeveen H, Kemp B, de Boer IJM 2015. Technical note: Validation of sensor-recorded lying bouts in lactating dairy cows using a 2-sensor approach. Journal of Dairy Science. 98: 7911-7916.

Mattachini G, Riva E, Bisaglia C, Pompe JCAM, Provolo G 2013. Methodology for quantifying the behavioral activity of dairy cows in freestall barns. Journal of Animal Science. 91: 4899-4907.

McGowan JE, Burke CR, Jago JG 2007. Validation of a technology for objectively measuring behaviour in dairy cows and its application for oestrus detection. Proceedings of the New Zealand Society of Animal Production 67: 136-142.

Munksgaard L, Reenen CG, Boyce R 2006. Automatic monitoring of lying, standing and walking behaviour in dairy cattle. Journal of Animal Sci. 84 (Suppl. 1): 304.

Rice CA, Eberhart NL, Krawczel PD 2017. Prepartum lying behaviour of Holstein dairy cows housed on pasture through parturition. Animals 7: 1-9.

Rutter SM, Atkins NE, Birch SA 2014. The accuracy of the automatic recording of lying behaviour is affected by whether dairy cows are inside or outside. Proceedings of the 48th Congress of the International Society of Applied Ethology, Vitoria-Gasteiz, Spain. Pg. 73.

Sepúlveda-Varas P, Weary DM, von Keyserlingk MAG. 2014. Lying behavior and postpartum health status in grazing dairy cows. Journal of Dairy Science 97: 6334-6343.

Tolkamp BJ, Haskell MJ, Langford FM, Roberts DJ, Morgan CA 2010. Are cows more likely to lie down the longer they stand? Applied Animal Behaviour Science 124: 1-10.

Umstatter C, Morgan-Davies J, Waterhouse T 2015. Cattle responses to a type of virtual fence. Rangeland Ecology & Management 68: 100-107.

Ungar ED, Nevo Y, Baram H, Arieli A 2018. Evaluation of the IceTag leg sensor and its derivative models to predict behaviour, using beef cattle on rangeland. Journal of Neuroscience Methods 300: 127-137.

Watson PF, Petrie A 2010. Method agreement analysis: A review of correct methodology. Theriogenology 73: 1167-1179.

Relationship between body condition score and pregnancy rates following artificial insemination and subsequent natural mating in beef cows on commercial farms in New Zealand

F Weik[a]*, JA Archer[b], ST Morris[a], DJ Garrick[a] and RE Hickson[a]

[a]*School of Agriculture and Environment, Massey University, Private Bag 11222, Palmerston North 4442, New Zealand;* [b]*AbacusBio Ltd, PO Box 5585, Dunedin 9054, New Zealand*

**Corresponding author:* Email: f.weik@massey.ac.nz

Abstract

Body condition scoring is an efficient on-farm visual-assessment tool used to describe the energy reserves of animals. Cow body condition score (BCS) at crucial time points throughout the year is likely to influence reproductive performance. The aim of this experiment was to examine the influence of BCS before calving, before mating and at weaning on reproductive performance of mature beef cows. Percentage of cows conceiving to a single artificial insemination (AI) at a synchronised oestrus and pregnancy rate after 49 days of mating were determined for a total of 2,683 individual cows. Cows with a greater than average BCS had greater pregnancy rate to AI than did those with low BCS ($P<0.001$). The percentage of animals conceiving to AI was on average 54.8% but was lower at 42.5% for pre-mating BCS 4.5 or greater at 64.5% for BCS 9.0 ($P<0.001$). Cows had greater overall pregnancy rate after 49 days of mating with greater BCS; ranging from 88.3%, 75.7% and 79.7% for BCS 4.5 before calving, before mating and at weaning, respectively, to 93.5%, 93.3% and 93.3% for BCS 8.0 at the same time points. Increasing BCS up to 7 is likely to improve overall pregnancy rate, and most benefit tends to come from improving BCS in lower-conditioned cows to achieve high pregnancy results.

Keywords: beef cows; BCS; reproductive performance; pregnancy rate; artificial insemination

Introduction

Body condition scoring is an easy and efficient tool to assess the energy reserves of livestock which reflects their recent nutritional management. It is used to evaluate energy reserves of the animals based on their body fat and muscle reserves (Bishop et al. 1994; Wagner et al. 1988) and is a better predictor of body fat than is live weight (Russel et al. 1969). The assessment of body condition score (BCS) should not simply reflect the live weight of the animals nor be influenced by factors like gut-fill, mature size or weight of the conceptus in pregnant cows. BCS can be used to evaluate the body reserves of cows at crucial time points throughout the year to improve feed planning, which is known to influence reproductive performance (Morris et al. 2006). Typically, BCS is evaluated through visual assessment that is easily implemented on-farm, without the need for any off-site training or further equipment. In New Zealand BCS in beef cows is typically assessed on a 1-10 (Hickson et al. 2017; Smeaton et al. 2000) or a 0-5 (Morris et al. 2002) scale. A report by Hickson et al. (2017) using the 10-point scale suggested a target BCS of 6 at mating, 7 at weaning and 5 throughout the winter months.

Reproductive performance has been reported as being influenced by BCS, in terms of pregnancy rates or inter-calving interval, in NZ sheep (Kenyon et al. 2014), USA beef cattle (Ciccioli et al. 2003; Renquist et al. 2006) and NZ dairy cows (Buckley et al. 2003). According to Selk et al. (1988) BCS before calving and at the start of mating are the main factors influencing pregnancy rates in beef cows. Similarly, DeRouen et al. (1994) reported a significant positive effect of BCS at calving on subsequent pregnancy rate. However, few studies have been conducted to describe this relationship for beef cows in New Zealand. Morris et al. (2006) reported higher pregnancy rates for cows with greater BCS at joining than for lower-conditioned cows. Tait et al. (2017) indicated that cows that had higher BCS at mating or at pregnancy diagnosis were more likely to have reproductive success.

Artificial insemination (AI) is an efficient reproductive technology with the potential to incorporate favoured genetics into the herd to increase productivity and genetic gain (Vishwanath 2003). AI is widespread within the New Zealand dairy industry, but not yet as well established in beef cow herds (Smeaton et al. 2003). This is mainly due to management issues as beef cattle are not yarded together on a regular basis. One approach to overcome this limitation has been the introduction of oestrus synchronisation. There is scope for a wider use of AI programs within the industry to further improve the beef herd (Morris & Archer 2007). To the authors' knowledge, there is no published literature that examined the relationship between BCS and AI success rate in New Zealand beef cows. However, some studies around the New Zealand dairy industry (Roche et al. 2007) as well as the beef industry outside New Zealand (Ayres et al. 2014; Sprott et al. 1998) have identified higher pregnancy rate to AI for cows with higher than average BCS.

The aim of this study was to evaluate and quantify the relationship of BCS before calving, before mating and at weaning with pregnancy rate to AI and overall pregnancy rate following a 49-day mating period of beef breeding cows on commercial hill-country farms in New Zealand.

Materials and methods

Dataset

The beef progeny test and all related procedures were approved by the AgResearch Ethical Committee.

The dataset consisted of an ongoing beef progeny test (BPT) carried out by Beef + Lamb NZ Genetics on four large-scale commercial farms in New Zealand. The farms are located on North Island (Gisborne, Central Northern plateau, Southern Hawkes Bay) and South Island (North Canterbury) hill country with varying climatic conditions and, therefore, diverging seasonal trait recordings. Data were collected over a period of five years from November 2014 to September 2019. Each year, beef cows were artificially inseminated with semen from New Zealand or foreign bulls. Bull breeds used for mating were Angus, Hereford, Stabilizer, Simmental and Charolais. Data for this experiment was taken from the base population of the BPT, including all cows that built up the population at the start of the progeny test as well as all replacement animals from within the property. Consistent with normal farm practices, animals were typically managed separately in different mobs. However, the overall recording scheme followed the same system for each of those mobs within farm and year. All animals included in this analysis were mixed-aged beef breeding cows (3-10+ years of age) with their second or later calf at foot. BCS and pregnancy data representing a total of 5,484 pregnancy outcomes of 2,683 cows with a total of 16,105 BCS recordings were available for this experiment. All cows in the project were Angus or Hereford. Consistent with normal farm practices, cows failing to conceive were culled following weaning of their calves.

Measurements

BCS was recorded within each herd for all base cows in the dataset on three events throughout the year: pre-calving (July – September), pre-mating (November – January) and weaning (February – April). Timing of these events varied among farms and years, but was consistent for all cows within farm and year. BCS was scored on a 1-10 scale with 0.5 increments (1=emaciated and 10=obese; Hickson et al. (2017)). Birth years were recorded for each cow. All cows included in the analysis were inseminated once by fixed-time AI at a synchronised oestrus before bulls were introduced to the herd, generally two to three days following AI and always less than 21 days after AI. Treatments for oestrus synchronisation were based on a three-yarding protocol for most farms. Cows were given 100 µg of gonadorelin (Ovurelin, Bayer New Zealand Ltd., Auckland, New Zealand) on day 0 and were treated with an intravaginal P4-releasing device (Cue-mate, Bayer New Zealand Ltd., or CIDR, Zoetis New Zealand Ltd., Auckland, New Zealand) from days 0-7. At the day of device removal, cows received 200 µg cloprostenol (Ovuprost, Bayer New Zealand Ltd.) and 200 µg gonadotrophin (Pregnecol, Bayer New Zealand Ltd.). A second treatment of 100 µg of gonadorelin was given on day 10 at the time of AI. One farm used a four-yarding protocol, where the final treatment was conducted the day prior to AI. Bulls remained with the herd for a minimum of seven weeks after AI. Date of AI was recorded with corresponding sire ID. Pregnancy diagnosis (PD) was conducted approximately 90 days after AI using trans-rectal ultrasound by an experienced commercial operator. Fetal age was recorded at pregnancy scanning based on a combination of characteristics. Pregnancy was recorded as either 0 (not pregnant) or 1 (pregnant) at the time of PD.

Data manipulation

Pregnancy rates represent the number of pregnant cows as a proportion of total number of cows with pregnancy records at the time of PD. Day of conception was calculated from the fetal age recorded at PD. A gestation length of 282 days (Burris & Blunn 1952) was assumed to compute probable calving dates based on the fetal age at PD. The interval from this probable calving date to the following AI date was calculated and is referred to as "days from previous calving" (DfPC). The fetal age record was used to determine whether each cow had conceived to AI or natural mating. Cows were defined as conceived to AI when the days between the estimated conception date and AI-Date were less than eight days. Similarly, fetal age records were used to determine pregnancy rate, where cows for which the fetal age indicated they conceived more than seven weeks after AI were recoded as not pregnant to allow calculation of a standardised 49-day pregnancy rate. Age of cows was calculated from their birth year. Cows were grouped according to their age into four categories: 3-year olds, 4-year olds, 5-9-year olds and 10 or more years old. BCS ranks with fewer than five records for each time point were excluded from this study, leaving a range of BCS from 4.0 to 9.0 for further analysis (Table 1).

Statistical analysis

Binomial regression analysis was performed using R (R Core Team 2019) to evaluate the relationship between pre-calving BCS, pre-mating BCS and BCS at weaning on reproductive performance. Percentage of cows conceiving to a single AI, and pregnancy rate after 49 days of mating, were analysed using logit transformation for categorical data analysis. Age of cow (3, 4, 5-9 and 10+) was considered as a class effect but was not significant for any model and was excluded from the final models. BCS and DfPC were included as covariates for each model. BCS was fitted as a linear and quadratic effect to test for deviation from linearity. The covariates for each model were standardized prior to analysis by subtracting the overall mean and dividing by the standard deviation (SD) (Table 1). A contemporary group (herd:season:mob) and the sire used for AI were fitted as random effects. An ANOVA was conducted to test for significance of the model effects and the form of relationship between the predictor and the response variables. Probabilities of pregnancy rate to AI and pregnancy rate after 49 days of mating were calculated for each level of BCS. In a second approach, BCS was fitted as a fixed effect in each model to estimate least-square means (lsmeans) for each category of BCS. All probabilities and estimates were calculated based on the mean DfPC in this experiment of 71.6 days.

Table 1 Number (n) of cow records for each body condition score (BCS), mean and standard deviation (SD) of BCS and days from previous calving date to first day of mating (DfPC), pregnancy rate to AI (cows pregnant to a single artificial insemination by cows with pregnancy records, %) and 49-day pregnancy rate (cows pregnant after a 49-day mating period by cows with pregnancy records, %) recorded before calving, before mating and at weaning.

	Before calving	Before mating	At weaning
BCS records[a]			
4	57	5	13
4.5	263	30	58
5	539	154	212
5.5	719	305	358
6	1,116	593	717
6.5	736	564	789
7	922	1,023	1,309
7.5	602	874	772
8	389	1,168	841
8.5	86	426	225
9	6	99	135
Total n of records	5,435	5,241	5,429
BCS: Mean ± SD	6.33 ± 1.01	7.14 ± 0.97	6.92 ± 0.97
DfPC: Mean ± SD	71.63 ± 15.74	71.68 ± 15.80	71.63 ± 15.73
49-day pregnancy rate (%)	90.82	91.01	90.88
AI pregnancy rate (%)	54.98	55.43	54.93

[a]BCS was scored on a 1-10 scale with 1=emaciated and 10=obese.

Table 2 Standardized coefficients and standard errors (Estimates ± SE) with P values and unstandardized coefficients (log odds) for all variables in the model to describe the relationship of body condition score (BCS) before calving, before mating and at weaning with pregnancy rate to AI (cows pregnant to a single artificial insemination by cows with pregnancy records) and 49-day pregnancy rate (cows pregnant after a 49-day mating period by cows with pregnancy records) on the logit scale.

Model	Pregnancy rate to AI			49-day pregnancy rate		
	Estimates ± SE	P value	Log odds	Estimates ± SE	P value	Log odds
Model 1 – before calving						
Intercept	0.21 ± 0.07	0.005	-1.9332	2.36 ± 0.07	<0.001	-0.3499
BCS	0.17 ± 0.04	<0.001	0.1660	0.19 ± 0.05	<0.001	0.1833
DfPC[b]	0.24 ± 0.03	<0.001	0.0152	0.34 ± 0.04	<0.001	0.0216
Model 2 – before mating						
Intercept	0.22 ± 0.06	<0.001	-2.4601	2.41 ± 0.06	<0.001	-6.3034
BCS	0.19 ± 0.03	<0.001	0.2000	1.75 ± 0.53	<0.001	1.8072
BCS^2				-1.49 ± 0.54	0.006	-0.1105
DfPC[b]	0.28 ± 0.04	<0.001	0.0175	0.34 ± 0.05	<0.001	0.0215
Model 3 – at weaning						
Intercept	0.19 ± 0.07	0.006	-5.0968	2.42 ± 0.07	<0.001	-5.6681
BCS	1.08 ± 0.33	0.001	1.1186	1.68 ± 0.48	<0.001	1.7366
BCS^2	-0.96 ± 0.33	0.004	-0.0723	-1.46 ± 0.49	0.003	-0.1101
DfPC[b]	0.24 ± 0.03	<0.001	0.0150	0.32 ± 0.05	<0.001	0.0202

[a] Blank cells were not included in the analysis.

[b]Days from previous calving date to first day of mating.

Results

AI pregnancy rate

The overall percentage of animals conceiving to AI was 54.8%. Cows tended to have greater pregnancy rate (P<0.001) to AI with increasing BCS for all measured time points, ranging from 45.5% (95% CI 40.1-51.0) to 65.7% (95% CI 60.3-70.8) for BCS 4.0-9.0 pre-calving, 40.1% (95% CI 34.3-46.1) to 64.5% (95% CI 60.5-68.3) for BCS 4.0-9.0 pre-mating and 33.1% (95% CI 24.7-42.8) to 57.5% (95% CI 53.7-61.2) for BCS 4.0-8.0 at weaning (Fig. 1). No quadratic relationship between the predictor and the response variable could be identified for pre-calving and pre-mating BCS (P>0.05), however, BCS at weaning showed a significant quadratic (P<0.01) relationship (Table 2). In addition, cows that calved early in the previous mating season had a significantly greater chance (P<0.001) of conceiving to AI the following year.

Forty-nine-day pregnancy rate

The 49-day pregnancy rate for all cows was 90.8%. Pregnancy rate was significantly (P<0.001) associated with

Figure 1 Relationship of body condition score (BCS) before calving (a), before mating (b) and at weaning (c) with pregnancy rate to AI (cows pregnant to a single artificial insemination by cows with pregnancy records); solid line: predicted probabilities from regression analysis, dashed line: 95% CI, dots: least square means for each level of BCS; results are based on an average 71.6 days between previous calving date and first day of mating.

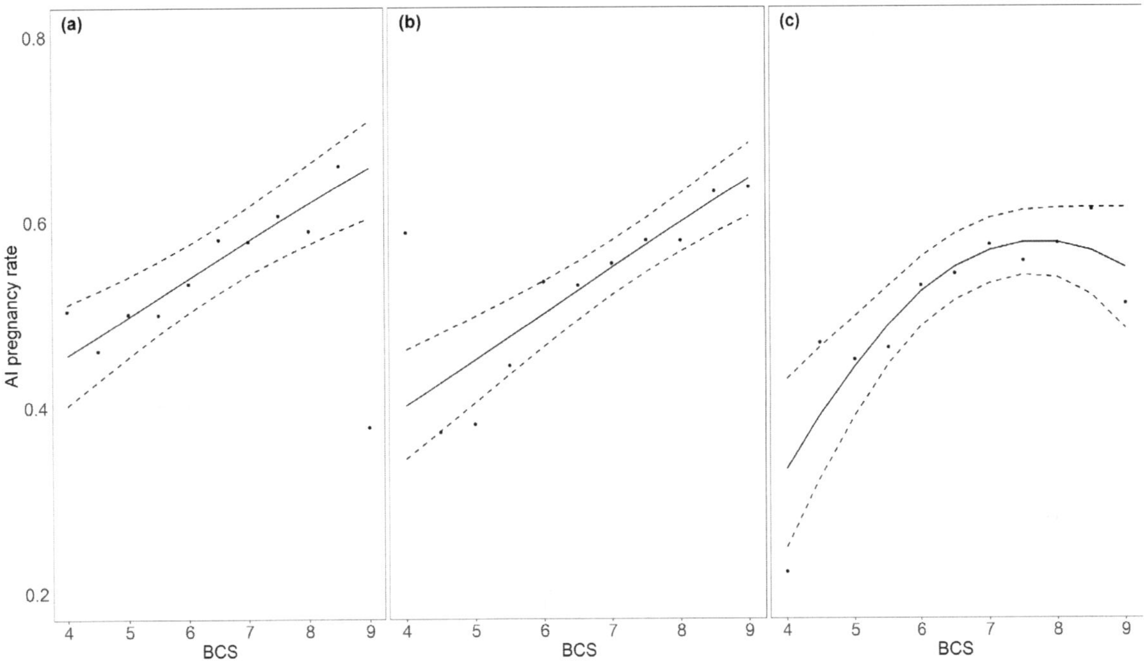

Figure 2 Relationship of body condition score (BCS) before calving (a), before mating (b) and at weaning (c) with 49-day pregnancy rate (cows pregnant after a 49-day mating period by cows with pregnancy records); solid line: predicted probabilities from regression analysis, dashed line: 95% CI, dots: least square means for each level of BCS; results are based on an average 71.6 days between previous calving date and first day of mating.

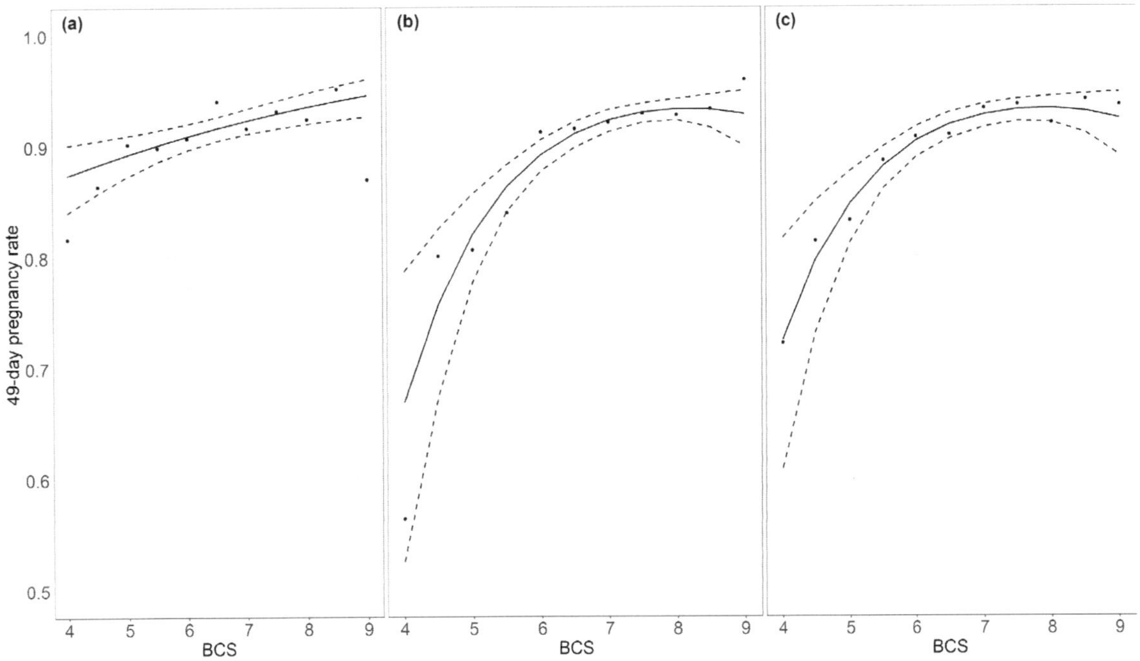

BCS before calving, before mating or at weaning (Table 2), with a higher proportion of cows conceiving at greater BCS. Cows with a greater than average BCS had greater pregnancy rates; ranging from 87.4% (95% CI 84.0-90.1) to 94.5% (95% CI 92.6-96.0) for BCS 4.0-9.0 pre-calving, 66.9% (95% CI 52.5-78.7) to 93.3% (95% CI 92.3-94.2) for BCS 4.0-8.0 pre-mating and 72.4% (95% CI 60.8-81.6) to 93.3% (95% CI 92.0-94.4) for BCS 4.0-8.0 at weaning (Fig. 2). Pre-mating BCS and BCS at weaning followed a quadratic function with little increase in pregnancy rate for BCS above 7. In contrast, pre-calving BCS was linearly related to 49-day pregnancy rate. Forty-nine-day pregnancy rate increased ($P<0.001$) as the time increased between the preceding probable calving date and the first day of mating.

Discussion

AI pregnancy rate

Nutritional status has been demonstrated to influence reproductive performance in beef cows (Sprott et al. 1998; Whitman 1975). BCS as a measure of nutritional status can, therefore, be manipulated in order to improve reproductive performance. From a management perspective, a high percentage of cows conceiving early in the breeding season is desired and may subsequently lead to higher calf weaning weights (Lesmeister et al. 1973).

Regression analysis showed a positive association between BCS and pregnancy rate to AI, indicating that a higher BCS would result in a greater proportion of cows conceiving to AI early in the mating season. The form of relationship between BCS before calving and before mating and the pregnancy rate to AI was linear. This implies that any increase in BCS around calving and before mating would result in improved pregnancy rate to AI. Ayres et al. (2014) found that Zebu beef cows were more likely to conceive to first mating by AI when they were at their greatest BCS at parturition. Similarly, studies on dairy cows reported a positive effect of higher BCS at calving on pregnancy rate at first mating by AI (Roche et al. 2007), while cows in poor condition at parturition tended to have lower pregnancy rates (Lopez-Gatius et al. 2003). Ayres et al. (2014) did not identify a relationship between BCS around mating and AI conception rate, whereas Roche et al. (2007) reported a significant effect.

Results from this experiment support the conclusion that beef cows need to be in BCS of at least 6, around the time of calving and/or mating, to achieve approximately 50% conception to a single synchronised AI, and that greater BCS will likely lead to further improvements in conception rate. Adequate number of days between previous calving and the start of mating and good BCS at calving has been demonstrated to increase the probability of oestrus (Sprott et al. 1998; Whitman 1975). In agreement with this, our experiment showed that an increase in time from previous calving results in greater pregnancy rate to AI at the start of mating, indicating that cows that calved early were more likely to conceive to AI at the following breeding.

Forty-nine-day pregnancy rate

The mean pregnancy rate reported by McFadden et al. (2005) was 91% for a total of 1,005 beef cow herds in New Zealand and matches the findings of this study with an overall pregnancy rate of 90.8-91.0% across all herds and years.

Several studies have described the relationship between pre-calving BCS and BCS around mating on pregnancy rate. Pre-calving BCS had a significant effect on 49-day pregnancy rate in this experiment, which agrees with the findings of DeRouen et al. (1994) and Selk et al. (1988), however, neither Morris et al. (2006) nor Tait et al. (2017) found an effect of calving BCS on pregnancy rate. Pre-mating BCS and BCS at weaning were significantly related to 49-day pregnancy rate in the current study. Renquist et al. (2006) and Morris et al. (2006) demonstrated an increase in pregnancy rate for higher BCS at joining, whereas Tait et al. (2017) did not report a significant relationship of BCS at joining or PD with pregnancy rates.

Pre-mating BCS and BCS at weaning were quadratically related to 49-day pregnancy rate in the current experiment. Improving condition around mating to BCS 7 is beneficial whereas further increase is unlikely to result in greater pregnancy rates. This outcome could explain the absence of a significant relationship between BCS at joining and PD on pregnancy results reported by Tait et al. (2017), as the cows in their study were all above BCS 6, and based on the results found in this experiment, a strong response would have been unlikely. Compared to the curvilinear trend for pre-mating BCS and BCS at weaning, pre-calving BCS followed a linear relationship. This indicates that increasing pre-calving BCS would result in higher pregnancy rates without a detrimental effect of very high BCS. This finding concurs with Renquist et al. (2006), who also reported a quadratic relationship between BCS around breeding and a linear relationship between BCS at calving on pregnancy rates. This experiment outlines an optimum BCS between 6 and 7 at mating and weaning, whereas overall higher pre-calving BCS would be advantageous. From a commercial perspective, this demonstrates the value of separating lower-conditioned cows and increasing their feed levels to ensure sufficient BCS gain. However, increasing BCS before calving is associated with higher feed costs for grazing cows compared to after calving when more feed is becoming available as a response to increased pasture growth in early spring. The results found in this experiment tend to agree with industry targets outlined by Hickson et al. (2017), which seem to be adequate guidelines to improve pregnancy results.

Compared among pre-calving BCS, pre-mating BCS and BCS at weaning, the pre-mating BCS tends to be the most valuable in predicting pregnancy rates and might therefore be a key point for achieving pregnancy rate targets. Those findings coincide with those of Renquist et al. (2006) who identified a greater variation in pregnancy rate being explained by BCS at breeding compared to BCS at calving. Nevertheless, BCS at weaning is often the only measurement available for New Zealand farmers in their day-to-day practices. Cows that are in better condition at weaning may be more likely to have gained or at least maintained condition over the mating period compared with cows that were in poorer condition at weaning. This could explain why those cows with greater BCS at weaning were more likely to have conceived during the mating period.

Pre-calving BCS did have an influence on 49-day pregnancy rate in the current experiment, but the slope of the relationship at lower BCS was greater before mating than before calving. This suggests that the focus for management should be to ensure that cows achieve a minimum BCS of 6 to 7 at time of mating. Based on the relationship persisting through to weaning, it seems that it is likely that maintaining target BCS of 6 to 7 at least across the mating period may also improve 49-day pregnancy rates.

Conclusion

This study quantified the relationship of BCS before calving, before mating and at weaning with AI and 49-day pregnancy rate. Increasing BCS tends to be advantageous to achieve higher pregnancy rates. The linear relationship between BCS and AI pregnancy rate suggests that aiming for the highest possible BCS before calving and before mating would lead to improved outcomes from AI programmes. For overall pregnancy rate (after 49 days of natural mating post-AI), the curvilinear relationship with BCS suggests that most value can be obtained by reducing the percentage of low-conditioned cows in the herd.

Acknowledgements

The primary author is funded by Massey University. The authors gratefully acknowledge Beef + Lamb NZ Genetics for funding the research, Craig Foote, Geoff Purchas and the participating progeny test farms for collecting and supplying the data and the team at AbacusBio Ltd for the assistance provided.

References

Ayres H, Ferreira RM, Torres-Júnior JRS, Demétrio CGB, Sá Filho MF, Gimenes LU, Penteado L, D'Occhio MJ, Baruselli PS 2014. Inferences of body energy reserves on conception rate of suckled Zebu beef cows subjected to timed artificial insemination followed by natural mating. Theriogenology 82: 529-536. doi 10.1016/j.theriogenology.2014.04.026.

Bishop DK, Wettemann RP, Spicer LJ 1994. Body energy reserves influence the onset of luteal activity after early weaning of beef cows. Journal of Animal Science 72: 2703-8. doi 10.2527/1994.72102703x.

Buckley F, O'Sullivan K, Mee JF, Evans RD, Dillon P 2003. Relationships among milk yield, body condition, cow weight, and reproduction in spring-calved Holstein-Friesians. Journal of Dairy Science 86: 2308-2319. doi 10.3168/jds.S0022-0302(03)73823-5.

Burris MJ, Blunn CT 1952. Some factors affecting gestation length and birth weight of beef cattle. Journal of Animal Science 11: 34-41. doi 10.2527/jas1952.11134x.

Ciccioli NH, Wettemann RP, Spicer LJ, Lents CA, White FJ, Keisler DH 2003. Influence of body condition at calving and postpartum nutrition on endocrine function and reproductive performance of primiparous beef cows. Journal of Animal Science 81: 3107-3120. doi 10.2527/2003.81123107x.

DeRouen SM, Franke DE, Morrison DG, Wyatt WE, Coombs DF, White TW, Humes PE, Greene BB 1994. Prepartum body condition and weight influences on reproductive performance of first-calf beef cows. Journal of Animal Science 72: 1119-1125. doi 10.2527/1994.7251119x.

Hickson RE, Morris ST, Thomson BC. 2017. Beef Cow Body Condition Scoring. https://beeflambnz.com/knowledge-hub/PDF/beef-cow-body-condition-scoring [accessed 20 March 2020].

Kenyon PR, Maloney SK, Blache D 2014. Review of sheep body condition score in relation to production characteristics. New Zealand Journal of Agricultural Research 57: 38-64. doi 10.1080/00288233.2013.857698.

Lesmeister JL, Burfening PJ, Blackwell RL 1973. Date of first calving in beef cows and subsequent calf production. Journal of Animal Science 36: 1-6. doi 10.2527/jas1973.3611.

Lopez-Gatius F, Yaniz J, Madriles-Helm D 2003. Effects of body condition score and score change on the reproductive performance of dairy cows: a meta-analysis. Theriogenology 59: 801-812. doi 10.1016/s0093-691x(02)01156-1.

McFadden AM, Heuer C, Jackson R, West DM, Parkinson TJ 2005. Reproductive performance of beef cow herds in New Zealand. New Zealand Veterinary Journal 53: 39-44. doi 10.1080/00480169.2005.36467.

Morris CA, Archer JA 2007. Application of new technologies in New Zealand for beef cattle and deer improvement. New Zealand Journal of Agricultural Research 50: 163-179. doi 10.1080/00288230709510289.

Morris ST, Kenyon PR, Burnhham DL 2002. A comparison of two scales of body condition scoring in Hereford x Friesian beef breeding cows. Proceedings of the New Zealand Grassland Association 64: 121-123.

Morris ST, Morel PCH, Kenyon PR 2006. The effect of individual liveweight and condition of beef cows on their reproductive performance and birth and weaning weights of calves. New Zealand Veterinary Journal 54: 96-100. doi 10.1080/00480169.2006.36619.

R Core Team 2019. R: A Language and Environment for Statistical Computing.

Renquist BJ, Oltjen JW, Sainz RD, Calvert CC 2006. Relationship between body condition score and production of multiparous beef cows. Livestock Science 104: 147-155. doi 10.1016/j.livsci.2006.04.004.

Roche JR, Macdonald KA, Burke CR, Lee JM, Berry DP 2007. Associations among body condition score, body weight, and reproductive performance in seasonal-calving dairy cattle. Journal of Dairy Science 90: 376-391. doi 10.3168/jds.S0022-0302(07)72639-5.

Russel AJF, Doney JM, Gunn RG 1969. Subjective assessment of body fat in live sheep. The Journal of Agricultural Science 72: 451-454. doi 10.1017/S0021859600024874.

Selk GE, Wettemann RP, Lusby KS, Oltjen JW, Mobley SL, Rasby RJ, Garmendia JC 1988. Relationship among weight change, body condition and reproductive performance of range beef cows. Journal of Animal Science 66: 3153-3159. doi 10.2527/jas1988.66123153x.

Smeaton DC, Bown MD, Clayton JB 2000. Optimum liveweight, feed intake, reproduction, and calf output in beef cows on North Island hill country, New Zealand. New Zealand Journal of Agricultural Research 43: 71-82. doi 10.1080/00288233.2000.9513410.

Smeaton DC, Harris BL, Xu ZZ, Vivanco WH 2003. Factors affecting commercial application of embryo technologies in New Zealand: a modelling approach. Theriogenology 59: 617-634. doi 10.1016/S0093-691X(02)01244-X.

Sprott LR, Harris MD, Richardson JW, Gray AW, Forrest DW, Northcutt-Dolezal S, Cundiff LV 1998. Pregnancy to artificial insemination in beef cows as affected by body condition and number of services. The Professional Animal Scientist 14: 231-235. doi 10.15232/S1080-7446(15)31835-0.

Tait IM, Morris ST, Kenyon PR, Garrick DJ, Pleasants AB, Hickson RE 2017. Effect of cow body condition score on inter-calving interval, pregnancy diagnosis, weaning rate and calf weaning weight in beef cattle. Proceedings of the New Zealand Society of Animal Production 77: 23-28.

Vishwanath R 2003. Artificial insemination: the state of the art. Theriogenology 59: 571-584. doi 10.1016/S0093-691X(02)01241-4.

Wagner JJ, Lusby KS, Oltjen JW, Rakestraw J, Wettemann RP, Walters LE 1988. Carcass composition in mature hereford cows: estimation and effect on daily metabolizable energy requirement during winter. Journal of Animal Science 66: 603-612. doi 10.2527/jas1988.663603x.

Whitman RW 1975. Weight change, condition and beef-cow reproduction. PhD. Dissertation Colorado State University. Fort Collins.

BRIEF COMMUNICATION: Influence of birth rank on cause of lamb deaths prior to weaning

BC Thomson*, NB Smith, KR Ward and PD Muir

On-Farm Research Ltd. PO Box 1142, Hastings, New Zealand

**Corresponding author:* Email: bev@on-farm.co.nz

Abstract

Post-mortem examinations were carried out on 1098 lambs that died between birth and weaning at 12 weeks of age to evaluate the causes of mortality in a high-fertility flock. These comprised 95% of all lamb deaths from a total of 14732 lambs born over nine years. Starvation/exposure was the biggest cause of lamb deaths (26%) followed by infection (20%), hypoxia (16%) and prenatal deaths (16%). Prenatal deaths were 18%, 12% and 10%; deaths due to hypoxia were 18%, 15% and 11% and to starvation were 28%, 26% and 12% for triplets, twins and singles respectively. There were no significant differences between birth ranks for deaths from infection.

Keywords: mortality; litter size; birth rank; dystocia; starvation; prenatal; single; twin; triplet; survival; sheep

Introduction

An increasing lambing percentage is associated with an increasing number of triplet lambs (Muir et al. 2005). Triplet survival rates vary widely, and a review by Kenyon et al. (2019) reported that triplet survival rates ranged from 50% to 88% with an average of 68%, compared to survival rates of 86% for twins and 90% for singles. Previously, survival rates at Poukawa averaged 76% for triplets compared to 89% and 91% for twin and single lambs, respectively, over six years (Thomson et al. 2004). The aim of this experiment was to evaluate cause of death and whether this differed between different litter sizes in a farm environment. An understanding of the causes of death in lambs born to high-fecundity ewes will assist in developing management practices to improve lamb survival and returns to farmers.

Materials and methods

Over nine years, lamb survival data was collected on a mixed-age crossbred ewe flock (East Friesian X Romney, Finn X Romney, Poll Dorset X Romney and Romney ewes aged 3 - 8 years and composite ewes aged 2-7 years). The work was carried out at the Poukawa Station in Hawkes Bay, NZ (GPS coordinates -39.745944, 176.731556, elevation 30m a.s.l.) from 2005 to 2015. The climate was winter warm and summer dry (annual average (±SD) temperature of 19.2 ± 3.6 ^{o}C and average rainfall (±SD) of 765 ± 102 mm) and the topography of the farm is flat to gently rolling. Prior to mating, ewes were weighed and body-condition scored (Jefferies 1961) with an average ewe mating weight (±SD) of 64.9 ± 9.6 kg and an average (±SD) body condition score of 3.5 ± 0.6. Data were collected on 8096 ewe-lambing events, 14732 lambs born and 1134 lamb deaths (1098 post-mortemed) between lambing and weaning at twelve weeks of age.

All ewes were vaccinated against clostridial diseases (Multine 5 in 1, MSD Animal Health), toxoplasmosis and campylobacter. Foetal number and age were assessed by a commercial operator using transabdominal ultrasound at or around 65 days of pregnancy. Ewes were rotationally grazed on established perennial ryegrass pastures until lambing. Prior to lambing, ewes were divided into early-, medium- or late-lambing mobs and the mob closest to lambing was divided into single-, twin- and triplet-bearing mobs. Ewes were set-stocked within 1-2 weeks of lambing with single-bearing ewes grazed on hill country on lower pasture covers (1000 kg DM/ha minimum) and twin-bearing ewes on flatter country with pasture covers around 1200 kg DM/ha minimum. Triplet-bearing ewes were set-stocked on higher pasture covers (1400 kg DM/ha minimum) in smaller, flatter, and sheltered paddocks.

All lambing mobs were checked at least twice a day with the triplet mob being checked more frequently. As soon as possible after birth (up to 12 hours after birth when born at night), lambs were tagged and sex and weight recorded. Ewes that had not lambed were quietly moved into another paddock every 1-2 days. When possible, dead lambs were autopsied up to weaning at 12 weeks (McFarlane 1965; Everett-Hincks & Duncan, 2008). Of all the lambs that died, 95% were autopsied. In some cases it was not possible to autopsy lambs for a number of reasons, e.g., partially eaten by hawk or too decomposed when found. Cause of death category was coded as prenatal death, dystocia, hypoxia, abnormal, exposure, starvation, infection, misadventure or unknown. Primary cause was determined by the symptom which occurred earliest. For example, cause of death was defined as dystocia if any dystocia symptoms were present regardless of starvation symptoms. Prenatal death was defined as a mummified foetus or presence of atrophy. Dystocia was defined as the presence of bruising or oedema around the head, shoulders or hind limb, internal bleeding or organ damage. Hypoxia was recorded when lambs had no physical symptoms of dystocia but failed to breathe properly and did not walk. Starvation was recorded when no milk was present in the stomach. Exposure was recorded when some or all of the heart and kidney fat reserves had been utilised. Infection covered a wide range of symptoms including navel infections, lesions, adhesions, scouring, arthritis and pleurisy. Within each death category there was no attempt to determine the reason for the death occurring.

Statistical analysis of the cause of death and survival data was carried out using the Nominal Logistic Regression in Minitab for Windows (version 14). Data was analysed across all lamb deaths and within cause of death category using litter size as the treatment effect. Other potential contributing factors such as birth weight, ewe breed, year etc were not fitted in the model. Cause of death was categorised in post-mortemed lambs up to weaning at 12 weeks of age, but age of death was not evaluated.

Results and discussion

Increasing mortality with increasing litter size is well established (e.g., Kenyon et al. 2019; Kerslake et al. 2005; Muir et al. 2005). In the present dataset, the large number of twin- and triplet-born lambs and their associated higher mortality rates relative to single-born lambs meant they made up the majority (86%) of the dead lambs (Table 1). Although single lambs made up 16.3% of lambs born, they only made up 8.5% of the lamb deaths. While 29% of the quadruplets and quintuplets died, they only made up 0.01% of total lambs born, so their contribution to overall flock mortality was small (5.3%).

The percentage of dead lambs that died prenatally increased with birth rank (9.6% in singles to 18.4% in triplets). Prenatal deaths included late pregnancy abortions, non-viable early lambs and mummified foetuses. There is a greater risk of placental insufficiency with increasing litter size and, thus, decreased lamb survival (Kenyon et al. 2007, Mellor & Stafford, 2004). In addition, triplet-bearing ewes generally have a greater chance of metabolic upset (e.g., pregnancy toxaemia), becoming immobilised (cast) or having a vaginal prolapse (Muir et al, 2005). It is hard to determine whether this prenatal category is included in many reports (e.g., Everett-Hincks et al. 2007; Everett-Hincks & Dodds, 2008: Kerslake et al. 2005).

Kerslake et al. (2005) identified that of the lambs that died, 30% failed to breathe and of those that breathed, 23% never walked. In the current study, the percentage of dead lambs that did not breathe fully (hypoxia classification) increased with increasing birth rank from 10.6% in singles to 17.7% in triplets. Duration of parturition increases with litter size (Cloete et al. 1993) and Everett-Hincks et al. (2007) found increased duration of parturition was associated with decreased lamb survival.

In single (Everett & Dodds, 2008) and twin lambs (Kerslake et al. 2005) higher birth weights were associated with increased deaths from dystocia. However, Thomson et al. (2004) found that death rates in single-born lambs only increased at birth weights above 8 kg. In triplets, however, Everett-Hincks and Dodds (2008) reported that lower birth weights increased dystocia death rates. In the current study, dystocia death rates in triplet lambs were relatively low, possibly due to the frequency of shepherding. Dystocia can also result in lambs being slower to suckle or less active, thus increasing the risk of starvation and like Kerslake et al. (2005), these lambs were also deemed to have died of dystocia. Nevertheless, the total level of dystocia in this flock (8.8% dead lambs) was lower than the 48% dystocia (range 3 to 80%) reported by Kerslake et al. (2005) for twin and triplet lambs and the 33% for twins and triplets reported by Kenyon et al. (2019). But both these studies only examined effects in the first few weeks of life when the deaths from dystocia occur, and didn't include later deaths from other causes.

In the present study, starvation rates increased with increasing litter size (Table 1) and accounted for 25.8% of total lamb deaths to weaning at 12 weeks of age. McCutcheon et al. (1981) found starvation/exposure accounted for about 30% of lamb deaths on farms. As lambs grow, their energy requirement increases and, in

Table 1 The pattern of lamb deaths (number of lambs (percentage of lambs)) from pre-birth to weaning at 12 weeks by litter size and cause of death as determined by post-mortem of lambs born to crossbred ewes over nine years in Hawkes Bay.

	Birth rank					
	1	2	3	4	5	Average
No born	2402	8892	3249	192	15	14732
No died/removed*	96	481	497	55	5	1134
% died	4.0[a]	5.4[a]	15[b]	28.8[ab]	33.3[ab]	11.4
Prenatal	9 (9.6)[a]	58 (12.4)[b]	88 (18.4)[c]	16 (30.2)[abc]	0	15.7
Hypoxia	10 (10.6)[a]	72 (15.4)[b]	85 (17.7)[c]	8 (15.1)[abc]	2 (40.0)[abc]	16.1
Dystocia	20 (21.3)	37 (7.9)	34 (7.1)	6 (11.3)	0	8.8
Exposure	3 (3.2)	17 (3.6)	16 (3.3)	2 (3.8)	0	3.5
Starvation	11 (11.7)[a]	121 (25.9)[b]	134 (28.0)[c]	17 (32.1)[abc]	0	25.8
Misadventure	4 (4.3)	10 (2.1)	10 (2.1)	0	0	2.2
Infection	22 (23.4)	108 (23.1)	81 (16.9)	3 (5.7)	1 (20.0)	19.6
Abnormal	6 (6.4)	18 (3.9)	7 (1.5)	1 (1.9)	1(20.0)	2.9
Other	0	4 (0.9)	0	0	1 (20.0)	0.4
Undiagnosed	9 (9.6)	22 (4.7)	24 (5.0)	0	0	5.0

*Includes lambs removed that lived. [abc]different superscripts indicate significant differences (P<0.05) between birth ranks based on a nominal logistic regression. Litters with 4 and 5 lambs were not significantly different due to insufficient numbers. No superscripts indicate no significant differences

multiples, this increased demand is less likely to be matched by increasing ewe milk supply (Muir et al. 2000; Peterson et al. 2006). Initially there is a limit to how much pasture a lamb is able to successfully substitute for the lack of ewe's milk and is probably why starvation deaths continue to occur for up to six weeks. The present study recorded for longer than most other studies (e.g., Everett- Hincks & Dodds, 2008; Kerslake et al. 2005) and includes lambs that died of starvation at older ages as well as those that died in the first few days after birth. A relatively mild climate and shelter (Muir et al, 2005) is associated with low rates of mortality and this may be why the deaths from exposure are low (3.5%) in this present study.

Infection appeared to cause high numbers of deaths in the current study (20% of all deaths) but it is difficult to know whether this is normal as most studies only report post-mortem data for the first three days after parturition. In older lambs, infections tended to be seen as adhesions or lesions around the liver, heart and lungs. It is possible that our mild lambing environment meant that more lambs with minor issues survived but were more vulnerable to infections.

This study's results differ from previous studies (e.g., Everett-Hincks et al. 2007; Everett-Hincks & Dodds, 2008: Kerslake et al. 2005) in that deaths were monitored up until weaning at twelve weeks in high-fecundity sheep, and lambing occurred in a different environment. The wider time frame and inclusion of deaths prior to parturition means that the proportions of lambs that died in each category differs from these previous studies and varies with litter size. This means that the type of changes in management required to reduce death rates will change as lambing percentage increases. In addition, the importance of the deaths from starvation, infection and those that occur shortly before the start of parturition means that further work is needed on why this is happening and how they can be prevented is needed.

Acknowledgements

The authors would like to acknowledge the assistance of John Lane, Stuart MacMillan, Graham Wallace and Rebecca Woodhouse for helping with the lambing and autopsy data collection. This work was funded by B+LNZ.

References

Cloete SWP, Halderen A, Schneider DJ 1993. Causes of perinatal lamb mortality amongst Dormer and Mutton Merino lambs. Journal of South African Veterinary Association 64: 121-125.

Everett-Hincks JM, Dodds KG, Kerslake JI 2007. Parturition duration and birthing difficulty in twin and triplet lambs. Proceedings of the New Zealand Society of Animal production 67: 55-60.

Everett-Hincks JM, Dodds KG 2008. Management of maternal-offspring behaviour to improve lamb survival in easy care sheep systems. Journal of Animal Science 86: E259-E270.

Everett-Hincks JM, Duncan SJ 2008. Lamb post-mortem protocol for use on farm: to diagnose primary cause of lamb death from birth to 3 days of age. The Open Veterinary Science Journal 2: 55-62.

Jefferies BC 1961. Body condition scoring and its use in management. Tasmanian Journal of Agriculture 32: 19-21.

Kenyon PR, Roca Fraga FJ, Blumer S, Thompson AN 2019. Triplet lambs and their dams- a review of current knowledge and management systems. New Zealand Journal of Agricultural Research 62: 399-437.

Kenyon PR, Stafford KJ, Jenkinson CMC, Morris ST, West DM 2007. The body composition and metabolic state of twin- and triplet-bearing ewes and their foetuses in late pregnancy. Livestock Science 107: 103-112.

Kerslake, JL, Everett-Hincks JM, Campbell AW 2005. Lamb survival: a new examination of an old problem. Proceedings of the New Zealand Society of Animal Production 65: 13-18.

McCutcheon SN, Holmes CW, McDonald MF 1981. The starvation-exposure syndrome and neonatal lamb mortality: a review. Proceedings of the New Zealand Society of Animal Production 41: 209-217.

McFarlane D 1965. Perinatal lamb losses. 1. An autopsy method for the investigation of perinatal losses. New Zealand Veterinary Journal 13: 116-135.

Mellor DJ, Stafford KJ 2004. Animal welfare implications of neonatal mortality and morbidity in farm animals. Veterinary Journal 168: 118-133.

Muir PD, Thomson BC, Knight TW 2005. Factors affecting lamb survival. Proceedings from the 35th Seminar of the Society of Sheep and Beef Cattle Veterinarians NZVA. Pp 73-82.

Muir PD, Smith NB, Wallace GJ, Fugle CJ, Bown MB 2000. Maximising lamb growth rates. Proceedings of the New Zealand Grassland Association 62 :55-58.

Peterson SW, Kenyon PR, Morris ST 2006. Do ewes with twin and triplet lambs produce different yields of milk and does the grazing behaviour of their lambs differ? Proceedings of the New Zealand Society of Animal Production 66: 444-449.

Thomson BC, Muir PD, Smith NB 2004. Litter size, lamb survival, birth and twelve week weights in lambs born to cross-bred ewes. Proceedings of the New Zealand Grassland Association 66: 233-237.

Relationship between gamma-glutamyl transferase (GGT) concentrations and lying behaviour in dairy cattle

M Sutherland[a]*, F Huddart[a], G Lowe[a], N Cox[b], E Cuttance[c] and K Schütz[a]

[a]*AgResearch Ltd., Ruakura Research Centre, Hamilton 3216, New Zealand;* [b]*NeilStat Ltd, 9 Ngaere Ave, Hamilton 3210, New Zealand;* [c]*VetEnt, Te Awamutu 3800, New Zealand*

**Corresponding author.* Email: mhairi.sutherland@agresearch.co.nz

Abstract

Facial eczema (FE) in livestock results in liver damage, impaired production and welfare, and is a significant problem in New Zealand. The pathology of this disease has been described in sheep and cattle, however, few studies have investigated the behavioural response to FE and whether behaviour can be used as an indicator of FE. Therefore, the aim of this study was to evaluate lying behaviour of dairy cattle with FE. Six farms located in the North Island of New Zealand with confirmed cases of FE were selected (n=391 lactating cows). Blood samples were collected to analyse gamma-glutamyl transferase (GGT) concentrations and three days of continuous lying behaviour were recorded using accelerometers. There was no correlation between GGT concentrations and either lying times (r^2=0.0008) or lying bout frequency (r^2=0.0008) when all animals were included in the analysis. In addition, lying times (means±SEM: Low: 9±0.1 h/d, High: 9±0.1 h/d; P=0.347) and lying bout frequency (means±SEM: Low: 8±0.2 no. bouts/d, High: 8±0.2 no. bouts/d; P=0.149) did not differ between pair-matched cows with Low (≤ 89 IU/L) or High (≥ 123 IU/L) GGT concentrations. Therefore, it does not appear as though lying behaviour, measured using accelerometers, is associated with GGT levels in dairy cattle.

Keywords: facial eczema; gamma-glutamyl transferase; lying behaviour

Introduction

Facial eczema (FE) or pithomycotoxicosis, a disease that affects ruminants and camelids, is found in all temperate climate zones in the world and commonly occurs in late summer and autumn in the North Island of New Zealand. Animals get FE after eating large numbers of fungal spores produced by *Pithomyces chartarum* which contain the toxin sporidesmin. Ingestion of sporidesmin causes occlusion of the bile ducts and liver damage (Smith & Towers 2002). Photosensitivity then occurs when phylloerythrin, a breakdown product of chlorophyll, is not eliminated from the body but instead accumulates in the blood (Clare 1944). When phylloerythrin reaches high levels, photosensitisation of unpigmented and hairless areas of the skin occurs in response to sunlight (Clare 1944) and these areas can then become reddened, raised and oedematous (Mortimer & Ronaldson 1983). However, most animals affected with FE do not show clinical signs, though they still can have liver damage: for every cow in a herd with skin lesions, up to 10 or more may be affected sub-clinically (Faull 1986). Even though cattle may not show clinical signs of FE they may still be experiencing adverse effects. Serum GGT levels are commonly used to diagnose FE in sheep and cattle, as GGT concentrations have been shown to increase proportionally with sporidesmin-induced liver damage in both species (Towers & Smith 1978; Towers & Stratton 1978).

Facial eczema is generally not fatal, however, it causes liver damage, reduced feed intake, decreased production, and discomfort (Morris et al. 2004). Limited scientific research is available demonstrating the impact of this disease on ruminant behaviour. Anecdotally, once animals become photosensitive from FE, they will often seek shade and may respond to skin irritation by head shaking, skin rubbing and restlessness (Morris et al. 2004). There is little other scientific information regarding the behavioural response of cows with FE and whether animal behaviour can be used as an early indicator of animals with FE. It would, therefore, be of interest to assess how FE affects the behaviour of dairy cattle.

Lying behaviour is an important welfare indicator in cattle (Haley et al. 2000) and well-fed, pastured, lactating dairy cattle spend between 8.3 and 10.1 h/24 h lying down (Kendall et al. 2006; Tucker et al. 2007, 2008; Fisher et al., 2008; Schütz et al. 2013). Health status can affect lying behaviour in dairy cattle; for example, cows performed fewer and longer lying bouts during the three days before clinical diagnosis of metritis (Neave et al. 2018) and a similar pattern was observed in calves before clinical signs of neonatal calf diarrhoea appeared (Lowe et al. 2019). Therefore, lying behaviour could potentially be used as an indicator of FE, possibly even sub-clinical FE, in cattle. Lying behaviour can now be measured relatively non-invasively using accelerometer data loggers that have been validated for measuring lying behaviour of cattle (Ledgerwood et al. 2010). The aim of this study was to evaluate lying behaviour of dairy cattle with FE (e.g., elevated serum GGT concentrations).

Materials and methods

Between March and May 2018 (southern hemisphere autumn) six dairy farms located in the North Island of New Zealand were selected due to cows in those herds having current outbreaks of FE and high GGT concentrations. This study was part of a larger research project designed to determine both the cost and animal welfare implications of sub-clinical facial eczema in dairy cattle. All procedures involving animals were approved by the Ruakura Animal Ethics Committee (no. 14361) under the New Zealand Animal Welfare Act 1999.

Blood samples were collected from the coccygeal (tail) vein of cattle into tubes that contained no anticoagulant. Blood samples were left to sit at room temperature in an upright position for approximately 30 minutes. Serum samples were analysed for GGT enzyme activity at 37°C, using a Roche colorimetric method and Modular Analytics Model P analyser (Roche Diagnostics, Auckland, NZ).

In total, 413 cows from the six farms were selected based on GGT concentrations, days in milk, milk yield, calving date, age and breed. Cows with GGT concentrations ≥ 123 IU/L were match paired with cows with similar days in milk, milk yield, calving date, age and breed, but with GGT concentrations ≤ 89 IU/L. Due to missing data from some animals it was only possible to include 167 complete matched pairs in the analysis (n = 334 cows).

Once these cows were selected, a HOBO pendant G accelerometer data logger (64k, Onset Computer Corporation, Bourne, MA, USA) was attached to each cow to record lying behaviour continuously for at least three days. The time between blood sampling, selecting animals for inclusion in the trial and attaching the accelerometers to the cows meant that there was a delay between blood sampling and recording of lying behaviour of 14 to 30 days. Following the methodology described by Schütz et al. (2019), the accelerometers were set to record the y- and z-axes continuously at 1-min intervals. The accelerometers were placed in a fabric pouch held in position by Velcro patches and attached on the lateral side of the hind leg above the metatarsophalangeal joint. The data were downloaded using HOBOware Pro software (Onset Corp., Pocasset, MA) and converted to daily summaries of lying behaviour (total lying times and bout information) calculated in SAS 9.3 (SAS Institute Inc., Cary, NC, USA) using a code designed for this purpose (AWP UBC, 2015). Lying behaviour was analysed over three consecutive days (72 h in total) for each cow.

Statistical analysis

The lying data were analysed using a rank transformation, due to the data being clearly inconsistent with the normal distribution. An ANOVA was run in Genstat, version 19 (VSN International, Hemel Hempstead, UK) and the model included the blocking effects of farm and pair (within farm) and treatment effect for GGT category (Low or High).

Results

From the original 413 cows, data were successfully collected from only 391 cows due to accelerometer failure (lost accelerometers or corrupted files). Farm and animal information for these cows is summarised in Table 1.

Table 1 Farm and cow information for the six enrolled dairy farms located in the North Island of New Zealand between March and May 2018.

			Age		Days in milk			GGT concentrations (IU/L)		
Farm	Region	No. cows tested	Mean	Range	Mean	Range	Sampling gap[1]	Mean	SD	Range
1	Taranaki	71	12	(7 - 15)	216	(172 - 237)	14	961	1267.2	(2 - 5278)
2	Waikato	104	11	(8 - 15)	230	(195 - 265)	20	456	710.7	(1 - 3635)
3	Northland	42	11	(7 - 15)	240	(196 - 259)	17	333	440.8	(3 - 2055)
4	Taranaki	39	13	(8 - 15)	218	(170 - 249)	17	285	545.7	(4 - 2809)
5	Bay of Plenty	107	12	(5 - 15)	230	(171 - 289)	30	773	1058.4	(3 - 5158)
6	Waikato	28	13	(6 - 15)	223	(189 - 250)	30	513	786.2	(3 - 2495)

GGT = Gamma-glutamyl transferase

[1]Sampling gap is the number of days between cows being blood sampled and when lying behaviour was recorded.

Table 2 Mean (± SD) gamma-glutamyl transferase (GGT) concentrations, daily lying times and frequency of lying bouts for cows categorised as having Low or High GGT concentrations (n = 167 matched pairs) on six dairy farms in the North Island of New Zealand between March and May 2018.

		GGT concentrations (IU/L)				Lying time (h/24 h)				Lying bouts (no./24 h)			
Farm	Cows (no.)	Low	SD	High	SD	Low	SD	High	SD	Low	SD	High	SD
1	46	37.3	25.01	1783.3	1161.4	9.7	1.47	9.6	1.62	7.8	2.38	7.4	1.81
2	92	19.5	12.90	883.6	736.3	9.7	1.46	9.6	1.66	9.1	3.07	8.7	2.51
3	32	23.8	18.36	675.7	509.7	7.7	1.38	7.8	1.12	7.1	2.16	7.2	2.20
4	38	16.8	11.24	567.2	669.3	9.9	1.69	9.0	1.31	9.1	1.97	8.1	1.72
5	100	22.1	19.09	1509.4	1112.1	9.0	1.75	8.9	1.73	10.3	2.57	10.1	2.70
6	26	22.2	9.38	1056.5	864.6	8.8	2.99	9.1	3.18	6.7	2.00	7.5	2.35

Figure 1 Relationship between daily lying times and gamma-glutamyl transferase (GGT) concentrations in dairy cattle (n = 391) on six dairy farms in the North Island of New Zealand between March and May 2018.

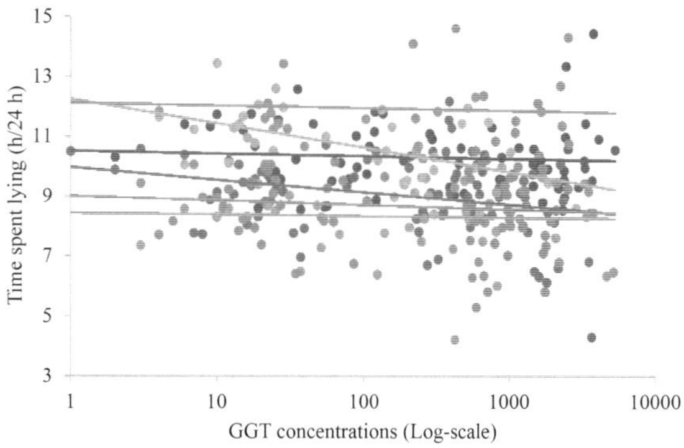

Figure 2 Relationship between number of lying bouts and gamma-glutamyl transferase (GGT) concentrations in dairy cattle (n = 391) on six dairy farms in the North Island of New Zealand between March and May 2018.

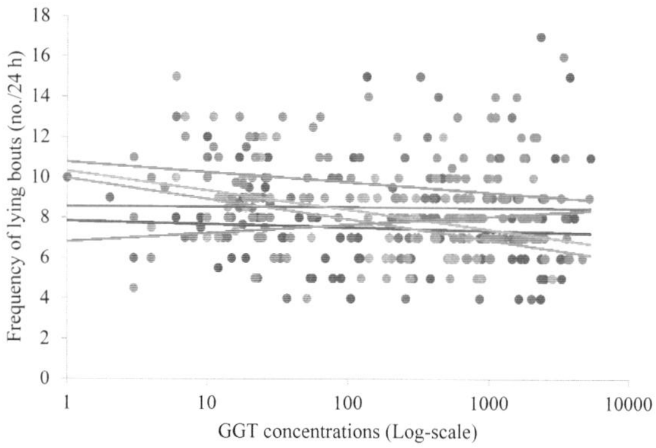

Daily lying times and number of lying bouts, averaged over the three data-collection days, are plotted against the GGT concentrations for each animal in figures 1 and 2, respectively. There was no relationship between GGT concentrations and lying times ($r^2 = 0.0008$) or number of lying bouts ($r^2 = 0.0008$) when all 391 cows were included in the analysis.

Due to missing data from some cows, data analysis was based only on 167 matched pairs (n = 334 cows). The range of GGT concentrations for cows categorised as Low and High, across all matched pair cows on the six farms, was 1 – 89 IU/L and 123 – 5278 IU/L, respectively. GGT concentrations, daily lying times and frequency of lying bouts for cows categorised as having Low or High GGT concentrations on the six study farms are presented in Table 2.

Time spent lying, averaged over three days and the six farms, did not differ between the Low and High cows (mean ± SEM: Low: 9 ± 0.1 h/d, High: 9 ± 0.1 h/d; P = 0.347). The frequency of lying bouts, averaged over three days and the six farms, did not differ between the Low and High cows (mean ± SEM: Low: 8 ± 0.2 no. bouts/d, High: 8 ± 0.2 no. bouts/d; P = 0.149).

Discussion

There appeared to be no relationship between GGT concentrations and lying behaviour in dairy cattle; however, two farms did show a slight negative correlation between lying times and GGT concentrations. Due to logistical reasons, lying behaviour was not measured at the same time, or directly after, blood samples were taken to determine GGT concentrations. Depending on the farm, lying behaviour was measured 14 to 30 days after blood samples were taken. It is, therefore, likely that GGT concentrations at the time that lying behaviour was recorded were different than those initially measured. However, previous studies in cattle and sheep suggest that GGT concentrations rise within two weeks after a naturally or experimentally induced sporidesmin challenge and can remain elevated for several weeks after this initial exposure (Blackshaw 1978; Towers & Smith 1978; Towers & Stratton 1978). Therefore, cattle with elevated GGT levels in the current study may still have had elevated GGT concentrations at the time lying behaviour was measured, but concentrations might have changed and not be reflected in the analysis. There is still limited evidence for how GGT levels develop with a natural challenge on-farm and with previous exposure of sporidesmin. It would have been ideal to know the actual GGT concentrations of the cows at the time lying behaviour was recorded. For example, GGT concentrations of 'High' cattle may have declined or GGT concentrations of 'Low' cows may have been in the process of increasing. Without being able to confirm when these animals were exposed to sporidesmin, or how often they were exposed, it is not possible to know what stage of infection or degree of liver damage these animals would have been experiencing, hence, the results in the present study need to be interpreted with caution, and we recommend that more research is undertaken to investigate the relationship between behaviour and FE. It is also worth noting that the cows enrolled in this study, which were selected based on GGT concentrations and their matched pairs, ended up being older animals; the mean age ranged between 11 and 13 years, and we speculate that previous exposure to FE might have affected the livers of these animals ability to produce GGT. Hence, this could have influenced our results, and we recommend that more research investigating the effect of history of liver damage on the excretion of GGT and how this in turn influences animal responses, is needed.

It is unclear why farms 2 and 4 showed a slight negative correlation between lying times and GGT concentrations. The gap between blood sampling and measuring lying behaviour on farms 2 and 4, was 20 and 17 days, respectively. No correlation between lying times and GGT concentrations were observed on farm 1, which only had a sampling gap of 14 days. Therefore, timing of sampling likely does not explain the slight negative correlations observed on farms 2 and 4. In addition, as mentioned earlier, previous exposure to sporidesmin and possible liver damage may have accounted for the variation in the responses we observed among farms.

The lying times recorded in the present study are, in general, within the range of studies with well-fed lactating dairy cattle in New Zealand (Kendall et al. 2006; Tucker et al. 2007, 2008; Fisher et al. 2008; Schütz et al. 2013) except for one farm in Northland where cows had low lying times (a reduction > 1 h/24 h) compared to the other farms. We did not measure weather conditions at the time of testing, but it was noted that it was very warm at the time of recording of lying times on the Northland farm. It is well-known that cows spend less time lying in warm weather (Tucker et al. 2008; Schütz et al. 2010) and this could be a potential explanation for the lower lying times on the Northland farm.

Lying behaviour in an important welfare indicator in cattle and can be measured relatively non-invasively, and with minor labour input, using accelerometer data loggers. Therefore, we chose to investigate whether lying behaviour could be used to detect FE in cattle in the present study. Since feed intake and milk production is affected by FE (Morris et al. 2004), other behaviours such as grazing would have been beneficial to measure, however, it was not feasible in the present study. Up until recently, it has not been possible to measure grazing activity automatically, though with recent developments in technology, this is now feasible, and we encourage further research investigating the behavioural responses of cows to FE.

In summary, clinical signs of FE are the result of photosensitisation causing unpigmented and hairless areas of skin to become irritated (Mortimer & Ronaldson 1983). Anecdotaly, animals respond to the discomfort and pain caused by photosensitisation by seeking shade, head shaking, skin rubbing and restlessness (Morris et al. 2004). Animals that show these clinical signs of FE, and possibly cows with sub-clinical FE, are likely to experience discomfort from the disease process and possible negative affective states, such as pain and perhaps nausea. We, therefore, recommend further studies investigating behavioural responses of cattle with FE, in particular sub-clinical FE.

Acknowledgments

The authors gratefully acknowledge the technical assistance from AgResearch staff and the farmers who kindly agreed to participate in this study. This project was funded by the Ministry of Primary Industry Sustainable Farming Fund and by the Ministry of Business, Innovation and Employment (Wellington, New Zealand, contract no. C10X0813).

References

Blackshaw C 1978. Serum gamma-glutamyl transferase in the diagnosis of liver disease in cattle. New Zealand Veterinary Journal 26: 1-2.

Clare NT 1944. Photosensitivity diseases in New Zealand. III The photosensitizing agent in facial eczema. The New Zealand Journal of Science and Technology 25: 202-220.

Faull BW 1986. Facial eczema surveillance. Surveillance, New Zealand 13: 3-4.

Fisher AD, Roberts N, Bluett SJ, Verkerk GA, Matthews LR 2008. Effects of shade provision on the behaviour, body temperature and milk production of grazing dairy cows during a New Zealand summer. New Zealand Journal of Agricultural Research 51: 99-105.

Haley DB, Rushen J, Passillé AM 2000. Behavioural indicators of cow comfort: activity and resting behaviour of dairy cows in two types of housing. Canadian Journal of Animal Science 80: 257-63.

Kendall PE, Nielsen PP, Webster JR, Verkerk GA, Littlejohn RP, Matthews LR 2006. The effects of providing shade to lactating dairy cows in a temperate climate. Livestock Science 103: 148-157.

Ledgerwood DN, Winckler C, Tucker CB 2010. Evaluation of data loggers, sampling intervals, and editing techniques for measuring the lying behavior of dairy cattle. Journal of Dairy Science 93: 5129-5139.

Lowe GL, Sutherland MA, Waas JR, Schaefer AL, Cox NR, Stewart M 2019. Physiological and behavioral responses as indicators for early disease detection in dairy calves. Journal of Dairy Science 102: 5389-5402.

Morris CA, Towers NR, Hohenboken WD, Maqbool N, Smith BL, Phua SH 2004. Inheritance of resistance to facial eczema: a review of research findings from sheep and cattle in New Zealand. New Zealand Veterinary Journal. 52: 205-215.

Mortimer PH, Ronaldson JW 1983. Fungal-toxin-induced photosensitization. In: Keeler RF, Tu AT eds. Handbook of Natural Toxins. New York, Marcell Dekker. Vol 1. Pg. 361–419.

Neave HW, Lomb J, Weary DM, LeBlanc SJ, Huzzey JM, von Keyserlingk MAG 2018. Behavioral changes before metritis diagnosis in dairy cows. Journal of Dairy Science 101: 4388-4399.

Schütz KE, Rogers AR, Poulouin YA, Cox NR, Tucker CB 2010. The amount of shade influences the behavior and physiology of dairy cattle. Journal of Dairy Science 93: 125-133.

Schütz KE, Cox NR, Macdonald KA, Roche JR, Verkerk GA, Rogers AR, Tucker CB, Matthews LR, Meier S, Webster JR 2013. Behavioral and physiological effects of a short-term feed restriction in lactating dairy cattle with different body condition scores at calving. Journal of Dairy Science 96: 4465-4476.

Schütz KE, Cave VM, Cox NR, Huddart FJ, Tucker CB 2019. Effects of three types of bedding surface on dairy cattle behavior, preference, and hygiene. Journal of Dairy Science 102: 1530-1541.

Smith BL, Towers NR 2002. Mycotoxicosis of grazing animals in New Zealand. New Zealand Veterinary Journal 50: 28-345.

Towers NR, Smith BL 1978. The protective effect of zinc sulphate in experimental sporidesmin intoxication of lactating dairy cows. New Zealand Veterinary Journal 26: 199-202.

Towers NR, Stratton G 1978. Serum gamma-glutamyl-transferase as a measure of sporidesmin-induced liver damage in sheep. New Zealand Veterinary Journal 26: 109-12.

Tucker CB, Dalley DE, Burke J-LK, Clark DA 2007. Milking cows once daily influences behavior and udder firmness at peak and mid lactation. Journal of Dairy Science 90: 1692-1703.

Tucker CB, Rogers AR, Schütz KE 2008. Effect of solar radiation on dairy cattle behaviour, use of shade and body temperature in a pasture-based system. Applied Animal Behaviour Science 109: 141-154.

UBC AWP. 2013. UBC Animal Welfare Program: SOP - HOBO Data Loggers. pp. 1 - 23. University of British Columbia, Vancouver, Canada

Effect of breed and paddock activity on bone mass and strength in three beef cattle breeds

L Bijen[c], MJ Gibson[ab], PJ Back[ab], RE Hickson[b], A van Knegsel[c] and CW Rogers[ab]

[a]*School of Veterinary Science, Massey University, New Zealand,* [b]*School of Agriculture and Environment, Massey University, New Zealand ,* [c]*Wageningen University & Research, Wageningen, The Netherlands.*

Corresponding author: Email: c.w.rogers@massey.ac.nz

Abstract

There are obvious phenotypic differences among beef cattle breeds, but, to date, there are limited data on the effect of breed and pasture-based management systems on the bone mass and strength of the distal limb bone (metacarpals). The left 3rd/4th metacarpal bones were collected from a cohort of Angus (AA) (n= 17), Angus × Friesian (AF) (n=13), and Angus × Jersey (AJ) (n=13) cows aged nine years at slaughter. Prior to slaughter the cohort had been intensively monitored as part of longevity- and GPS-based paddock-activity trials. Measures of metacarpal bone mass and strength were assessed using peripheral quantitative computed tomography (pQCT) scanning at the mid-diaphysis after slaughter. Locomotion parameters, based on GPS data when grazing, were collected when four and five years old. The AA and AF cows had significantly greater slaughter weight than AJ (598±14 *vs* 586±18 *vs* 514±17 kg, P<0.01 respectively). AA cows had lower wither height than AF and AJ (1288±6 *vs* 1311±8 *vs* 1269±7 mm, P<0.01) and shorter metacarpal bone length (198±2, *vs* 207±2 *vs* 210±2 mm, P<0.05). At the mid-diaphyseal site, AF and AJ cows had greater bone mineral density $(BMD)_v$ than did AA cows (977±8 *vs* 1018±9 *vs* 1019±9 mg/cm^3, respectively, P<0.001), but had less cross-sectional area (882±16 *vs* 816±18 *vs* 731±18 g/cm^3, P<0.05 respectively). Across all breeds, there was a negative relationship of slaughter weight with BMD_v. No significant relationships were found between distance walked on moderate and steep terrain (GPS data) and the pQCT measures. Breed influenced the size and structure of the metacarpal bone, which altered the material properties (pQCT) measured. The limited amount of high-strain-rate exercise in these cattle may explain the lack of association between locomotion data and measures of bone mass and strength.

Keywords: bovine; bone; GPS; locomotion; beef

Introduction

Under commercial conditions, beef cattle are commonly grazed on areas of steep hill country, often in summer-dry regions with soil of low fertility. Most beef animals are farmed together with sheep, as the stock classes are complementary to one another with respect to animal health and pasture management (Geenty & Morris 2017). In addition to beef production, beef cattle contribute to pasture quality management and support optimal grass yield (McCall 1994).

To understand the effect of activity on bone mass and strength of cattle, knowledge on how cattle utilize differing slopes and terrain is important. Early work showed that cattle tended to use land with some slopes extensively, and others not at all, or only slightly (Cook 1966). The influence of slope steepness on the distribution of cattle on mountainous rangeland in the USA showed that 81% of the variation in relative grazing use was accounted for by slope steepness and distance upslope from the bottom (Mueggler 1965), and cattle preferred slopes less than 4% (Pinchak et al. 1991). More recent work in New Zealand (Martin et al. 2015) reported that beef breeding cows grazing hill country in winter generally avoided steep terrain; only about 5% of their movements were recorded on steep terrain. The preference of cattle for more level terrain is also influenced by herbage availability. Lower herbage availability resulted in a more-equal distribution of grazing over different types of terrain (Henkin et al. 2012).

In horses, increasing pasture exercise has been demonstrated to alter a number of measures of bone mass and strength (Rogers et al. 2008a; Rogers et al., 2008b). A study in the USA using Holstein calves demonstrated that the level of exercise, number of load cycles and relative velocity of the gait in particular, required to induce positive changes in the metacarpal bones were low compared to those published for horses (Logan et al. 2019). These data indicate that there may be an early developmental window for the stimulation of bone development in cattle and that the relative velocity required to induce change is lower than that observed in horses. The reasons for the between-species difference may be due to the initial starting values, as horses are a cursorial animal and start life with a very well-developed musculoskeletal system (Rogers & Dittmer 2019). In comparison, cattle as grazing ruminants would provide a much lower general baseline strain rate to the distal limb with a high proportion of activity based around standing and grazing, rather than bursts of high-speed activity such as canter and gallop.

Under commercial conditions however, management of cattle on steep hill country could provide exposure to brief periods of high-strain rates that, in theory, should be osteoinductive. Quantification of activity, and hence load cycles, on slopes of different aspect could help our understanding of the relative strains grazing on different slopes provides and the relative bone responses associated with these loads.

As present in New Zealand there are limited data published on measures of bone mass and strength in cattle managed under commercial conditions. Preliminary data on dairy cattle in relation to humeral fractures have demonstrated the value of using peripheral quantitative computed tomography (pQCT) to quantify bone mass and strength (Dittmer et al. 2016, Gibson et al. 2019).

The aim of this study was to quantify bone mass and strength in the metacarpus of a cohort of commercially-managed beef and beef-dairy cross cows that had been part of a productivity trial and, hence, had thorough documentation of management, reproduction and pasture activity.

Materials and methods

Animals

The beef breeding cows used in this study were a convenience sample (subset) of the cows (n=47) originating from the beef cow productivity study (Hickson et al. 2015;Martin et al. 2015). At the end of the experiment all cows were sent to slaughter at a local abattoir. At slaughter at the completion of the cows' ninth year, the left metacarpal bone (third and fourth metacarpal, Mc3/4) were collected from all the cows. The cows were of the following crosses: Angus × Angus (AA, n=17), Angus × Friesian (AF, n=13), and Angus × Jersey (AJ, n=13) crosses. Description of the management of the cows, productivity, and collection of slaughter weight and height of the cows are published in detail (Martin et al. 2015).

GPS data

The detailed account of the GPS measurement and observation was reported by Martin et al. (2015). In brief, the cows wore custom-made GPS collars that logged positional data whenever a cow moved ≥4 m, or at one-minute intervals if the cow did not move. The total distance walked per day and the daily distance walked on gentle (slope < 17°), moderate (17° ≥ slope <35°), and steep terrain (≥35° slope) were recorded for six days consecutively in either winter 2012 or 2013. Each breed (AA, AJ and AF) wasassigned a separate paddock during the observation period. The average total distance walked per day (TDW), the average distance walked on gentle terrain per day (DWG), the average distance walked on moderate terrain per day (DWM), and the average distance walked on steep terrain per day (DWS) were calculated for each cow.

pQCT scanning

At slaughter, the left Mc3/4 was dissected out and frozen (–20°C) until subsequent peripheral quantitative computed tomography (pQCT) scanning with an XCT-2000 scanner (pQCT; XCT 2000, Stratec Medical). The mid-diaphysis of each bone was scanned using pQCT with the bone being scanned at 50% of the total bone length starting from the distal end with a voxel size of 0.3 mm^3. Voxels were assigned, within the manufactuer's software, as either "trabecular" bone (≤710 mg/mL), or as "cortical" bone (>710 mg/mL). Data derived from the scan included measures of total bone content, cortical and subcortical bone content, cortical and subcortical density, trabecular content, trabecular density, total area, trabecular area, cortical and subcortical area, cortical content, cortical density, cortical area, cortical thickness, periosteal circumference, endosteal circumference, and the stress strain index.

Statistical analyses

Data were tested for normality using the Shapiro-Wilks test. Differences among breeds for GPS and bone parameters were tested using a general linear model. Multiple comparisons with *post hoc* tests were corrected for using a Bonferroni correction. All analyses were completed within Stata 12 (StataCorp LP, College Station, TX, USA) with significance set at P <0.05.

Results

The AA and AF cows had significantly greater slaughter weight than the AJ cows (598 ± 14 vs 586 ± 18 *vs* 514 ± 17 kg, respectively, P <0.01). Angus cows had lower withers height than AF and AJ (1288 ± 6 *vs.* 1311 ± 8 *vs.* 1269 ± 7 mm, P<0.01) and shorter metacarpal bone length (198 ± 2, 207 ± 2 *vs.* 210 ± 2 mm, P<0.05). The distance walked on gentle terrain and distance walked on moderate terrain primarily contributed to the total distance walked per cow per day (Figure 1).

The pQCT-derived bone measures of the mid-diaphysis of each breed are presented in Table 1. Within each parameter there was a significant breed effect (P<0.001). Angus cows had the largest bones with the greatest periosteal circumference (PeriC) and bone mineral content (BA, PeriC, and BMC). Despite the Angus cows having a lower volumetric bone mineral density, the greater

Table 1: pQCT-derived bone parameters from the mid-diaphyseal site (50% of bone length) for Angus (AA), Angus × Friesian (AF), and Angus × Jersey (AJ) cross breeding cows. Values represent least squares means (LSM) and standard error of the mean (SEM).

	Breed			
pQCT parameter	AA	AF	AJ	P value
BA (mm^2)	881.9±15.8^c	815.6±18.1^b	730.9±18.1^a	<0.001
PeriC (mm)	105.2± 0.9^c	101.1±1.1^b	95.8±1.1^a	<0.001
vBMD (mg/cm^3)	977.3±7.8a	1018.5±8.9^b	1019.4±8.9^b	<0.001
BMC (mg/mm)	860.9±12.6^c	829.0±14.4^{bc}	744.0±14.4^a	<0.001
EndoC (mm)	57.3±0.9^c	52.3±1.1^b	49.5±1.1^{ab}	<0.001
SSI (mm^3)	6121.3±149.9^c	5549.6±171.5^b	4653.4±171.5^a	<0.001

Footnote: PeriC – periosteal circumference, vBMD – volumetric bone mineral density, BMC – bone mineral content, EndoC – Endosteal circumference, SSI – Stress strain Index

Different superscript letters in the same row indicate significant differences among breeds (P<0.05).

Figure 1 The cumulative contribution of distance walked on gentle, moderate, and steep terrain as components of the total distance walked by beef cows (per day) monitored with GPS collars

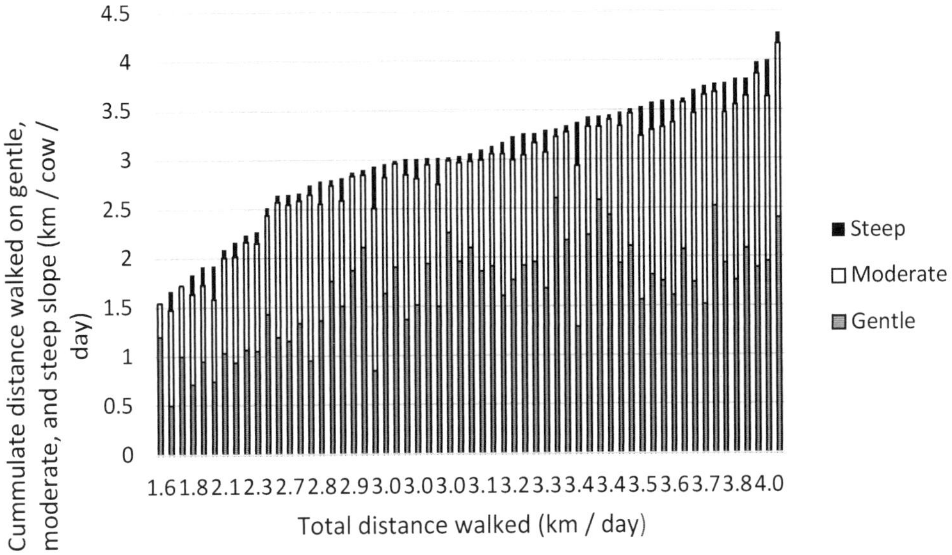

measures of bone size and content contributed to the Angus cows having the greatest bone strength (SSI), with the least variation in SSI values across the three breeds.

Discussion

The management of the cows was typical of that of beef cows in the lower North Island of New Zealand and, thus, the load cycles and respective strain rates on the limbs would be similar to that observed under typical New Zealand management conditions. The advantage with this cohort of cows was that they had been part of a longitudinal productivity trial and, thus, had a well-documented history with respect to management and reproductive performance. This study appears to be the first to document the effect of locomotion under typical commercial pasture-based management systems on bone parameters in the distal limb of beef and beef-dairy cross cattle.

A breed effect was consistent across all the bone parameters measured. The data from the beef-dairy cross cows (AF and AJ) were similar to the data described by (Gibson et al. 2019) for beef-dairy cross yearlings. This may imply that bone development and maturation is close to completion and, therefore, adult values are reached by the time these animals are one year old. The metacarpus being a distal limb bone, is likely to achieve maturation earlier during growth than the bones in the proximal limb (Pomeroy 978). Gibson et al. (2019) demonstrated that, even though comparisons were between beef-dairy cross yearlings and mixed-aged dairy cows, there were no differences in many parameters, supporting the hypothesis that much of the maturation in the metacarpus has occurred by one year of age.

The mechanostat theorem provides a mechanism to describe that, in any given bone, or location within the bone, the material properties will be such that there is optimisation within a relatively narrow range. Loads above this range result in increased strength, and lack of load leads to a reduction in material content and strength (Frost 2004). Thus the material properties of the bone (structure and relative deposition of mineral content) describe the relative loading it is exposed to. The different strategies used to achieve bone strength depend on the type of loading (flexion *vs* torsional strain), sex (oestrogen supresses bone size) (PeriC), and genetics. Within our population, there was large variation in some of the parameters for the beef-dairy cross cows compared to those in the Angus cows. This phenotypic variation reflects the morphological differences between the two dairy-cross breeds. The metacarpus bones of the Angus cows had greater periosteal (PeriC) and endosteal circumference (EndoC) and this was able to generate a greater stress strain index. In contrast to this increase in size strategy, the dairy cross breeds, particularly the JA cows, had much lower periosteal and endosteal circumference but required a greater BMD_v to achieve the appropriate SSI. There is a strong association of body weight (and hence, load) with measures of bone strength, particularly in the distal limb. However, the Angus cows had only 2% greater BW than did the Angus-Friesian but had a 10% greater SSI, and the relative difference between body weight and SSI was even greater compared with the Jersey cross (16% greater BW and 32% greater SSI). The lack of linearity of body weight with SSI across the breeds implies that the breed effect (Angus) may be having an amplification factor on the relationship of body weight and SSI. Hence, differences in morphology may mean that relative effect of body weight is distributed differently in metacapus of the Angus compared to the Angus dairy cross cows.

The GPS data indicated that the majority of the loading was at moderate strain rates that were unlikely to be osteoinductive as most of the behaviour was grazing and on gentle to moderate slopes. We had hypothesised that the steep slopes may provide sufficient strain rate to induce a focal bone response at the mid-diaphysis area. In theory, the number of high strain rates required could be achieved with relatively little time spent on the steep slopes, as across mammals, the number of load cycles required to induce a bone response if sufficient strain rate is applied, is low. In Holstein calves, sprint exercise on a 71-m concrete track was sufficient to induce quantifiable changes in BMD_v and resistance to fracture (Logan et al. 2019). The sprint exercise in these calves was approximately 3.6 ms^{-1} which was a lower velocity compared to the sprint exercise required to generate similar responses in horses. In foals and adult horses without short bursts of high-strain-rate activity there is not sufficient stimuli to promote, or maintain, higher bone-mineral density (Rogers & Dittmer, 2019; Firth et al. 2007). Given that the GPS data were collected two years prior to slaughter, some caution should be used when interpreting the relative load cycles on the limbs with the pQCT-derived data. However, despite some differences between years, there was limited variation in the relative distribution of loading as described by the time spent on the different slope gradients. This indicates that the GPS data may provide a relatively good indication of typical locomotor activity in beef cattle under commercial conditions and that most of the load cycles are of low magnitude.

Conclusion

These data indicate that breed may have an affect on the relative loads on the metacarpus and its material properties. The GPS data imply that load cycles on the distal limb of beef cows managed under typical New Zealand pasture conditions are of moderate strain rate and unlikely to stimulate dynamic bone response. The similarity of the material properties reported here with those of Gibson et al. (2019) support the hypothesis that much of the bone material properties observed in our cows may have been achieved by the time they were yearling and remained persistent up to nine years of age and after multiple pregnancies.

References

Cook CW 1966. Factors affecting utilization of mountain slopes by cattle. Journal of Range Management 19: 200-204.

Dittmer KE, Hitchcock B, Mcdougall S, Hunnam JC 2016. Pathophysiology of humeral fractures in a sample of dairy heifers. New Zealand Veterinary Journal 64: 230-7.

Firth EC, Rogers CW, Vanweeren PR, Barneveld A, Kawcak CE, Mcilwraith CW, Goodship AE, Smith RKW 2007. Changes in diaphyseal and epiphyseal bone parameters in thoroughbred horses after withdrawal from training. Journal of Musculoskeletal & Neuronal Interactions 7: 74-76.

Frost HM 2004. A 2003 update of bone physiology and Wolff's Law for clinicians. Angle Orthodontist, 74: 3-15.

Geenty K, Morris ST 2017. Guide to New Zealand cattle farming. Wellington Beef + Lamb New Zealand.

Gibson MJ, Rogers CW, Dittmer KE, Hickson RE, Pettigrew EJ, Back PJ 2019. Can bone measures of the bovine metacarpus predict humeral bone structure? New Zealand Journal of Animal Science and Production 79: 8-12.

Henkin Z, Ungar ED, Dolev A 2012. Foraging behaviour of beef cattle in the hilly terrain of a Mediterranean grassland. The Rangeland Journal, 34: 163-172.

Hickson RE, Corner-Thomas RA, Martin NP, Kenyon PR, Lopez-Villalobos N, Morris ST 2015. Stayability of beef-cross-dairy breeding cows to six years of age. Proceedings of the New Zealand Society of Animal Production 75: 159-163

Logan AA, Nielsen BD, Robison CI, Manfredi JM, Buskirk DD, Schott HC, Hiney KM 2019. Calves, as a model for juvenile horses, need only one sprint per week to experience increased bone strength. Journal of Animal Science 97: 3300-3312.

Martin NP, Hickson RE, Draganova I, Horne D, Kenyon PR, Morris ST 2015. BRIEF COMMUNICATION: Walking distance and energy expenditure of beef cows grazing on hill country in winter. Proceedings of the New Zealand Society of Animal Production 75: 164-166.

McCall DG 1994. The complementary contribution of the beef cow to other livestock enterprises. Proceedings of the New Zealand Society for Animal Production, 54: 323-328.

Mueggler WF 1965. Cattle distribution on steep slopes. Journal of Range Management 18: 255-257.

Pinchak WE, Smith MA, Hart RH, Waggoner JW 1991. Beef cattle distribution patterns on foothill range. Journal of Range Management 44: 267-275.

Pomeroy R 1978. Historical and general review of growth and development. IN H, DB & J, M (Eds.) Patterns of Growth and Development in Cattle. Current Topics in Veterinary Medicine. Springer, Dordecht. 3-11.

Rogers CW, Dittmer K 2019. Does Juvenile Play Programme the Equine Musculoskeletal System? Animals 9. https://doi.org/10.3390/ani9090646

Rogers CW, Firth EC, Mcilwraith CW, Barneveld A, Goodship AE, Kawcak CE, Smith RKW, Van Weeren PR 2008a. Evaluation of a new strategy to modulate skeletal development in racehorses by imposing track-based exercise during growth: The effects on 2-and 3-year-old racing careers. Equine Veterinary Journal 40: 119-127.

Rogers CW, Firth EC, Mcilwraitth CW, Barneveld A, Goodship AE, Kawcak CE, Smith RKW, Van Weeren PR 2008b. Evaluation of a new strategy to modulate skeletal development in Thoroughbred performance horses by imposing track-based exercise during growth. Equine Veterinary Journal 40: 111-118.

An association between circulating copper concentrations and gammaglutamyl transferase activity in sheep after exposure to the toxin sporidesmin

PL Johnson*[a] and NC Amyes[b]

[a]*AgResearch Invermay, Puddle Alley, Mosgiel, New Zealand;* [b]*AgResearch Ruakura, Private Bag 3123, Hamilton, New Zealand*

**Corresponding author.* Email: tricia.johnson@agresearch.co.nz

Abstract

Copper is a potent catalyst of the reaction in which sporidesmin generates damaging free radicals causing facial eczema in grazing livestock in New Zealand. This study sought to investigate whether circulating copper at the time an animal is dosed with the toxin, influenced the way the animal responds to sporidesmin and whether the action of sporidesmin on the liver in susceptible animals results in changes to circulating copper. Serum copper concentrations (CU) together with gamma glutamyl transferase (GGT) activity, an indicator of bile duct damage, were opportunistically collected on over 400 animals from nine flocks in which the animal's tolerance to sporidesmin was commercially assessed through measuring its response to a known dose of the toxin. The association between CU concentration before the animals were dosed and natural log transformed GGT activity measured 21 days after the animals had been dosed was not significant, but there was a suggestive ($P=0.06$) interaction between flock and CU. There was a significant positive association between natural log transformed GGT activity and CU concentrations measured 21 days after the animals had been dosed with the toxin ($P<0.0001$). For some individuals, the CU concentrations approached or met copper-toxicity thresholds (above 40 µmol/L). The specific biological mechanisms causing this association remain unknown, but given the role of copper in catalysing the sporidesmin reaction and the potential of toxic copper concentrations, further research is warranted.

Keywords: sheep; facial eczema; copper; gamma glutamyl transferase

Introduction

Facial eczema is caused by ruminants ingesting the toxin sporidesmin, which is produced by the fungus *Pithomyces chartarum* that proliferates in the presence of dead plant matter in warm humid conditions in parts of New Zealand. The primary site of action of the toxin in sheep is in the liver and bile ducts of animals that ingest the toxin, with the production of superoxide radicals (O_2^-) and a by-product of the reaction, hydrogen peroxide (Munday 1982).

In vitro copper has been shown to be a potent catalyst of the autoxidation of reduced sporidesmin in producing O_2^- (Munday 1985). It has been hypothesised that a mechanism through which zinc prevents facial eczema may be through decreasing intestinal copper absorption (Munday 1985). The liver is the major storage site of copper. There is evidence that under stressful conditions copper can be released from storage in the liver (Farquharson 1984). Alternatively, copper can be released from the liver as a result of damage to hepatocytes (Nederbragt et al. 1984). In high enough concentrations, copper can be toxic and can cause damage to the liver and bile duct through the generation of hydroxyl radicals (Nederbragt et al. 1984). Gamma glutamyl transferase which is used as indicator of bile duct damage in facial eczema (Amyes & Hawkes 2014), is similarly used in the diagnosis of copper toxicity in farmed animals (Johnston et al. 2014).

Despite the known *in-vitro* relationship, no *in-vivo* testing of the role of copper in the sporidesmin reaction has been conducted previously. The most appropriate study to test for a role would be to measure circulating and liver stored copper concentrations; however, as a first step, serum samples from sheep that were being dosed with sporidesmin as part of the Ramguard FE tolerance test were available to test for serum copper concentrations in addition to the routine gamma glutamyl transferase testing. The aim was to investigate whether circulating copper concentrations at the time of sporidesmin dosing influenced the way in which an animal responded to sporidesmin and/or whether the action of sporidesmin in susceptible or tolerant animals resulted in changes to circulating copper levels.

Materials and methods

This study utilised blood samples collected through the Ramguard programme. The Ramguard programme is described in detail by Amyes and Hawkes (2014). Briefly, an animal's tolerance to sporidesmin is determined through an animal being dosed by intraruminal intubation with a pre-determined amount of sporidesmin. The chosen dose rate reflects previous response levels in the flock the animal came from, and the animal's live weight and expressed as mg sporidesmin per kg live weight. Blood samples are collected either on the day the animal is dosed with the toxin (D0) or seven days prior (D-7; to check for pre-existing liver damage in animals grazed in areas where natural sporidesmin exposure had been possible) and again 21 days (D21) after exposure. For simplicity of reporting the pre-sporidesmin dosing time point will be referred to as D0. Ramguard blood samples are routinely analysed for serum gamma glutamyl transferase activity (IU/L 37°C; GGT) through a commercial laboratory (IDEXX, Hamilton, New Zealand).

Initially, a single Ramguard client was contacted (Flock 1), and permission obtained to also allow measurement of serum copper concentrations (µmol/L; CU) on the blood samples being collected for RamGuard testing. A total of 55 animals had been selected by the breeder for testing. The results from this flock supported the collection of more CU data in addition to the routinely collected GGT data.

An additional eight Ramguard clients (Flocks 2-9) were identified from the total Ramguard client list, with the aim of representing the mix of New Zealand's maternal breeds, including Romney, Perendale, and composites including Finnish Landrace and Texel genetics; a range of sporidesmin dose rates ranging from 0.27 to 0.55 mg per kg live weight; and geographical locations ranging from Northland to Otago. In all cases the number of, and specific animals dosed were chosen by the breeder as part of their breeding programme, and thus, in some instances, only low numbers of animals were tested. In total, between September 2018 and September 2019, CU data were collected for 414 lambs from nine flocks, representing approximately one third of all Ramguard-tested animals for that year. The breeders have been breeding for tolerance to FE from five to more than 30 years. The dose rates varied between flocks dependent on how many years testing they had undertaken, and the estimated tolerance of their flock (based on results from Ramguard testing in previous years). Day 21 CU data were available for all animals in the study, however, D0 data were only available for animals from seven breeders, representing 382 animals.

Data used in the analysis were D21 serum GGT (GGTD21) activity and D0 and D21 serum copper (CUD0 and CUD21) concentration. The ratio of CUD21:CUD0 was also calculated (CURATIO) where both CUD0 and CUD21 data were available. Due to D21 serum GGT activity data exhibiting a non-normal distribution (Amyes & Hawkes, 2014), the data were natural log-transformed prior to analysis (lnGGTD21). Each flock represented a unique combination of breed and dose rate, and as such breed and sporidesmin dose-rate data were confounded with flock, and therefore, only flock was fitted in models described below, with no attempt to interpret the results with respect to breed or sporidesmin dose rate. The GLM Procedure in SAS (SAS 2011) was used to undertake analysis of variance analysis to investigate the association between copper and GGT. Three models were fitted. In the first model lnGGTD21 was fitted as the dependent variable, with CUD0, flock and their interaction fitted as explanatory variables. CUD0 was fitted as a covariate, whilst flock was fitted as a fixed effect. In the second and third models CUD21 and CURATIO were fitted as dependent variables, with lnGGTD21, flock and their interaction fitted as explanatory variables. lnGGTD21 was fitted as a covariate. The results are presented whereby the R^2 of reduced models are reported in addition to the R^2 of the full model to determine which explanatory variables were explaining the largest amount of the variation reported. The first reduced model did not include flock or the interaction between flock and the covariate fitted, with the second reduced model also including flock but not the interaction, with the full model including the interaction. The R^2 of the reduced models were calculated by dividing the reported type-I sums of squares for the explanatory variables included in the reduced model (summed for the second reduced model) by the total model sums of squares. Two data sets were used in the analysis, the first just exploring relationships in Flock 1, as was carried out to inform the decision to do further data collection, with the second data set including data from all nine flocks. For the first data set, flock was not fitted as a fixed effect.

To graphically represent the data, individual animals were assigned to tolerance/susceptibility groups (GGTGRP) based on their GGTD21 results according to the standard groupings used within the Ramguard programme to estimate liver/bile duct damage, with GGT<71 IU/L low; GGT 71-300 IU/L slight; GGT 301-700 IU/L moderate and GGT> 700 IU/L high, with the CUD21 and CURATIO trait data plotted in a boxplot using GGTGRP as the category on the X axis.

Results

The summary statistics for GGTD21, CUD0, CUD21 and CURATIO for the nine Ramguard flocks are presented in Table 1. Flock 1 was the first flock where data were collected, and a preliminary analysis of these data led to the decision to collect additional data from additional flocks. For Flock 8 most animals exhibited high tolerance to their dose of sporidesmin with an average GGTD21 of only 73±53 IU/L, with a maximum GGTD21 of only 343 IU/L. For the other flocks there was a large range in GGTD21 concentrations, with all flocks recording GGTD21 levels greater than 1000 IU/L. The average CUD21 was elevated in most flocks compared to CUD0, except for Flock 4 which was a flock in which the tolerance to sporidesmin was also high, with an average GGTD21 of only 128 ± 170 IU/L. Serum copper concentrations >11 µmol/L are considered to indicate adequate copper, while those above 25 µmol/L are considered to be high (Laven & Smith 2008). Two animals in Flock 1 exceeded the serum copper toxicity concentration of 40 µmol/L, with a further 13 above 30 µmol/L across all flocks. In all flocks with CURATIO (except Flock 4), there was at least one animal that had double the concentration of copper between the two measurements.

In the analysis only including data from Flock ,1 which was the flock which copper data was first collected, there was a significant positive association between CUD0 and lnGGTD21 ($P<0.05$), lnGGTD21 and CUD21 ($P<0.0001$) and lnGGTD21 and CURATIO ($P<0.0001$). The results from the analyses including data from all nine flocks are presented in Tables 2 and 3. For the model considering the association between CUD0 and lnGGTD21 (Table 2), CUD0 was not significant, however, the interaction between flock and CUD0 was approaching significance ($P=0.06$). For the model considering the relationship between lnGGTD21 and CUD21 (Table 3), all explanatory variables were significant (lnGGTD21, flock and the interaction; $P<0.05$). For the model considering the relationship between lnGGTD21

Table 1 Summary statistics for gamma glutamyl transferase activity 21 days (GGTD21) and its natural log-transformed value (lnGGTD21) after animals were being dosed with the toxin sporidesmin and serum copper concentrations before (Day 0 or Day -7: CUD0) and after (Day 21: CUD21) dosing, together with their ratio (CURATIO) in nine Ramguard flocks.

		GGTD21		lnGGTD21		CUD0		CUD21		CURATIO	
Flock	n	Mean ± SD	Range	Mean ± SD	Range	Mean ± SD	Range	Mean ± SD	Range	Mean ± SD	Range
1	55	224 ± 299	41 - 1341	4.8 ± 1.1	3.7 - 7.2	19.9 ± 3.9	12 - 31	21.7 ± 7.0	12 - 44	1.1 ± 0.4	0.6 - 2.3
2	17	624 ± 525	43 - 1195	6.0 ± 1.2	3.8 - 7.1	14.6 ± 2.1	11 - 19	24.5 ± 6.9	13 - 35	1.7 ± 0.5	1 - 2.5
3	10	582 ± 563	49 - 1316	5.6 ± 1.5	3.9 - 7.2	na	na	22.3 ± 8.6	13 - 33	na	na
4	146	128 ± 170	45 - 1079	4.5 ± 0.6	3.8 - 7.0	14.7 ± 3.2	10 - 30	14.6 ± 3.4	11 - 27	1.0 ± 0.2	0.6 - 1.9
5	75	375 ± 349	44 - 1405	5.5 ± 1.0	3.7 - 7.2	14.5 ± 2.9	9.8 - 23	20.4 ± 4.8	11 - 32	1.4 ± 0.4	0.8 - 2.4
6	28	235 ± 297	41 - 1187	4.8 ± 1.0	3.7 - 7.1	na	na	15.8 ± 5.2	8.7 - 27	na	na
7	33	673 ± 608	48 - 1955	5.9 ± 1.3	3.9 - 7.6	17.0 ± 3.3	13.1 - 28.6	20.2 ± 6.1	9.2 - 31.4	1.2 ± 0.4	0.6 - 2.1
8	44	73 ± 53	41- 343	4.2 ± 0.4	3.7 - 5.8	13.3 ± 2.5	10 - 21	14.4 ± 4.1	7.4 - 28	1.1 ± 0.3	0.6 - 2.1
9	6	535 ± 289	59- 812	6.0 ± 1.0	4.1- 6.7	13.0 ± 2.1	9.7 - 15	22.3 ± 4.8	16 - 28	1.7 ± 0.4	1.1 - 2.3

na: Pre-dose CU was not measured in this flock

Table 2 Results for model fitted to determine relationship between explanatory variables, serum copper concentrations (CUDO) prior to dosing animals with the toxin sporidesmin, and flock, and the dependent variable gamma glutamyl transferase activity (natural log transformed) 21 days (GGTD21) after dosing in nine Ramguard flocks.

	Significance			Solution Est.	Model R^2		
	CUDO	Flock	CUDO*Flock	CUDO	Red. 1[1]	Red. 2[1]	Full[1]
lnGGTD21	0.41	<0.0001	0.06	-0.08	0.00	0.32	0.34

[1]Reduced model 1 only included CUD0; Reduced model 2 also included flock; Full model also included the interaction.

Table 3 Results for models fitted to determine relationship between explanatory variables, gamma glutamyl transferase activity (natural log transformed) 21 days (GGTD21) after dosing animals with the toxin sporidesmin and flock, and dependent variables of serum copper concentrations after dosing (CUD21) and the ratio of copper levels prior to and at day 21 after dosing (CURATIO) in nine Ramguard flocks.

	Significance			Solution Est.	Model R^2		
	lnGGTD21	Flock	lnGGTD21*Flock	lnGGTD21	Red. 1[1]	Red. 2[1]	Full[1]
CUD21	<0.0001	<0.0001	0.03	4.87	0.54	0.67	0.69
CURATIO	<0.0001	<0.0001	0.09	0.32	0.55	0.64	0.65

[1]Reduced model 1 only included GGTD21; Reduced model 2 also included flock; Full model also included the interaction.

and CUD21 (Table 3), all explanatory variables were significant (lnGGT21 and flock; P<0.0001) or approaching significance (the interaction between lnGGTD21 and flock; P<0.10). Considering the R^2 values for reduced models relative to the full models, lnGGTD21 explained most of the variation in both CUD21 and CURATIO, with flock explaining less of the variation, and the interaction between flock and GGTD21 contributing very little of the variation.

Graphical representation of the data is provided in Figure 1, with CURATIO trait data plotted in a boxplot using GGTGRP as the category on the X axis. This illustrates the relationships described in Table 2, in that animals with highly elevated GGTD21 had an elevated CURATIO; however, it also visualises that those with non-elevated GGTD21 had, on average, reduced CUD21 compared to CUD0 (CURATIO below one). Additionally, this plot illustrates that several animals that had moderate to highly elevated GGTD21 exceeded the ratio of 2.0 (n=15), above which animals can be at risk of copper toxicity.

Discussion

The range in GGTD21 (Table 1) was as expected for animals exposed to the toxin through the Ramguard programme. For CUD0 and CUD21 individual animals had values both below and above the adequate range for CU, although the flock average concentrations were within the adequate range. There was greater variability in CUD21, and one flock had an average CUD21 that was sitting on the "high" threshold for the adequate range.

The initial results from Flock 1 suggested that a significant association existed between lnGGTD21 and CUD0, with a very significant association between lnGGTD21 and CUD21 and CURATIO, supporting the collection of further copper data which was carried out,

Figure 1. Left: boxplot of the distribution of the copper concentration (μmol/L) measured 21 days (D21) after animals have been dosed with the toxin sporidesmin grouped by the level of liver response estimated by activity of Gamma Glutamyl Transferase (GGT) where Low: GGT<71IU/L; Slight: GGT 71-300 IU/L; Moderate: GGT 301-700 IU/L and High GGT> 700IU/L. Right: boxplot of the distribution of the ratio of copper concentration measured before animals were dosed with the toxin sporidesmin (D0) and 21 days later (D21) grouped by level of liver response estimated by GGT activity. There is a risk of copper toxicity where copper concentrations are above 40μmol/L or D21 concentrations are double or above D0 concentrations (indicated by the horizontal dashed line).

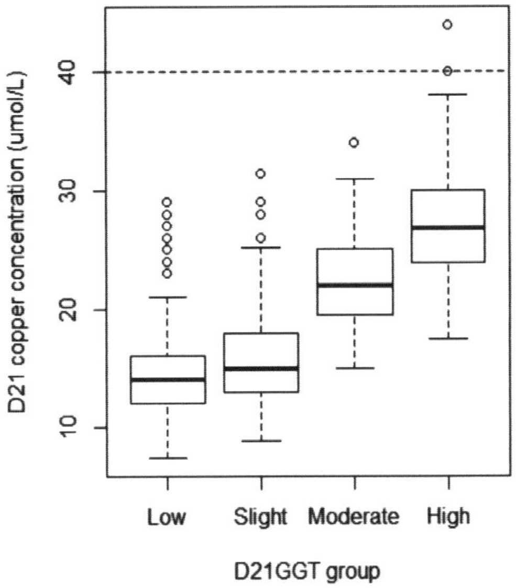

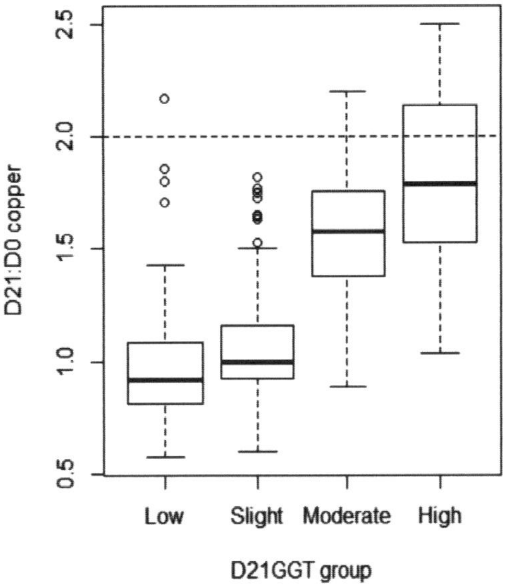

forming the full data set used in this study. In the full data set, the association between CUD0 and lnGGTD21 was not replicated (Table 2), although there was a significant (P=0.06) interaction between flock and CUD0, indicating that an association may exist in some flocks. There was a highly significant positive association observed between lnGGTD21 and CUD21 and CURATIO suggesting that the association is consistent across a range of dose rates, breeds and geographical regions. In addition to visualising the elevation in CUD21 in animals with high lnGGTD21, Figure 1 illustrates that animals with limited liver damage (low GGTD21) had similar or even lower CUD21 compared with CUD0 (values below one).

The level significance of the association between CUD21 and GGTD21 were a surprise. The absolute concentrations of CUD21 and the CURATIO, for some individuals put them at concentrations/ratios associated with copper toxicity in sheep (Figure 1). Serum copper concentrations of greater than 40 μmol/L (Gribbles 2020) can indicate toxicity, and two-fold changes in CU concentrations have been suggestive of an early onset of a copper toxicity event (McCosker 1968).

Copper toxicity has been observed in sheep in association with the ingestion of other plant secondary metabolites, such as a toxin associated with lupins (Gardiner 1966) and pyrrolizidine alkaloids produced by plants including *Echium plantaglneum* and *Heliotropium europaeum* (Seaman 1987). Whilst the most likely explanation for the observed result is liver hepatocyte damage caused by the sporidesmin toxin resulting in the release of stored copper (Nederbragt et al. 1984) alternative hypotheses do exist. An alternative hypothesis is that the increased CU is the result of lower copper excretion through the gall bladder, once it is damaged by the toxin, leading to a build-up of CU (even though the rate of excretion of the copper through bile is considered to be low (Søli & Rambaek 1978)). Another alternative is that the copper is actively released from the liver in response to the physiological stress of exposure to the toxin as described by Farquharson (1984). Whilst elucidating the cause of the rise is important, equally important is determining whether the rise in circulating copper goes on to play a role in catalysing further sporidesmin reactions, or if the increased circulating copper directly causes the generation of superoxide radicals and further liver and bile duct damage as can be observed in cases of copper toxicity (Johnston et al. 2014), in addition to that already caused by sporidesmin.

There is no relevant literature to consider potential mechanisms through which reduced circulating copper occurred in some tolerant animals.

The finding of a significant association between CU concentration and GGT activity after exposure to sporidesmin is novel. However, further studies are required to understand the cause and implications of this association. Stored liver copper could not be measured in this opportunistic data set. Although the relationship between lnGGTD21 and CUD0 was not consistent, it does not preclude stored liver copper at the time of dosing from contributing to the results observed at Day 21 given circulating and stored copper levels are not well correlated in normal animals (Johnston et al. 2014), and future studies should include measurement of liver copper concentration.

Although the underlying reason for the association between CUD21 and GGTD21 is not known, the results of this study do have practical relevance, as copper supplementation is common place, particularly in copper-deficient regions in New Zealand, and supplementation could further exacerbate the potential for copper toxicity in animals if given whilst copper concentrations are already elevated. As such, assessment of copper concentrations after facial eczema challenge should be made prior to any supplementation. Alternatively, if zinc supplementation has occurred, there is also the possibility that liver and serum copper concentrations may be low due to zinc supplementation driving decreased storage of copper (Smith et al. 2010). This further highlights the importance of testing both serum and liver copper concentrations to understand the status of a flock (or herd).

This study has shown, using an opportunistic data set, that a significant association exists between CUD21 and GGTD21. The cause of the association cannot be inferred from this study, however, irrespective of the cause, increased circulating concentration of copper is of potential importance given the proposed role of copper in catalysing the sporidesmin reaction, and the fact that copper can be toxic to the animal in high concentrations which were reached or approached in some animals in this data set. Further investigation of the association with blood samples collected at multiple time points between D0 and D21, including collection of liver copper data, is warranted to confirm whether the circulating copper elevations occur before or after rise in GGT activity. In addition, irrespective of the order, further investigation should determine whether the additional circulating copper further exacerbates liver and bile duct damage, either directly, or through further stimulation of the sporidesmin reaction. Ultimately, we seek to gain further understanding of biological mechanisms associated with sporidesmin toxicity to contribute towards the discovery of alternative preventative strategies.

Acknowledgements

The ability to obtain collect copper data was the result of permission from the individual sheep breeders using the Ramguard service. These breeders were interested in contributing to uncovering novel information that will lead to new solutions to combat facial eczema in their own, and their clients, flocks.

References

Amyes, NC, Hawkes, AD 2014. Ramguard – Increasing the Tolerance to Facial Eczema in New Zealand Sheep, Proceedings of the New Zealand Society of Animal Production 74**:** 154-157.

Farquharson, BC 1984. Some aspects of copper toxicity in sheep grazing New Zealand pastures. Doctor of Philosophy in Veterinary Science, Massey University, Palmerston North, New Zealand.

Gardiner, MR 1966. Mineral metabolism in sheep lupinosis. 2. Copper. Journal of Comparative Pathology 76: 107-120.

Gribbles 2020. Retrieved 01/02/2020, 2020, from https://www.gribblesvets.co.nz/copper/.

Johnston, H, Beasley, L, MacPherson, N 2014. Copper toxicity in a New Zealand dairy herd. Irish Veterinary Journal 67: 20.

Laven, RA, Smith, SL 2008. Copper deficiency in sheep: An assessment of the relationship between concentrations of copper in serum and plasma. New Zealand Veterinary Journal 56: 334-338.

McCosker, PJ 1968. Observations on Blood Copper in the Sheep: II. – Chronic Copper Poisoning. Research in Veterinary Science 9: 103-116.

Munday, R 1982. Studies on the mechanism of toxicity of the mycotoxin, sporidesmin. I. Generation of superoxide radicals by sporidesmin. Chemico-Biological Interactions 41: 361-374.

Munday, R 1985. Studies on the mechanism of toxicity of the mycotoxin sporidesmin. IV. Inhibition by copper-chelating agents of the generation of superoxide radicals by sporidesmin. Journal of Applied Toxicology 5: 69-73.

Nederbragt, H, van den Ingh, TS, Wensvoort, P 1984. Pathobiology of copper toxicity. The Veterinary Quarterly 6: 179-185, 235.

SAS 2011. SAS Institute Inc. SAS/STAT® 9.3 User's Guide. Cary, NC: SAS Institute Inc.

Seaman, JT 1987. Pyrrolizidine alkaloid poisoning of sheep in New South Wales. Australian Veterinary Journal 64: 164-167.

Smith, SL, Grace, ND, West, DM, Balemi, SC 2010. The impact of high zinc intake on the copper status of dairy cows in New Zealand. New Zealand Veterinary Journal 58: 142-145.

Søli, NE, Rambaek, JP 1978. Excretion of intravenously injected copper-64 in sheep. Acta pharmacologica et toxicologica 43: 205-210.

REVIEW: Critiquing the relationship between body condition and animal welfare

MW Fisher[a]*, KE Schütz[bc] and GA Verkerk[b]

[a]*Ministry for Primary Industries, PO Box 2526, Wellington 6140, New Zealand;* [b]*National Animal Welfare Advisory Committee, C/- Ministry for Primary Industries, PO Box 2526, Wellington 6140, New Zealand;* [c]*AgResearch Ltd., Ruakura Research Centre, Private Bag 3123, Hamilton 3240, New Zealand.*

**Corresponding author:* Email: Mark.Fisher@mpi.govt.nz

Abstract

Body condition has long been used when assessing animal health and productivity, both important indicators of animal welfare; however, assessments of animal welfare must also consider the extent to which animals' emotional needs are met. New Zealand's codes of welfare focus on using body condition score as a measure of emaciation, requiring action to be taken at very low scores and generally recommending higher scores. In anticipation of future code reviews, the National Animal Welfare Advisory Committee is exploring our understanding of body condition as a measure of welfare, with a view to incorporating standards that also take account of animals' affective or emotional states. Most of the scientific literature appears related to optimising animal health and production and body condition score is a good indicator of an animal's energy reserves. While affective or emotional state may be more difficult to assess, thinner animals seem more motivated to feed as they spend more time foraging and consume more feed than 'better' conditioned animals. In addition, animals losing condition were more interested, anxious or excited, suggesting higher feeding motivation and possibly hunger. A more nuanced understanding is needed that considers the circumstances of the animal; what individual animals are feeling; and that body condition *per se* may not necessarily reflect hunger. In addition, the stage at which compromises to body condition are deemed unreasonable or unnecessary, and the reserves required in extensive environments, suggest more complex research, regulatory and non-regulatory understandings and interventions will be required.

Keywords: body condition; survival; production; health; behaviour; feelings; animal-welfare standards

Introduction

Animals have physiological and behavioural mechanisms to overcome variation in nutritional resources, when energy demand exceeds availability, e.g., in winter, during pregnancy and lactation, or when unable to forage, e.g., during migration, transportation or when held in lairage. Conversely, animals in good condition reflect greater access to, or more efficient use of, resources, and consequently exhibit enhanced growth, reproduction, lactation and health (e.g., Roche et al. 2009; Kenyon et al. 2014). However, excessive resource provision and energy deposition, not only represent an inefficient utilisation of feed supplies, but predispose animals to obesity, and with it a variety of health problems (see D'Eath et al. 2009). The relationship between body condition and animal health and productivity has, perhaps, been most thoroughly investigated in the high-producing dairy cow: those in higher condition at calving are at greater risk of metabolic disorders (e.g., ketosis, milk fever) and lameness, while those in lower condition are more likely to suffer from metritis and mastitis and have difficulty getting pregnant again. Similarly, inappropriate body condition at lambing can predispose ewes to metabolic disease. Furthermore, throughout domestication and selection for desired traits, the animals are changing. While there is evidence of a decline in the average condition of New Zealand dairy cows (Macdonald et al. 2008), there are significant numbers of overweight and obese companion animals, especially dogs, cats and horses (German 2006; Giles et al. 2014; Sandøe et al. 2014).

Other than the impacts on animal production and health, there are relatively few reports examining the impacts of body condition on what the animal experiences or feels, knowledge crucial in understanding its welfare (Fraser 2003; Fisher 2009). New Zealand's codes of animal welfare focus on using body condition score as a measure of emaciation, requiring action to be taken at very low scores and recommending higher scores. However, as Kenyon et al. (2014) noted, the information on which the standards were based, are not clear, sentiments also expressed elsewhere (McGregor & Butler 2008).

The National Animal Welfare Advisory Committee (NAWAC) has expressed concerns relating to body condition of animals and, in particular, understanding the stage at which animals suffer or become susceptible to environmental conditions and diseases, and the extent to which minimum standards in codes of welfare are being met. When reviewing codes of welfare, the relationship between body condition and our understanding of the related indicators of the emotional or affective state of the animal, such as hunger and satiety, must also be considered, but there are extensive gaps in our knowledge of these relationships. In this paper we review scientific literature pertinent to our traditional understanding of the relationships between welfare and body condition, and emerging studies that link body condition with affective state. While livestock are given emphasis, reflecting NAWAC's wider role companion animals are included where relevant.

Survival

Longevity is affected by many factors (e.g., age, worn or missing teeth, breed, and lamb performance), and the survival of sheep in extensive hill conditions in Scotland

(Morgan-Davies et al. 2008; Annett et al. 2011) was reduced when body condition scores fell below 2.5-3 (scale 0-5). Along with provision of shelter and additional and higher-quality feed, having animals in good condition is one of the major ways livestock are protected, or buffered, against cold weather. For example, on US ranges, younger cows grazing in less-sheltered country lost live weight and condition during winter compared with mature animals that used the available topography for shelter, as well as better use of the available pasture (Beaver & Olson 1997). One of the most poignant examples of the impact of body condition on animal survival is the retrospective analysis of the relationship between body condition and death from hypothermia in Angora goats (McGregor & Butler 2008). Twenty-four hours of heavy rain and wind, five weeks after shearing, resulted in significant mortality amongst yearling wethers. Deaths increased sharply when condition scores were <2 (scale 0-5), exacerbated by higher stocking rates and when the goats were grazing with sheep, presumably because the goats, under the stress of poor weather, were unable to consume adequate feed as pasture availability declined.

Health

While increased risk of death is a definitive arbiter of welfare, there are many physiological indicators of increased risks to animal health. For instance, while ewes deal with extreme nutritional conditions, those in either poorer (below 1.5 or 2, scale 0-5) or better condition (above 3 or 3.5) are more susceptible to metabolic imbalances and a greater risk of, for example, pregnancy toxaemia (Calderia et al. 2007a,b). Similarly, relatively small differences in the body condition of dairy cattle over the calving period can compromise reproduction; those in lower condition were more prone to reproductive compromise, while fatter cows had increased risk of metabolic and other diseases (Roche et al. 2013). Poor body condition predisposes dairy cows to lameness (Randall et al. 2015, 2018) and increases the risk of lameness worsening in cull dairy cows being transported (Dahl-Pedersen et al. 2018).

Companion animal ill-health associated with obesity has also been well documented (see Sandøe et al. 2014), reducing lifespan and health-related quality of life, with the potential for animal suffering. Reducing weight, primarily through dietary and/or exercise interventions increases dogs' quality of life, according to owners' assessments of animal activity, pain, sociability, aggression, anxiety, enthusiasm, happiness, and mobility (German et al. 2012). However, the issue is complicated by the bond between human and animal, the latter indulged as "fellow-humans" and related to human obesity and the social status of owners (Sandøe et al. 2014).

Production

There have been many studies highlighting the effects of body condition on various indices of animal production (see Roche et al. 2009; Kenyon et al. 2014). They include scanning rate in ewes, the number of lambs born, their birth weight and subsequent growth rates. In beef cattle, the timing of first oestrus and pregnancy rates are similarly affected. Some of these associations are quite precise and defined. For instance, slightly thinner ewes (3-3.5, scale 0-5) outperformed fatter ewes (>3.5) in the total weight of lambs weaned (Mathias-Davis et al. 2011). Others are quite subtle: for example, ewes that maintain body condition in late pregnancy may provide a more suitable maternal environment for their lambs (Everett-Hincks et al. 2004). Finally, it is worth remembering that there are differences among ages, individuals and genetic strains (e.g., Smeaton et al. 2000) suggesting optimal condition-score targets may differ among animals (Morris et al. 1985).

Although how an animal performs is one good indicator of animal welfare, it is not necessarily always the case. For example, Webster (2005), summarising the physiology of what motivates the high-yielding cow (namely hunger, satiety, the unbalanced absorption of ammonia, and the desire to do something other than eat, for example, rest), stated "her feelings may be defined, with brutal accuracy, as simultaneously hungry, tired, full up and feeling sick". Thus, it is necessary to consider what animals experience.

Behaviour

Thinner sheep had greater voluntary food intake than did those with more condition during a period when both were putting on weight and condition (Sibbald & Rhind 1997). When feed is readily available, dairy cattle in lower condition spend more time eating (Tucker et al. 2007; Matthews et al. 2012). Naturally occurring variations in body condition (2.5 to 8.5, scale 1-10) do not appear to affect dairy cow welfare markedly during lactation, at least when provided with generous pasture allowances with or without supplements (Matthews et al. 2012). While thinner cows appeared to be able to achieve their nutritional requirements, they spent more time foraging at the expense of lying. However, although lactating cows showed marked behavioural and physiological responses (e.g., vocalisation, aggression, fat metabolism) to several days of feed restriction, they were not affected by body condition score (3.4-5.4, scale 1-10) at calving (Schütz et al. 2013). As lactation progressed in dairy cows, time spent grazing and ruminating increased with decreasing body condition (Matthews et al. 2012). Sheep with a lower body condition score (2, scale 0-5) were more motivated to obtain food than those in better condition (2.9 and 3.7). Ewes deprived of food were similarly more motivated and displayed differences in their affective state, being more preoccupied with seeking food (e.g., Verbeek et al. 2011; 2014). Food-deprived animals were more motivated to obtain food. Sheep walked further for food (i.e., larger distances walked were considered to reflect greater motivation as the animals were prepared to pay a 'higher cost'), and ate more, when they had been deprived of food for 14 h (Doughty et al. 2016) and cows walked greater distances for food the longer they were deprived of it (Schütz et al. 2006). Overall, these results suggest that animals in lower condition are more motivated to feed as they spend more time foraging and consume more feed, and are, thus, probably hungrier. In addition to hunger, thinner animals are likely more susceptible to cold conditions due to the lack of fat reserves. Tucker et al. (2007) reported that thinner cows without shelter mobilised less fat and spent less time eating when the weather got colder and more time lying in postures indicative of conserving their energy, perhaps indicative of a greater thermoregulatory challenge than in those cows in better condition.

Animals' experiences

Animals, like humans, experience an array of affective states or feelings associated with provision of food and water, e.g., hunger, sated, thirsty, nauseous, and bloated. While it is difficult to assess animal feelings and experiences objectively, just like humans it is possible to 'read' their behaviour or body language (Wemelsfelder et al. 2001), something good stockmen and owners probably do intuitively in making husbandry decisions. An animal's body language or demeanour reflects not just its physical or physiological state, but also its mental or psychological state. For example, observers have described or scored sheep who walked further for food as hungry/searching/excited, whereas those who didn't were curious/intimidated/uneasy. Although not without its challenges (see Fleming et al. 2016), Qualitative Behavioural Assessment is a technique that allows the common patterns or consensus in observers' descriptions, to be objectively analysed. Stockman et al. (2014) took 21 pregnant sheep with a body condition score of 3 (scale 0-5) and fed them to either maintain or lose condition to a score of 2. The motivation of the sheep to walk for a food reward was then filmed and observers asked to describe the animals' behavioural expressions seen in video clips of each animal. While ewes with a body condition score of 3 were described as more calm/bored/comfortable, ewes with a slowly declining body score were described as more interested/anxious/excited, suggesting they were "exhibiting an affective state indicative of hunger." Although Qualitative Behavioural Assessment has been used to investigate the emotional state of companion animals, e.g., horses and dogs, to our knowledge this has not been assessed in relation to their body condition.

Another method is judging the bias animals may have towards ambiguous stimuli depending on the affective state they are in, e.g., animals from enriched environments judge ambiguous stimuli more optimistically than those from unpredictable environments, who were more pessimistic (unpredictability is a well-known stressor of animals, including humans). Similarly, hungry people shift their attention to images of food and gaze at them longer. Judgement bias, optimistic or pessimistic, along with biased attention to food-related cues, may give an insight into what animals feel. Verbeek et al. (2014) used these methods to suggest that food-restricted sheep have altered affective states.

Discussion

Not surprisingly, much of the literature on body condition relates to optimising herd or flock performance (production and reproduction) and its impact on animal survival and health, both well accepted indicators of animal welfare. However, the relationship between animal production and animal welfare is not always positive: high-performing animals can be more susceptible to ill-health and high-performance systems can be associated with poor welfare, for example, when animals are kept in confined and barren environments, such as those in stalls and cages. There are other indicators of an animal's welfare, including its affective state or what it is experiencing, usually interpreted in its behaviour (e.g., posture) or appearance, which must also be assessed.

While many animals in low condition may experience increased motivation to feed, and possibly prolonged hunger, body condition is, more accurately, a measure of an animal's energy reserves, reflecting its history and indicating its potential production and the risks it may face in its circumstances. Animals in good, even excessive, condition may still experience hunger (and its impacts such as weakness and nausea), especially those selected for high growth rates where, as has been suggested, hypothalamic mechanisms regulating appetite have been altered (Rauw et al. 1998). Animals in similar condition may also have different feelings depending on whether they are gaining, maintaining or losing condition. As a measure of energy reserves, then, how much can it be taken as a measure of hunger? Schütz et al. (2013) suggest little. For example, there is natural variation in body condition among individuals and breeds, as well as species. Even within a more normal range of scores, body condition may have its limitations. Roche et al. (2013), after monitoring milk production, health, and udder and uterine health, concluded that body condition score (at least between 3.5 and 5.5, scale 1-10) "is not a sufficiently sensitive measure to be reflective of cow welfare" in early lactation, despite it appearing optimal for production, reproductive performance and general health. This was because body condition did not reflect metabolic changes and, for example, did not affect the cows' ability to mount an inflammatory response. Furthermore, keeping animals within a recommended range may involve restricting their diet, thereby making them hungry, and can result in aggression, stress and the development of aberrant behaviour, all indicators of reduced animal welfare. The dilemma (Sandøe 2018) between giving animals freedom from hunger or optimising performance and reducing their risk of disease has been well noted in companion animals – 'lean and mean' or 'fat and friendly' (Sandøe et al. 2014). Similarly, for example, in broiler or meat chicken breeders, feed restrictions to ensure the birds remain healthy and reproductively competent mean they are chronically hungry (Mench 2002).

These insights make welfare code review that effectively incorporates measures of affective state in relation to adequacy of feeding for good welfare challenging. While most information relates to mid-range condition scores, the standards in codes of animal welfare, with some exceptions, relate more to the extremes, especially emaciation. Hunger, a feeling or sensation motivating animals to forage, likely differs from a more chronic sensation of discomfort and exhaustion associated with emaciation. Perhaps there should be a greater distinction between the use of the former, its foundation in optimising animal production, and the latter, arguably of most relevance in maintaining and enhancing animal welfare. However, there is relatively little information to support animal welfare, perhaps partly explaining the scarcity of such information and rationales in the reports accompanying codes of welfare. In the absence of reasoning, standards would seem, then, to rely on common sense – emaciated or obese animals represent poor welfare. However, even at low condition scores there may be questions regarding the value of the standards, since the weight of fat may be overestimated; animals emaciated at several of the lower condition scores, not just at the lowest score (Gregory et al. 1998). When standards require remedial action at low body condition scores (e.g., 1 on a scale of 0-5 in the sheep and beef cattle code), the animals will likely have already faced lengthy periods of starvation and suffering, thus alleviating actions should have been implemented much earlier.

It is suggested that numerical indices of extreme body conditions should not be held as definitive at the expense of the common sense upon which most seem to be based. Body condition is both a dynamic state and a subjective assessment and the danger of appearing objective (e.g., scales having ½ points) may not only obscure the complexity of factors it reflects but give a deceptive impression of its precision. On the one hand, less precise measures, for example, 'thin', 'fit', or 'fat' (Phythian et al. 2011), or the less subjective and more specific 'if vertebrae bumps show along her back, she is too thin' (Grandin 2018), might be more valuable, at least in terms of assessing animal welfare in particular animals. On the other hand, automated systems being investigated (e.g., Halachmi et al. 2013) could provide that precision and prove valuable in tracking changes over time at least in production systems where animals can be repeatedly and routinely assessed. Perhaps the tension between precise and common descriptors reflects the distribution of animals in a population – those in the middle part of the range of most interest in optimising animal production, those at the extremes most pertinent to animal welfare.

Difficulties in maintaining animals in good condition may also reflect changing genetics (e.g., selection for production can be at the expense of body condition – Roche et al. 2017) and management (e.g., a lack of skills in managing pasture, perhaps exacerbated by farming to generalised recipes rather than having the skills to adapt to individual situations). In contrast, companion animals, being 'honorary' people, are susceptible to some of the problems more commonly associated with human lifestyles (Sandøe et al. 2014). The divergence calls for understanding the different motivations for intensifying animal production, and of the complex emotional interactions with companion animals.

Body condition is an indicator of past access to nutritional resources, as well as factors such as disease and parasitism, and thus, an indication of the animal's ability to deal with the constraints of the future environment, be it climate, production or need for veterinary care. Perhaps this is reflected in a 'farmer view' that the greater matter of concern is the availability of 'feed in front of the animals' rather than whether they are a 'bit thin'. It is arguably also an 'iceberg' indicator, i.e., a key indicator of overall welfare inferring that animal care is of high quality and welfare good (Farm Animal Welfare Council 2009) reiterating the common and long-held view that animals in good condition reflect good care. However, in terms of regulatory and non-regulatory animal welfare standards and guidelines, perhaps there is room for a more nuanced understanding, and explanation of, aspects such as the reserves required to deal with different circumstances, especially in extensive environments (for example, beef cattle exposed to hard winters and reduced forage, compared with those in more forgiving environments). Furthermore, any interventions will need to acknowledge the circumstances of those in charge of animals, as well as what the animals are likely experiencing.

Acknowledgements

Representatives of the New Zealand Veterinary Association (Sheep & Beef Cattle, Dairy, and Companion Animal special interest branches) and the Ministry for Primary Industries (Compliance, Verification Services, Legal, and Regulation and Assurance branches) are thanked for providing invaluable insights in responding to a questionnaire from NAWAC in 2015.

References

Annett RW, Carson AF, Dawson LER, Irwin D, Gordon AW, Kilpatrick DJ 2011. Comparison of the longevity and lifetime performance of Scottish Blackface ewes and their crosses within hill sheep flocks. Animal 5: 347-355.

Beaver JM, Olson BE 1997. Winter range use by cattle of different ages in southwestern Montana. Applied Animal Behaviour Science 51: 1-13.

Caldeira RM, Belo AT, Santos CC, Vazques MI, Portugal AV 2007a. The effect of body condition score on blood metabolites and hormonal profiles in ewes. Small Ruminant Research 68: 233-241.

Caldeira RM, Belo AT, Santos CC, Vazques MI, Portugal AV 2007b. The effect of long-term feed restriction and over-nutrition on body condition score, blood metabolites and hormonal profiles in ewes. Small Ruminant Research 68: 242-255.

Dahl-Pedersen K, Herskin MS, Houe H, Thomsen PT 2018. Risk factors for deterioration of the clinical condition of cull dairy cows during transport to slaughter. Frontiers in Veterinary Science 5: 297 doi.org/10.3389/fvets.2018.00297

D'Eath RB, Tolkamp BJ, Kyriazakis I, Lawrence AB 2009. 'Freedom from hunger' and preventing obesity: the animal welfare implications of reducing food quantity or quality. Animal Behaviour 77: 275-288.

Doughty AK, Ferguson D, Matthews LR, Hinch GN 2016. Assessing feeding motivation in sheep using different behavioural demand models and measures. Applied Animal Behaviour Science 180: 43-50.

Everett-Hincks JM, Blair HT, Stafford KJ, Lopez-Villalobos N 2004. The effect of ewe nutrition on maternal behaviour score and litter survival. Proceedings of the New Zealand Society of Animal Production 64: 188-191.

Farm Animal Welfare Council. 2009 Farm Animal Welfare in Great Britain: Past, Present and Future. Farm Animal Welfare Council, London. https://assets.publishing.service.gov.uk/government/uploads/system/uploads/attachment_data/file/319292/Farm_Animal_Welfare_in_Great_Britain_-_Past__Present_and_Future.pdf (accessed 17 December, 2018).

Fisher MW 2009. Defining animal welfare – does consistency matter? New Zealand Veterinary Journal 57: 71-73.

Fleming PA, Clarke T, Wickham SL, Stockman CA, Barnes AL, Collins T, Miller DW 2016. The contribution of qualitative behavioural assessment to appraisal of livestock welfare. Animal Production Science 56: 1569-1578.

Fraser D 2003. Assessing animal welfare at the farm and group level: the interplay of science and values. Animal Welfare 12: 433-443.

German AJ 2006. The growing problem of obesity in dogs and cats. Journal of Nutrition 136: 1940S-1946S.

German AJ, Holden SL, Wiseman-Orr ML, Reid J, Nolan AM, Biourge V, Morris PJ, Scott EM 2012. Quality of life is reduced in obese dogs but improves after successful weight loss. The Veterinary Journal 192: 428-434.

Giles SL, Rands SA, Nicol CJ, Harris PA 2014. Obesity prevalence and associated risk factors in outdoor living domestic horses and ponies. PeerJ 2:e299 doi.org/10.7717/peerj.299

Grandin T 2018. Welfare problems in cattle, pigs, and sheep that persist even though scientific research clearly shows how to prevent them. Animals 8: 124 doi:10.3390/ani8070124

Gregory NG, Robins JK, Thomas DG, Purchas RW 1998. Relationship between body condition score and body composition in dairy cows. New Zealand Journal of Agricultural Research 41: 527-532.

Halachmi I, Klopčič M, Polak P, Roberts DJ, Bewley JM 2013. Automatic assessment of dairy cattle body condition score using thermal imaging. Computers and Electronics in Agriculture 99: 35-40.

Kenyon PR, Maloney SK, Blache D 2014. Review of sheep body condition score in relation to production characteristics. New Zealand Journal of Agricultural Research 57: 38-64.

Macdonald KA, Verkerk GA, Thorrold BS, Pryce JE, Penno JW, L. McNaughton LR, Burton LJ, Lancaster JAS, Williamson JH, Holmes CW 2008. A comparison of three strains of Holstein-Friesian grazed on pasture and managed under different feed allowances. Journal of Dairy Science 91:1693-1707.

Matthews LR, Cameron C, Sheahan AJ, Kolver ES, Roche JR 2012. Associations among dairy cow body condition and welfare associated behavioural traits. Journal of Dairy Science 95: 2595-2601.

Mathias-Davis HC, Shackell GH, Greer GJ, Everett-Hincks JM 2011. The association of ewe body condition score with weight of lamb weaned. Proceedings of the New Zealand Society of Animal Production 71: 62-65.

McGregor BA, Butler KL 2008. Relationship of body condition score, live weight, stocking rate and grazing system to the mortality of Angora goats from hypothermia and their use in the assessment of welfare risks. Australian Veterinary Journal 86: 12-17.

Mench, JA 2002. Broiler breeders: feed restriction and welfare. World's Poultry Science Journal 58: 23-29.

Morgan-Davies C, Waterhouse A, Pollock ML, Milner JM 2008. Body condition score as an indicator of ewe survival under extensive conditions. Animal Welfare 17: 71-77.

Morris CA, Cullen NG, Carson PA, Morley GA 1985. Differences among and within crossbred beef cow groups in body condition and live weight. Proceedings of the New Zealand Society of Animal Production 45: 167-169.

Phythian CJ, Michalopoulou E, Jones PH, Winter AC, Clarkson MJ, Stubbings LA, Grove-White D, Cripps PJ, Duncan JS 2011. Validating indicators of sheep welfare through a consensus of expert opinion. Animal 5: 943-952.

Randall LV, Green MJ, Chagunda MGG, Mason C, Archer SC, Green LE, Huxley JN 2015. Low body condition predisposes cattle to lameness: an 8-year study of one dairy herd. Journal of Dairy Science 98: 3766-3777.

Randall LV, Green MJ, Chagunda MGG, Green LE, Mason C, Archer SC, Huxley JN 2018. The contribution of previous lameness events and body condition score to the occurrence of lameness in dairy herds: a study of 2 herds. Journal of Dairy Science 101: 1311-1324.

Rauw WM, Kanis E, Noordhuizen-Stassen EN, Grommers FJ 1998. Undesirable side effects of selection for high production efficiency in farm animals: a review. Livestock Production Science 56: 15-33.

Roche JR, Friggens NC, Kay JK, Fisher MW, Stafford KJ, Berry DP 2009. Body condition score and its association with dairy cow productivity, health, and welfare. Journal of Dairy Science 92: 5769-5801.

Roche JR, Macdonald KA, Schütz KE, Matthews LR, Verkerk GA, Meier S, Loor JJ, Rogers AR, McGowan J, Morgan SR, Taukiri S, Webster JR 2013. Calving body condition score affects indicators of health in grazing dairy cows. Journal of Dairy Science 96: 5811-5825.

Roche JR, Berry DP, Bryant AM, Burke CR, Butler ST, Dillon PG, Donaghy DJ, Horan B, Macdonald KA, Macmillan KL 2017. A century of change in temperate grazing dairy systems. Journal of Dairy Science 100: 10189-10233.

Sandøe P, Palmer C, Corr S, Astrup A, Bjørnvad CR 2014. Canine and feline obesity: a One Health perspective. Veterinary Record 175: 610-616.

Sandøe P 2018. A one health perspective on companion animal obesity. Proceedings of the Food Safety, Animal Welfare and Biosecurity Branch of the New Zealand Veterinary Association, Hamilton, New Zealand, pp 69-71.

Schütz K, Davison D, Matthews L 2006. Do different levels of moderate feed deprivation in dairy cows affect feeding motivation? Applied Animal Behaviour Science 101: 253-263.

Schütz KE, Cox NR, Macdonald KA, Roche JR, Verkerk GA, Rogers AR, Tucker CB, Matthews LR, Meier S, Webster JR 2013. Behavioral and physiological effects of a short-term feed restriction in lactating dairy cattle with different body conditions scores at calving. Journal of Dairy Science 96: 4465-4476.

Sibbald AM, Rhind SM 1997. The effect of previous body condition on appetite and associated insulin profiles in sheep. Animal Science 64: 247-252.

Smeaton DC, Bown MD, Clayton JB 2000. Optimum liveweight, feed intake, reproduction, and calf output in beef cows on North Island hill country, New Zealand. New Zealand Journal of Agricultural Research 43: 71-82.

Stockman CA, Collins T, Barnes AL, Miller D, Wickham SL, Verbeek E, Matthews L, Ferguson D, Wemelsfelder F, Fleming PA 2014. Qualitative behavioural assessment of the motivation for feed in sheep in response to altered body condition score. Animal Production Science 54: 922-929.

Tucker CB, Rogers AR, Verkerk GA, Kendall PE, Webster JR, Matthews LR 2007. Effects of shelter and body condition on the behaviour and physiology of dairy cattle in winter. Applied Animal Behaviour Science 105: 1-13.

Verbeek E, Waas JR, McLeay LR, Matthews LR 2011. Measurement of feeding motivation in sheep and the effects of food restriction. Applied Animal Behaviour Science 132: 121-130.

Verbeek E, Ferguson D, Lee C 2014. Are hungry sheep more pessimistic? The effects of food restriction on cognitive bias and the involvement of ghrelin in its regulation. Physiology and Behavior 123: 67-75.

Webster, J 2005. Animal Welfare: Limping Towards Eden. UK, Blackwell.

Wemelsfelder F, Hunter TE, Mendl MT. Lawrence AB 2001. Assessing the 'whole animal': a free choice profiling approach. Animal Behaviour 62: 209-220.

Impact of the proximity of the water source on survival and growth of triplet lambs – a case study

S McCoard[a]*, J Wing[b], T Smith[b] and S-Y Hea[a]

[a]AgResearch Limited, Grasslands Research Centre, Tennent Drive, 4442 Palmerston North, New Zealand; [b]Freestone Farm, Te Anau, Southland, New Zealand

**Corresponding author:* Email: sue.mccoard@agresearch.co.nz

Abstract

The objective of this study was to evaluate whether the provision of greater access to watering sites two weeks prior to lambing and at least one week after lambing impacts lamb survival and growth to weaning, using triplets as a model. Triplet-bearing ewes (n=206, 116-131 days gestation) were randomly allocated to either the control (one water trough/paddock) or treatment group (2-3 water troughs/paddock) balanced for ewe live weight, body condition score and stage of gestation, at a stocking density of 8.6-9.1 ewes/ha with three replicated paddocks/treatment. Lamb survival was determined via DNA parentage and lamb growth recorded at docking, weaning and at six months of age. Lamb survival (60 vs 62%, P=0.690) and lamb growth (P=0.452) did not differ between the treatment and control groups. The key finding of this study was that increasing the availability of a water supply to triplet-bearing ewes in late pregnancy and early lactation did not influence lamb survival or growth.

Keywords: sheep; triplets; water; lamb survival

Introduction

Lamb survival is a major animal health and production issue, with the majority of deaths occurring within the first three days of life (McCoard et al. 2017). Water is an important nutrient for maintenance and productivity of livestock and contributes to all vital bodily functions (digestion, absorption, metabolism, nutrient transport, waste elimination and thermoregulation), and is particularly important for lactation. Water consumption varies greatly depending on the type and size of the animal, level of activity, climatic conditions and the animal's physiological state (Beed 1994). Water availability around lambing may be potentially limiting because large paddocks used for lambing often have a single water source (water trough or creek). Further, as ewes select lambing sites up to 24 hours before lambing and can remain at those sites for up to 12-24 hours after lambing, there is the potential for the ewes to not consume water for 1-2 days, potentially resulting in dehydration. Water deprivation can alter the endocrine and metabolic balance of the animal (Jaber et al. 2004; Li et al. 2000). In sheep and goats, water deprivation for 72 hours negatively affects milk production (50% reduction) by reducing feed intake and causes an increase in the viscosity of milk (Agana 1992). Because triplet-bearing ewes spend more time giving birth and establishing the ewe-lamb bond immediately after birth, there is potential for triplet-bearing ewes to be more at risk of dehydration than ewes bearing one or two lambs. Therefore, triplet-bearing ewes were selected as the model for this study.

A recent study by Corner-Thomas et al. (2019) reported no effect of increased access to water on ewe live weight or birth weight of their lambs with the water content of the pasture meeting the requirements of ewes in late pregnancy. However, the potential for improving access to a water source on lamb survival in NZ sheep farming systems has not been evaluated. The objective of this study was to evaluate whether the provision of greater access to water two weeks prior to lambing and at least one week after lambing in triplet-bearing ewes increases lamb survival and growth in a commercial farming system. We hypothesised that increasing water availability in lambing paddocks through provision of a greater number of water troughs around the paddocks would increase survival and growth of triplet-born lambs.

Materials and methods

The study was conducted in the 2018 lambing season at Freestone Farm near Te Anau (a high fecundity flock) in the South Island of New Zealand. This study did not require additional manipulation of animals beyond current standard farm practice and, thus, no ethics approval was required (notification #115, AgResearch Grasslands Animal Ethics Committee). This was because the only change in farm management beyond current practice was the provision of additional water troughs in some of the lambing paddocks. The animal performance data selected for reporting was based on records already collected on this farm as part of standard farm recording for this flock.

This study used triplet-bearing ewes (n=206). The ewes were randomly allocated to one of two treatment groups at set stocking (28th August 2018) at approximately 116-131 days of gestation (mean 121 days). The treatments were applied at the paddock level, with three paddocks (replicates) allocated to each treatment group. Paddock sizes are presented in Table 1. The control group (n=103) was provided with access to one water trough per paddock. The treatment group (n=103) was provided with access to two or three troughs per paddock. The maximum walking distance to a drinking water source in the control paddocks was 233±33m compared to 107±3m in the treatment paddocks.

Table 1 Paddock size, number of triplet lambs scanned, weaned, hand reared and fostered in the control (single drinking-water source) and treatment (2-3 drinking-water sources) groups in each replicate (paddock).

Paddock	Group	Paddock size (ha)	No. lambs at scanning	No. lambs weaning	Lamb survival to weaning (%)	No. lambs hand reared	No. lambs fostered
A32	Control	3.7	90	53	59%	4	2
A34	Treatment	3.7	87	42	48%	8	1
A35	Control	4.5	114	62	54%	6	1
A36	Treatment	4.1	112	68	61%	4	2
A40	Control	4.2	105	64	61%	1	2
A42	Treatment	4.4	114	65	57%	5	0

All ewes were fetal-aged at pregnancy scanning (transabdominal ultrasonography using a commercial operator) within an estimated five-day range (e.g., 65, 70, 75 days gestation). Ewes were set stocked in groups with a 10-day range in expected lambing date on 28th August 2018 according to their expected lambing dates at 8.8-9.1 ewes per hectare (standard farm practice).

Scanning data were used as a proxy for the number of lambs born, and survival of lambs determined through DNA parentage to establish the number of live lambs per ewe at docking and weaning. Fetal loss between mid-pregnancy scanning and lambing is typically low (~5%; Edwards et al., 2016; Juengel et al., 2015). Therefore, the number of lambs scanned is a relatively accurate reflection of the number of lambs born. All data used in this study were downloaded from Sheep Improvement Limited (SIL). Any lambs removed from the ewes and reared artificially, or lambs fostered onto ewes were recorded.

The ewes were offered a ryegrass/white clover mixed pasture. Pasture covers at set stocking were 2300-2700 kg/DM/ha and were 2100-3100 kg/DM/ha on 21st September 2018. Only sheep were set stocked in the trial paddocks. Cows and calves were introduced into the paddocks to manage pasture covers after all ewes had lambed. Feed budgets were calculated using the FeedPlus program (in-house Pāmu software developed by AgResearch). Dry matter allowances were calculated based on ewes mated on the 20th April 2018 at an average live weight of 80 kg, expected lambing date of 17th September 2018, a potential 300% lambing (i.e., three lambs/ewe) and 270% at docking (i.e., 2.7 lambs/ewe) with an average lamb birth weight of 3.9 kg. The calculations were based on an estimated pasture energy content of 11.5 MJ ME/kgDM from April to the end of August 2018, and 12.0 MJ ME/kgDM from September to weaning in early January 2019 at an average lamb live weight of 33 kg.

Pasture samples were collected from each of the paddocks at set stocking (30 August 2018) and were analysed for chemical composition by Hill Laboratories (Hamilton, New Zealand). Pasture samples were oven dried at 62°C and ground to pass through a 1.0-mm screen. Dry matter was measured by weight loss on drying at 105°C for a minimum of 24 hours. Nitrogen was estimated by NIR, calibration based on nitrogen by Dumas combustion. Crude protein was calculated by multiplying nitrogen by 6.25. Digestibility of organic matter in dry matter (DOMD) was calculated from organic matter digestibility (OMD) using the Australian Fodder Industry Association (AFIA) Standard Equation. OMD was estimated by NIR, calibration based on AFIA pepsin-cellulase procedure. Metabolisable energy was calculated from DOMD using AFRC and Lincoln University standard formulae.

All ewes were vaccinated with Covexin 10 (MSD Animal Health, Wellington, New Zealand) four weeks prior to lambing and all ewes received a Flexidine injection (Bayer Animal Health, Auckland, New Zealand) on the 12th of July. The two-year-old ewes were also given a booster Campy Vax vaccination (Campyvax4®, MSD Animal Health) prior to mating. Prior to and during lambing, ewes were monitored three times a day and birthing assistance was provided if required. Water meters (Arad M Water Meters, ADM25-EV, WaterForce Winton, New Zealand) were installed in two paddocks (A40 - control and A42 - treatment) and paddock water intake was monitored from 1st September to 9th October 2018. Water use in these paddocks is presented as average intake per ewe in each group.

A generalised linear mixed model with a logit link function and random intercept for paddock was used to estimate the effect of paddock treatment on the proportion of lambs surviving from birth to weaning. The experimental unit was the paddock, as the treatments were applied at the paddock level, and the observational unit was the ewe. Variables included in the model were the paddock treatment at set stocking, ewe age (2, 3, 4, 5, 6+), body condition score (BCS; 1-5 scale, Jefferies 1961) and live weight before lambing, and the estimated age of the fetus at set stocking.

For the analysis of lamb live weights from docking to six months of age, a linear mixed model with weights nested within lambs, within ewe, within paddock was used. Variables included in the model were the ewe paddock treatment at set stocking, ewe age (2, 3, 4, 5, 6+), ewe BCS and live weight before lambing, the estimated fetal age at set stocking (as a proxy for lamb age), lamb sex, lamb rearing rank at docking, and the weighing time (docking, weaning and six months). The ewe BCS and live weights, and the estimated fetal age at set stocking variables were centred by subtracting each recorded value by their respective sample means. All statistical analyses were undertaken using the statistical software R (R Core Team, 2018).

No statistical analysis was undertaken for the ewe live weight or BCS data. Live weight and BCS records were taken prior to set stocking and, thus, prior to treatment. This raw data is included for the purposes of describing the populations.

Analysis of lamb survival was based on the number of lambs weaned (including fostered lambs) relative to the number of lambs scanned. Lambs that were hand reared were considered "dead" for this analysis.

Results and discussion

Pasture quality and water use

The chemical composition (as a % DM) of the pasture in the control versus treatment groups at the time of set stocking was: DM 23% for both groups, crude protein 22 *vs.* 21% DM, 12.6 *vs.*12.5MJ/ME kgDM, and 85 *vs.*84 digestibility of organic matter in dry matter. The chemical composition of the pastures indicates that good-quality pasture was offered to all groups at set stocking.

Ewe survival, assisted births, live weight and body condition score (BCS)

Based on the number of ewes present at scanning versus the number of ewes present at weaning, ewe deaths ranged from 3 to 12% among the paddocks (average of 6.5%). Lamb losses from these ewes were not included in the analysis of lamb survival but highlights another significant area of lost opportunity.

The live weight of the control *vs.* treatment ewes at mating was 75±0.1 *vs.* 74±0.1 kg, at pregnancy scanning was 82±1.3 *vs.* 85±1.1 kg and two weeks prior to set stocking was 90±1.1 *vs.* 90±1.1. The BCS of the control and treatment ewes at mating was 3.7±0.05 *vs.* 3.7±0.05, at pregnancy scanning was 3.6±0.04 *vs.* 3.7±0.05 and two weeks prior to set stocking was 3.6±0.04 *vs.* 3.6±0.04. On average, ewes in both groups had similar live weights and BCS (mean and variation) throughout gestation. The increase in live weight over time is expected because of advancing gestation.

Lamb survival

On average 48-61% of lambs survived from scanning to weaning (Table 1) and the number of lambs hand reared or fostered onto ewes was low and was similar across all replicates. There was no difference in lamb survival between the treatment and control group (60 *vs.* 62%, P=0.690). Furthermore, ewe age (P=0.460), BCS (P=0.450), ewe live weight (P=0.350) and fetal age at set stocking (P=0.250) had no effect on lamb survival in this population. It is important to note, that except for age, which was variable (2-6+ years) the ewes were of similar BCS, live weight and gestational age, therefore, it is not surprising that these traits did not influence lamb survival in this population. In this population, only three ewes (1.5%) lost 1 BCS unit from pregnancy scanning to lambing, and all other ewes either lost 0.5 BCS units (27%), maintained BCS (60%) or gained 0.5 BCS units (12%). This reflects the careful attention to detail of feeding management of the ewes.

Lamb survival was lowest for two-year-old ewes (52%, CI 44–59%) and while on average it was the greatest in six-year-old ewes, there was a much-higher population variation (72.5%, CI 49-88%; Figure 1). These results are consistent with previous studies (McCoard et al., 2018; Juengel, McCoard, Johnstone unpublished data). The level of mortality observed in this study (39-52% across the different paddocks) is similar to values observed in previous

Figure 1 The effect of ewe age (two to six years) on the proportion of lambs surviving from pregnancy scanning to weaning ~12 weeks post-partum in triplet-bearing ewes with increased access to a water supply (treatment; 2-3 drinking-water sources per paddock) compared to standard farm practice (control; 1 drinking-water source per paddock). Data presented as predicted mean and 95% confidence intervals.

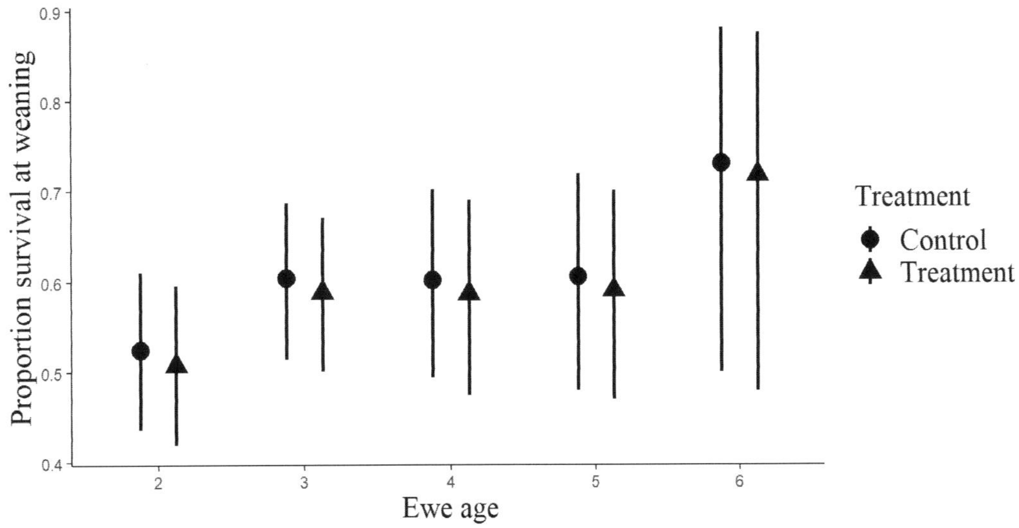

Figure 2 Live weight of female (solid lines) and male lambs (dashed lines) at docking, weaning and ~ six months of age. Sex × time interaction (P =0.003). Data are presented as means ± SEM.

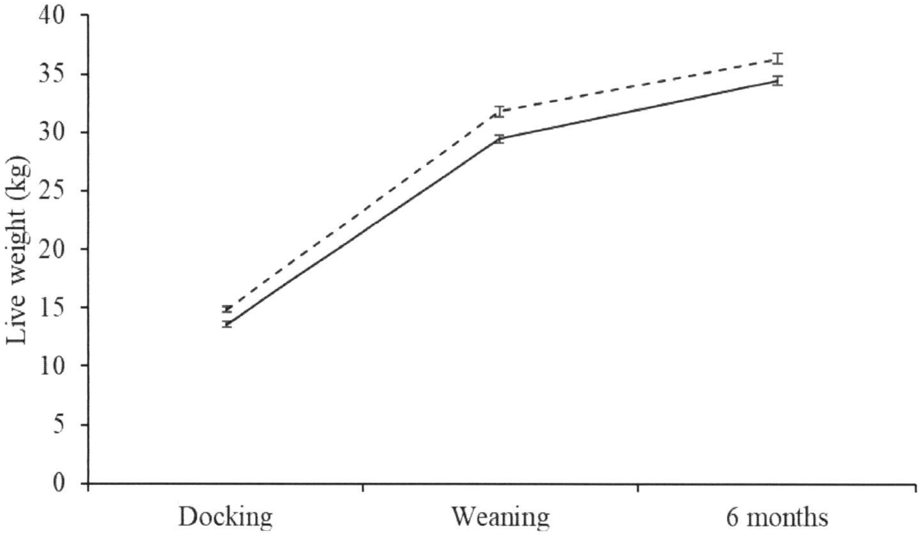

Figure 3 Water usage in one control (single-drinking water source) and one treatment (2-3 drinking-water sources) paddock during the trial from set stocking to one week after lambing.

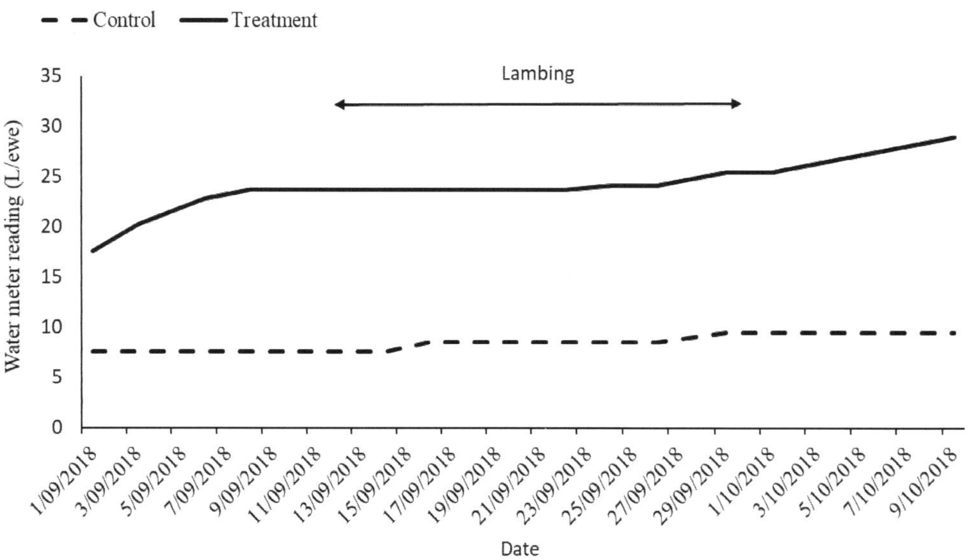

studies in New Zealand (25-40%; West et al. 2008; Stafford 2013), Australia (Hinch & Brien, 2014) and other areas of the globe (Rowland et al. 1992; Dwyer et al. 2007).

The key finding from this study is that increasing availability of a water supply to triplet-bearing ewes in late pregnancy and early lactation, by reducing the walking distance to drinking water troughs, did not influence lamb survival or growth. The intake of water per ewe was estimated to be 2-3-fold higher in the treatment compared to control group (Figure 3), likely resulting from the shorter walking distance. While the water intakes remain to be verified in a larger study, these preliminary results illustrate that, when a nearby water source is provided, water intake increases even when pasture water content is high. Water deprivation for 72 hours negatively affected milk production (50% reduction) in sheep and goats by reducing feed intake and caused an increase in the viscosity of milk (Agana 1992) which can affect the ability of the lamb to extract colostrum/milk from the gland. However, Casamassima et al. (2008) reported that reducing water consumption by 20-40% daily had no effect on milk yield, composition or feed intake. In the present study, reducing the walking distance to a water source and/or increasing water intake did not appear to influence lactational performance of the ewes as

Figure 4 Estimated daily rainfall and minimum and maximum temperatures during the trial period from set stocking to one week after lambing. Data source: www.worldweather.com.

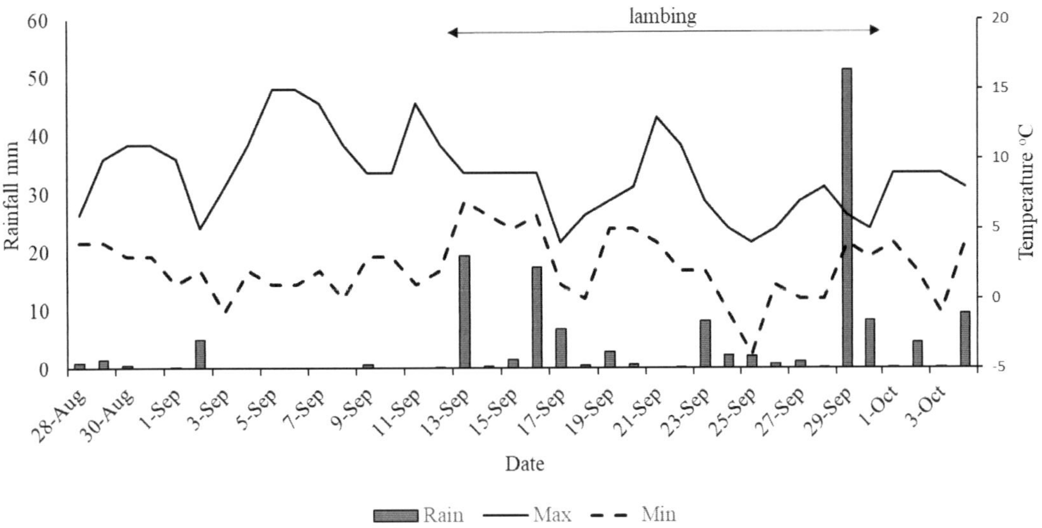

indicated by similar lamb survival and growth between the groups. Furthermore, there was no apparent effect on the formation of the ewe-lamb bond/mis-mothering which can occur when ewes leave their birth site.

Sheep can tolerate a water loss greater than 20% (Jaber et al. 2004) due to their forestomach which is able to accumulate water to use when water availability is low. It is likely that this adaptive capacity, coupled with the high-water content of the pasture (i.e., <25% DM) was able to mitigate against the risk of water deprivation during the parturition period, or that a single water source was able to provide sufficient water to cover their requirements. A limitation of this study was that due to the requirement to minimise contact with the ewes to avoid disruption of the birth process and to achieve commercial farming practice, no direct physiological measures on the ewes prior to or at lambing could be undertaken to determine their level of hydration. Such measures could be considered in future studies when animals are housed or under experimental conditions that enable individual animal handling. During the lambing period, a total of 138 mm of rainfall was recorded accompanied by relatively cool temperatures (Figure 4). Furthermore, there was only one day during lambing when no rainfall was recorded. Sun et al. (2017) reported that in cattle, the number of wet days rather than total rainfall significantly impacted daily water intake from troughs. Therefore, it is possible that the ewes were able to gain access to water from puddles in the paddocks, in addition to water in and on pasture, thereby reducing the need to visit the reticulated water supply.

Lamb growth

There was no effect of treatment on lamb growth (P=0.578). Sex (P<0.001, males > females), weighing time (P<0.001), ewe live weight at lambing (P=0.002), rearing rank at docking (P<0.001), fetal age at set stocking (P=0.001) and the interaction between sex and time (P=0.003; Figure 2) were significant predictors of lamb live weight. At docking the lambs were on average 14±0.4 kg live weight, 30±0.4 kg live weight at weaning and 35±0.4 kg live weight at six months of age. Ewe BCS and age were not significant predictors of lamb weight from docking to weaning.

The relatively high ewe losses (3-12) and lamb losses (39-58%) across the paddocks irrespective of treatment group, highlights the challenges associated with triplet-bearing ewes. The causes of the high losses were not investigated in this study but are within the range reported in the literature (Kenyon et al. 2019) and losses could be contributed to a variety of causes as previously described (McCoard et al. 2017; Kenyon et al. 2019) Increasing access to a fresh water supply by reducing the walking distance did not influence lamb survival or growth in this study. A recent study by Corner-Thomas et al. (2019) reported no effect of increased access to water on ewe live weight or birth weight of their lambs with the water content of the pasture meeting the requirements of ewes in late pregnancy. While it was not possible to determine the frequency of visits to the troughs by the ewes in the current study, the results suggest that the water content of the pasture and presence of one water trough was sufficient to meet the requirements of the ewes, or that they were able to visit the water sources frequently enough to not adversely affect lamb survival or growth. It is important to note that the paddock sizes used in this study (3.7-4.4 ha) may be considered small in comparison to some extensive production systems. Whether similar results would be observed in environments where paddock sizes are much larger or where feed quality and/or terrain differs, warrants further investigation.

Further research is required to identify practical intervention strategies to improve survival of triplet-bearing ewes and their progeny. There are substantial eco-efficiency gains to be realised through capitalising on increased fecundity (Mackay et al. 2011; 2019). However, novel strategies are yet to be discovered and implemented to realise this potential even on high-performing farms such as the Freestone Farm where best-practice feeding and animal-management strategies including increased shepherding around lambing time are implemented.

Acknowledgements

This work was funded by AgResearch's Strategic Science Investment Fund (SSIF) with on-farm trial, data collection and capture funded in-kind by Pāmu and Focus Genetics LP.

References

Agana AA 1992. Water utilization by sheep and goats in northern Nigeria. World Animal Review. FAO 73: 9-14.

Beed DK. 1994. Water: the most important nutrient for dairy cattle. Presented at the 31st Florida Dairy Production Conference; Gainesville, FL, USA: University of Florida.

Casamassima D, Pizzo R, Palazzo M, D'Alessandro AG, Martemucci G. 2008. Effect of water restriction on productive performance and blood parameters in comisana sheep reared under intensive condition. Small Ruminant Research 78: 169-175. Doi: 10.17221/144/2015-VETMED

Corner-Thomas RA, Winchester N, Draganova IG, Burkitt LLO, Kenyon PR. 2019. The impacts of reticulated water on sheep performance during winter in the Manawatu. New Zealand Journal of Animal Science and Production 79: 202 (abstract).

Dwyer CM. 2007. The welfare of the neonatal lamb. Small Ruminant Research 76: 31–41. Doi: 10.1016/j.smallrumres.2007.12.011.

Hinch GN, Brien F. 2014. Lamb survival in Australian flocks: a review. Animal Production Science 54: 656–666. https://doi.org/10.1071/AN13236

Jaber LS, Habre A, Rawda N, Abi Said M, Barbour EK, Hamadeh S. 2004. The effect of water restriction on certain physiological parameters in Awassi sheep. Small Ruminant Research. 54: 115-120. https://doi.org/10.17221/144/2015-VETMED

Jefferies BC. 1961. Body condition scoring and its use in management. Tasmanian Journal of Agriculture 32: 19-21.

Kenyon PR, Roca Fraga FJ, Blumer S, Thompson AN. 2019. Triplet lambs and their dams – a review of current knowledge and management systems. New Zealand Journal of Agricultural Research 62(4): 399-437. Doi/org/10.1080/00288233.2019.1616568

Mackay AD, Rhodes AP, Power I, Wedderburn ME. 2011. Has the eco-efficiency of sheep and beef farms changed in the last 20 years? Proceedings of the New Zealand Grassland Association 73: 119-124.

Mackay AD, Scobie DR, Rhodes TR, Devantier D. 2019 INVITED PAPER. Has progress been made in increasing the eco-efficiency of livestock systems? New Zealand Journal of Animal Science and Production 79: 43-55.

McCoard SA, Sales FA, Sciascia QL. 2017. Invited review: impact of a specific nutrient interventions during mid-late gestation on physiological traits important for survival of multiple-born lambs. Animal. Doi:10.1017/S1751731117000313.

Nowak R, Poindron P. 2006. From birth to colostrum: early steps leading to lamb survival. Reproduction Nutrition and Development 46(4): 431-446. doi: 10.1051/rnd:2006023.

R Core Team 2018. R: A language and environment for statistical computing. R Foundation for Statistical Computing, Vienna, Austria. Available online at https://www.R-project.org/.

Rowland JP, Salman MD, Kimberling CV, Schweitzer DJ, Keefe TJ. 1992. Epidemiologic factors involved in perinatal lamb mortality on four range sheep operations. American Journal of Veterinary Research 53: 262–267.

Stafford KJ. 2013. Welfare of sheep and goats. Animal welfare in New Zealand. Occasional publication no 16. New Zealand Society of Animal Production, Cambridge, New Zealand, pp. 56–71.

Steiger Burgos M, Senn M, Sutter F, Kreuzer M, Langhans W. 2001. Effect of water restriction on feeding and metabolism in dairy cows. American Journal of Physiology-Regulatory, Integrative and Comparative Physiology 280: R418–27. doi: 10.1152/ajpregu.2001.280.2.R418

Sun LZ, Auerswald K, Wenzel R, Schnyder H. 2014. Drinking water intake of grazing steers: The role of environmental factors controlling canopy wetness. Journal of Animal Science 92: 282-291.

West DM, Bruere AN, Ridler AI. 2008. The sheep: health, disease and production, (3rd edition). Vet Learn Foundation, Wellington, New Zealand.

Genetic parameters, breed and heterosis effects for conformation scores in cows milked once a day

NW Sneddon[a,b], DJ Donaghy[a] and N Lopez-Villalobos[a]

[a]School of Agriculture, Massey University, Private Bag 11222, Palmerston North 4410, New Zealand. [b] Fonterra, On-Farm Research and Development, Palmerston North, New Zealand.

*Corresponding author: Email: nick.sneddon@fonterra.com

Abstract

The use of conformation traits to aid selection for functional cows becomes more important as once-a-day (OAD) milking for whole or part season becomes more common. In 2013, Massey University Dairy 1 farm transitioned their mixed-breed herd milked twice-a-day (TAD) to an OAD spring-calving system. All cows on the farm were scored for 14 inspector-scored type traits and four farmer-scored traits, for a total of 1,617 lactation records over seven seasons (2013-2019, 168 to 258 cows per year). Genetic parameters, breed and heterosis effects were obtained from an animal model that included the fixed effects of year of scoring and cow age at scoring, and the covariates of proportion Holstein-Friesian, heterosis between Holstein-Friesian and Jersey, and the random effects of permanent environment of cow and random additive genetic effect of animal. Stature and live weight were found to have the greatest heritability estimates (0.46 and 0.41 respectively), while leg angle and body condition score had the lowest (0.03 and 0.04 respectively). Breed had a significant effect on all type scores, with heterosis also having significant effects; this is an important consideration with the increasing importance of type scores for cows in OAD milking systems. Jersey cows had greater front udder and udder support scores than did Holstein-Friesians ($P<0.05$), while Holstein-Friesians had greater stature and liveweight scores ($P<0.05$). From this study, genetic selection for improved udder conformation would see beneficial gains over time, whilst body condition score is heritable, would not be similarly improved.

Keywords: Traits other than production; once-a-day milking; genetic parameters

Introduction

Breed and heterosis effects are often highlighted as areas of consideration for the transition to once-a-day (OAD) milking systems (Rocha et al. 2017a), however, the reporting of these parameters is often limited to production and reproduction traits (Lembeye et al. 2016). As part of the transition to OAD from a twice-a-day (TAD) system, conformation traits are considered in the selection and culling of cows. These conformation traits, termed 'Traits other than Production' (TOP traits), are separated into four farmer-scored traits and 14 inspector-scored traits. The farmer-scored traits are milking speed, shed temperament, adaptability to milking and overall opinion, while the inspector-scored traits are stature, live weight, body capacity, rump angle, rump width, leg angle, udder support, front udder, rear udder, front-teat placement, rear-teat placement, udder overall, dairy conformation and body condition score (Advisory Committee on Traits other than Production 2014). The use of these scores to improve conformation and cow survival has previously been demonstrated (Cue et al. 1996; Berry et al. 2005; Rocha et al. 2017a, 2017b; Sneddon et al. 2019). The current study is the first to present genetic parameters for TOP traits in cows milked OAD. These parameters can be used to investigate the scope to change in phenotype over time and under selection.

Materials and methods

Since 2013, Massey University Dairy 1 farm has transitioned a previously TAD mixed-breed herd to an OAD spring-calving system. Since then, all cows on the farm have been scored annually for 14 inspector-scored TOP traits and four-farmer scored TOP traits. All scores (inspector- and farmer-scored) are on 1-9 scales, details of which are outlined in the TOP inspector manual (Advisory Committee on Traits other than Production 2014). The inspections all occurred between November and January each season when certified TOP inspectors were available. The breed compositions of all cows were available in 16ths: these breed proportions were used to classify the cows into Holstein-Friesian (F), Jersey (J), or F×J crossbred categories, any remaining 16ths were assigned to an "other" breed. Either F or J was designated for an animal with a breed proportion ≥87.5% of the respective breed, while F×J crossbreds were designated as all animals intermediate to those two proportions. Coefficients of specific heterosis were calculated between F and J breeds using the following identities (Dickerson 1973): $h_{F\times J} = \alpha_{sF}\alpha_{dJ} + \alpha_{sJ}\alpha_{dF}$ where $h_{F\times J}$ is the coefficient of expected heterosis between fractions of breeds F and J in the progeny, α_{sF} and α_{sJ} are proportions of breeds F and J in the sire, respectively, and α_{dF} and α_{dJ} are proportions of breed F and J in the dam, respectively. There were a total of 538 animals scored a total of 1615 times over the seven seasons; the pedigree file contained 994 identities over four generations.

Statistical analysis

The mean conformation scores were produced using the GLM procedure in SAS 9.4 (SAS Institute Inc., Cary, NC, USA), fitting a model that included the fixed effects of age of animal at scoring (two years old, three years old, four years old, five years old and over six years old) and the year of scoring (to adjust for differences between inspectors and timing), proportion of F and the heterosis effects for F×J fitted as covariates, and the repeated effect of cow. Estimates of genetic parameters and (co)variance components were obtained using the Restricted Maximal Likelihood procedure in ASReml package (Gilmour et al. 2009) of VSN International Ltd., fitting a repeatability animal model that included the fixed effects of year of scoring and cow age at scoring, and the covariates of proportion F, heterosis between F and J, and the random effects of permanent environment of cow and random additive genetic effect of animal. Heritability (h^2) of a trait was calculated as:

$$h^2 = \sigma_a^2 / (\sigma_a^2 + \sigma_p^2 + \sigma_e^2).$$

Repeatability (rep) of a trait was calculated as:

$$\text{rep} = (\sigma_a^2 + \sigma_p^2) / (\sigma_a^2 + \sigma_p^2 + \sigma_e^2)$$

where:
σ_a^2 is the animal additive genetic variance,
σ_p^2 is the cow permanent environmental variance,
σ_e^2 is the residual error variance.

Results

Least-squares means for the TOP values for each breed group are presented in Table 1. It was found that the F×J cows had the lowest scores for both front and rear udder, as well as the lowest score for udder overall. This was not due to greater age, as the median and mean ages of the F×J cows were not different to the other breeds (data not presented). Holstein-Friesian had the greatest scores for stature, live weight and rump width, whilst the J cows had the lowest, and F×J were intermediate. Jerseys and F were not different ($P<0.05$) for udder support, rear udder, or dairy conformation. The three breed groups were not different ($P>0.05$) for capacity, rump angle or body condition score. The breed and heterosis effects are presented in Table 1; stature, live weight, udder support and udder overall had heterosis effects which were significantly different to zero. Increasing the proportion of F in the cow had significant effects on stature, live weight, leg angle and rump width compared to a baseline of J cows. For the farmer scores, there was no significant effect of heterosis or proportion of F; for all four of these traits the effect was smaller than the associated standard error of the mean.

Estimates of variance components and genetic parameters are presented in Table 2. Heritability estimates were greatest for stature and live weight followed by rear teat placement (0.46, 0.41 and 0.34 respectively). Heritabilities were lowest for body condition score (0.04) and leg angle (0.03), with these two traits also having the lowest repeatabilities (0.07 and 0.09 respectively). Rear teat placement had the greatest repeatability (0.51), followed by stature (0.48). Udder traits all showed moderate heritabilities (0.16-0.34), and these traits also all showed moderate repeatabilities. The farmer-scored traits had lower overall variance than did the inspector-scored traits, as fewer scores are used.

Discussion

The use of TOP traits in selection of cows suited to OAD milking has been proposed previously in literature, with udder traits having the largest influence on survival (Berry at al. 2005; Rocha et al. 2017a). This has been

Table 1 Regression coefficients of Holstein-Friesian (β_F; F) (relative to Jersey(J)) and heterosis F × J ($h_{F\times J}$) and least-square means for F, J and first cross F×J cows for traits-other-than-production values scored on cows milked once a day.

Trait	β_F	$h_{F\times J}$	F	F×J	J
Farmer scored					
Adaptability to milking	0.06 ± 0.07	0.09 ± 0.09	7.34ᵃ ± 0.04	7.40ᵃ ± 0.03	7.30ᵃ ± 0.05
Temperament	-0.05 ± 0.07	0.17 ± 0.09	7.91ᵇ ± 0.04	8.02ᵃ ± 0.03	7.96ᵃᵇ ± 0.04
Milking speed	0.11 ± 0.08	0.03 ± 0.11	6.91ᵃ ± 0.05	6.86ᵃ ± 0.03	6.84ᵃ ±0.05
Overall opinion	0.09 ± 0.08	0.18 ± 0.11	7.85ᵃᵇ ± 0.05	7.92ᵃ ± 0.04	7.74ᵇ ± 0.06
Inspector scored					
Stature	2.21‡ ± 0.11	0.36‡ ± 0.12	6.75ᵃ ± 0.04	6.18ᵇ ± 0.03	4.59ᶜ ± 0.04
Live weight	1.99‡ ± 0.11	0.30‡ ± 0.12	5.91ᵃ ± 0.04	5.42ᵇ ± 0.03	4.05ᶜ ± 0.04
Body capacity	0.21 ± 0.08	-0.09 ± 0.11	6.97ᵃ ± 0.04	6.88ᵃ ± 0.03	6.85ᵃ ± 0.04
Leg angle	-0.40 ± 0.05	-0.14 ± 0.07	5.25ᶜ ± 0.03	5.41ᵇ ± 0.02	5.69ᵃ ± 0.03
Rump angle	-0.07 ± 0.07	0.09 ± 0.09	4.56ᵃ ± 0.04	4.63ᵃ ± 0.03	4.55ᵃ ± 0.04
Rump width	1.12‡ ± 0.13	0.04 ± 0.16	6.69ᵃ ± 0.06	6.26ᵇ ± 0.04	5.56ᶜ ± 0.06
Udder support	-0.04 ± 0.12	-0.46‡ ± 0.16	6.67ᵃ ± 0.06	6.41ᵇ ± 0.04	6.73ᵃ ± 0.06
Front udder	-0.21 ± 0.17	-0.51 ± 0.21	6.11ᵇ ± 0.08	5.78ᶜ ± 0.05	6.34ᵃ ± 0.08
Rear udder	-0.05 ± 0.13	-0.25 ± 0.17	6.71ᵃ ± 0.06	6.46ᵇ ± 0.05	6.76ᵃ ± 0.07
Front teats	-0.13 ± 0.08	-0.01 ± 0.11	4.57ᵇ ± 0.04	4.58ᵇ ± 0.03	4.72ᵃ ± 0.04
Rear teats	0.26 ± 0.16	0.25 ± 0.19	6.03ᵃ ± 0.06	6.02ᵃ ± 0.05	5.77ᵇ ± 0.07
Udder overall	-0.19 ± 0.15	-0.49‡ ± 0.18	6.24ᵇ ± 0.07	6.02ᶜ ± 0.05	6.45ᵃ ± 0.07
Dairy conformation	-0.01 ± 0.07	-0.06 ± 0.10	6.87ᵃ ± 0.04	6.76ᵇ ± 0.03	6.94ᵃ ± 0.04
Body condition score	0.05 ± 0.09	0.02 ± 0.12	4.43ᵃ ± 0.06	4.47ᵃ ± 0.06	4.37ᵃ ± 0.06

Values with ‡ are significantly different to zero $P<0.05$.
[a,b,c] Means with different letters denote significant differences ($P<0.05$).

Table 2 Variance components, heritabilities (h^2) and repeatabilities (rep) with associated standard errors for traits-other-than-production values scored on cows milked once a day.

Trait[1]	σ^2_a	σ^2_p	σ^2_e	σ^2_{total}	h^2	rep
Farmer scored						
Adaptability to milking	0.08	0.01	0.39	0.48	0.17 ± 0.07	0.19 ± 0.05
Temperament	0.05	0.02	0.31	0.38	0.13 ± 0.07	0.17 ± 0.05
Milking speed	0.09	0.08	0.34	0.51	0.17 ± 0.08	0.33 ± 0.04
Overall opinion	0.10	0.01	0.59	0.70	0.14 ± 0.07	0.16 ± 0.05
Inspector scored						
Stature	0.33	0.02	0.37	0.72	0.46 ± 0.06	0.48 ± 0.03
Live weight	0.31	0.04	0.41	0.76	0.41 ± 0.07	0.46 ± 0.03
Body capacity	0.14	0.01	0.60	0.75	0.19 ± 0.04	0.20 ± 0.03
Leg angle	0.01	0.03	0.40	0.44	0.03 ± 0.03	0.09 ± 0.03
Rump angle	0.11	0.07	0.31	0.49	0.23 ± 0.06	0.37 ± 0.03
Rump width	0.37	0.05	1.05	1.47	0.25 ± 0.06	0.29 ± 0.03
Udder support	0.25	0.16	0.90	1.31	0.19 ± 0.06	0.31 ± 0.03
Front udder	0.69	0.06	1.61	2.36	0.29 ± 0.06	0.32 ± 0.03
Rear udder	0.31	0.07	1.27	1.65	0.19 ± 0.05	0.23 ± 0.03
Front teats	0.10	0.09	0.44	0.63	0.16 ± 0.06	0.30 ± 0.03
Rear teats	0.56	0.29	0.81	1.65	0.34 ± 0.07	0.51 ± 0.03
Udder overall	0.49	0.09	1.16	1.74	0.28 ± 0.06	0.33 ± 0.03
Dairy conformation	0.09	0.02	0.52	0.63	0.14 ± 0.05	0.17 ± 0.03
Body condition score	0.05	0.04	1.12	1.21	0.04 ± 0.03	0.07 ± 0.03

[1] σ^2_a = animal additive genetic variance, σ^2_p = cow permanent environment variance, σ^2_e = residual error variance, σ^2_{total} = sum of all variances

evident in the introduction of TOP traits within the Livestock Improvement Corporation OAD selection index (LIC 2019). The inclusion of TOP traits into a greater range of breeding objectives allows for increased rates of genetic gain in those traits than could occur with farmer-only directed selection.

Most of the traits relating to size and shape of the animal were as would be expected, with F animals having the largest frame size (stature, live weight and rump width), however, this increased size was not as strong in relative traits such as body capacity. The trait of body capacity attracts a high amount of farmer interest, as they see it as an indication of the animals' "strength" or ability to eat greater amounts, however, the score actually relates to the heart room between the front legs (Advisory Committee on Traits other than Production 2014). In the current study, it was found that a large (greater scores in stature and live weight) animal did not mean that the capacity increased at the same rate and while F had a numerically greater mean, this capacity score was not significantly greater than those of the J or F×J animals. Interestingly, the farmer-score traits showed the F×J cows having a higher overall opinion score than did the J animals, despite having lower values for udder overall, front udder, rear udder and udder support. This can highlight another aspect found in previous studies, where farmer-scored traits (adaptability to milking, temperament, milking speed and overall opinion) had poor correlations with estimated breeding values (Sneddon et al. 2019). This difference may be influenced by farmer training or understanding of the scoring system as well as inherent bias - as the scores are more subjective than objective, there is potential for both farmer and inspector scores to be influenced in this manner. Inspector scoring is often more consistent, as there is a calibration training and assessment course before the inspector can undertake scoring, and this improves the chance of getting unbiased results.

Estimates of variance components are essential for the planning of selection indices and breeding objectives, as they are used in the prediction of the genetic response to selection pressures and essential factors in the genetic evaluation of any trait. This study is the first to present variance component estimations to the authors' knowledge for TOP traits from cows milked OAD in New Zealand.

Conclusion

As the proportion of New Zealand dairy farms milking OAD continues to increase, the requirement for TOP scores to be collected and analysed on a greater number of cows across more herds for breeding decisions and culling choices is a logical step. The resulting genetic parameters can then be used to strengthen the national breeding objective. The current study found that genetic selection for udder traits would see beneficial gains over time, whereas leg angle and body condition scores have low genetic variability and have lower potential for genetic selection in cows milked OAD.

References

Advisory Committee on Traits other than Production 2014. Evaluation system for traits other than production (TOP) for dairy cattle in New Zealand. https://www.dairynz.co.nz/media/1205535/TOP_Booklet_A4.pdf [Accessed 20/2/2020]

Berry DP, Harris BL, Winkelman AM, Montgomerie WA. 2005. Phenotypic associations between traits other than production and longevity in New Zealand dairy cattle. Journal of Dairy Science 88: 2962-2974.

Cue RI, Harris BL, Rendel JM 1996. Genetic parameters for traits other than production in purebred and crossbred New Zealand dairy cattle. Livestock Production Science 45: 123-135.

Dickerson GE 1973. Inbreeding and heterosis in animals. Proceedings of the Animal Breeding and Genetics Symposium in honor of Dr. Jay L. Lush, held July 29, 1972, at Virginia Polytechnic Institute and State University, Blacksburg, Virginia. Pp 54-77.

Gilmour AR, Gogel BJ, Cullis BR, Thompson R 2009. ASReml User Guide Release 3.0. Hemel Hempstead, HP1 1ES, UK: VSN International Ltd.

Lembeye F, Lopez-Villalobos N, Burke JL, Davis SR 2016. Estimation of genetic parameters for milk traits in cows milked once- or twice-daily in New Zealand. Livestock Science 185: 142-147.

LIC 2019. Once-a-day selection index. https://www.lic.co.nz/products-and-services/artificial-breeding/alpha/once-day-milking/ [accessed 20/2/2020]

Rocha JF, Lopez-Villalobos N, Burke JL 2017a. Culling reasons in once-a-day milking cows and differences in production and type traits between retained and culled cows. Proceedings of the New Zealand Society of Animal Production 77: 200-204.

Rocha JF, Lopez-Villalobos N, Burke JL, Sneddon NW, Donaghy DJ 2017b. Factors that influence the survival of cows milked once a day. New Zealand Journal of Agricultural Research 61: 42-56.

Sneddon NW, Lopez-Villalobos N, Garrick DJ, Rocha JF, Donaghy DJ 2019. Regression of traits-other-than-production for cows milked once-a-day on estimated breeding values from cows milked twice-a-day. New Zealand Journal of Animal Science and Production 79: 140-143.

Genetic evaluation for farm profitability in a commercial grazing dairy herd of Uruguay

D Laborde[a] and N Lopez-Villalobos[b*]

[a]*El Pedregal, Castiglioni 453, 8500 Trinidad, Uruguay;* [b]*School of Agriculture and Environment, Massey University, Private Bag 11-222, Palmerston North, New Zealand*

**Corresponding author.* Email: N.Lopez-Villalobos@massey.ac.nz

Abstract

The objective of this study was to develop a genetic evaluation model for farm profitability in a seasonally calving pasture-based dairy herd in Uruguay using crossbred cows. Total lactation yields of milk (MILK), fat (FAT) and protein (PROT) were calculated for each cow-lactation using the test-interval method. Somatic cell score (SCS) was calculated as the average of $\log_2$ (somatic cell count) for each cow-lactation. Mating records were used to calculate days from start of mating to conception (SMCO). Cow live weight (LWT) was recorded once per lactation. Cows were scored annually for udder depth (UD), udder support (US), front and rear teat placement (FT and RT). In total there were 4,081 lactations from 2,371 cows recorded from 2015 to 2017. The cows were the progeny of 97 sires. Breeding values (BV) for MILK, FAT, PROT, LWT, SMCO, SCS, UD, US, FT and RT were estimated with a multi-trait repeatability animal model that included the fixed effects of contemporary group (year-lactation number) and deviation from median calving date, and the random effects of animal, cow permanent and residual error. Estimates of BVs for these traits were combined in a selection index to rank cows for farm profitability. The index was calculated as $I = -0.074\times BV_{MILK} + 2.13\times BV_{FAT} + 7.25\times BV_{PROT} - 1.48\times BV_{LWT} - 3.60\times BV_{SMCO} - 36.84\times BV_{SCS} + 30.86\times BV_{UD} + 19.67\times BV_{US} + 21.10\times BV_{FT} + 20.07\times BV_{RT}$. The index has been used to select the best cows as mothers of future replacements, cull the cows with the lowest selection index value, and for the selection and culling of heifer replacements.

Keywords: genetic evaluation; genetic parameters; selection index; Uruguay

Introduction

Milk production systems in Uruguay are characterized by grazing herds, with 70% of the diet being grazed pasture, hay and silage with the remainder being grain-based concentrates (Fariña & Chilibroste 2019). Milk payment is based on a differential payment per kilogram of fat and protein with a penalty for milk volume, which is similar to the payment system used in New Zealand. The national evaluation scheme for dairy cattle currently only includes purebred Holstein and Jersey cattle (Aguilar 2016). The genetic evaluation system of Uruguay produces predicted transmitting abilities for lactation yields of milk, fat and protein, daughter pregnancy rate and somatic cell score (SCS), and animals (cows and bulls) are ranked on an economic index called Productive Economic Index. The relative emphases assigned to each trait are the following: 18.5% for milk yield, 10.1% for fat yield, 36.4% for protein yield, 7.4% for daughter pregnancy rate, and 27.6% for SCS (Evaluaciones Geneticas Lecheras 2018). The methodology used to obtain the economic values for traits considered in a breeding objective for a dairy cattle breeding program of Uruguay was reported by Rovere et al. (2014).

Herds with crossbred cows are not be included in the system of genetic evaluation and these cows cannot be ranked for farm profit. The objective of this study was to develop a model for the genetic evaluation of Uruguayan crossbred cows for farm profitability in a grazing dairy herd with seasonal calving.

Material and methods

Feeding system and cow management

The farm is located in Uruguay (33°32'0" S latitude, 56°53'0" W longitude) managed commercially with a stocking rate of 2.2 cows/ha. The herd is winter calving, grazing fresh pasture with strategic use of concentrates and other forages. The amount of silage and concentrate received by the cows varied during the season according to grass availability but the average diet during the year is 45% grazed pasture, 23% silage (sorghum and grass silage) and 32% concentrate (mainly wet sorghum grain and sunflower meal). The herd is mated for 2 months with artificial insemination (1st September-1st November) followed by natural mating for two further months.

Data

The cows had 3 to 4 herd tests during each production season (June to April) from 2015 to 2018. Total lactation yields of milk (MILK), fat (FAT) and protein (PROT) were calculated for each cow-lactation using the test-interval method (Sargent et al. 1968) implemented in the SW-Dr Sola recording system (SW Agropecuaria, San Martin, Santa Fe, Argentina). Somatic cell score was calculated as $SCS = \log_2(SCC/100{,}000) + 3$, and an average value was obtained for each cow-lactation. Mating records were used to calculate days from start of mating to conception (SMCO). Cow live weight (LWT) was recorded annually. In total there were 4,081 lactations from 2,371 cows recorded from 2015 to 2017. The cows were the progeny of 97 sires.

Cows were scored annually for udder depth (UD), udder support (US), front and rear teat placement (FT and RT respectively) by a qualified inspector on a nine-point scale. To score US, the depth of the cleft is measured at the base of the rear udder, between rear teats. The ligament forming a clear and very deep cleft between the rear quarters, receives score 9. If the ligament cannot be seen, the ligament is called broken and receives score 1. Udder depth is measured by comparing the distance between the deepest part of the udder and hock. A cow with score 1 has the udder bottom below the hock level and cow with a score 9 has the udder bottom above the hock level.

Teat placement is scored by teats closer to the center of the udder receive scores closer to 9, and those closer to the side of the udder obtain score 1: the ideal score is a centrally placed 5. Cows with rear teats that are very close and are placed inside the quarter close to the ligament, obtain score 9. If the rear teats are placed in the middle of the quarter, they are scored 4, whereas rear teats placed afar and on the outside of the quarter, receive a score 1.

Estimating breeding values

Estimated breeding values for each trait were computed simultaneously using the ASReml 3.0 software package (Gilmour et al. 2009) to apply best linear unbiased prediction (BLUP) to a multiple-trait animal model. In matrix notation, the model can be represented as:

$$\begin{bmatrix} \mathbf{y}_1 \\ \vdots \\ \mathbf{y}_{10} \end{bmatrix} = \begin{bmatrix} \mathbf{X}_1 & \cdots & \mathbf{0} \\ \vdots & \ddots & \vdots \\ \mathbf{0} & \cdots & \mathbf{X}_{10} \end{bmatrix} \begin{bmatrix} \mathbf{b}_1 \\ \vdots \\ \mathbf{b}_{10} \end{bmatrix} + \begin{bmatrix} \mathbf{Z}_1 & \cdots & \mathbf{0} \\ \vdots & \ddots & \vdots \\ \mathbf{0} & \cdots & \mathbf{Z}_{10} \end{bmatrix} \begin{bmatrix} \mathbf{a}_1 \\ \vdots \\ \mathbf{a}_{10} \end{bmatrix} + \begin{bmatrix} \mathbf{e}_1 \\ \vdots \\ \mathbf{e}_{10} \end{bmatrix}$$

where $\mathbf{y}_i$ = vector of phenotypic measures for trait i, $\mathbf{b}_i$ = vector of fixed effects for trait i, $\mathbf{a}_i$ = vector of additive genetic effects (random effects of animal) for trait i, $\mathbf{e}_i$ = vector of random residual effects (residual errors not accounted for by the fixed and random effects) for trait i; and $\mathbf{X}_i$ and $\mathbf{Z}_i$ are design matrices relating the fixed and additive genetic effects to the phenotypes of trait i, respectively. Fixed effects included in $\mathbf{b}_i$ were contemporary group (herd-lactation number) and deviation from median calving date.

The following assumption was considered, with E indicating the expectation: $E(\mathbf{y}_i) = \mathbf{X}_i \mathbf{b}_i$, $E(\mathbf{a}_i) = 0$ and $E(\mathbf{e}_i) = 0$. The random effects were assumed to be normally distributed with zero mean and the co(variance) structure was assumed as;

$$\text{var}\begin{bmatrix} \mathbf{a}_1 \\ \vdots \\ \mathbf{a}_{10} \end{bmatrix} = \begin{bmatrix} \mathbf{A}\sigma^2_{a_1} & \cdots & \mathbf{A}\sigma_{a_{1,10}} \\ \vdots & \ddots & \vdots \\ \mathbf{A}\sigma_{a_{1,10}} & \cdots & \mathbf{A}\sigma^2_{a_{10}} \end{bmatrix}$$

and

$$\text{var}\begin{bmatrix} \mathbf{e}_1 \\ \vdots \\ \mathbf{e}_{10} \end{bmatrix} = \begin{bmatrix} \mathbf{I}\sigma^2_{e_1} & \cdots & \mathbf{I}\sigma_{e_{1,10}} \\ \vdots & \ddots & \vdots \\ \mathbf{I}\sigma_{e_{1,10}} & \cdots & \mathbf{I}\sigma^2_{e_{10}} \end{bmatrix}$$

where **A**= is the numerator relationship matrix among animals, $\sigma^2_{a_i}$ = additive genetic variance for trait i and $\sigma_{a_{ij}}$ = additive genetic covariance between trait i and trait j, **I** = is an identity matrix which corresponds to the number of ewes with records, $\sigma^2_{e_i}$ = residual variance for trait i and $\sigma_{e_{ij}}$ = residual covariance between trait i and trait j.

Genetic and residual variances and covariances required for genetic evaluation were derived from genetic parameters presented in Table 1. Heritability and genetic correlations are averages of values published in the literature (Cue et al. 1996; Spelman & Garrick 1997; Berry et al. 2003; Berry et al. 2004; Pryce & Harris 2006). Phenotypic standard deviations and phenotypic correlations were obtained from the data set with the GLM procedure of SAS (Statistical Analysis System, version 9.4; SAS Institute Inc., Cary, NC, USA) using a linear model that included the fixed effect of year, lactation number and the deviation from the median calving date per year. When published estimates of genotypic and phenotypic correlations were not found, genetic correlations were assumed to be equal to phenotypic correlations produced by the current data set. The proportions of Holstein, Holstein-Friesian, Jersey or other breeds was not available for each cow, dam or sire. This information is required to calculate the coefficient of heterosis for each animal and, therefore breed, and heterosis effects were not included in the model. The matrix of genetic (co)variances was found to be non-positive definitive and was transformed to be positive definitive using the bending procedure of Jorjani et al. (2003). The new estimates of the genetic (co)variances were not greatly different from the original values.

Estimation of economic values and selection index

The selection index was calculated by including estimated breeding values for MILK, FAT, PROT, LWT, SMCO, SCS, UD, FT and RT and their respective economic values. The economic values for MILK, FAT, PROT and LWT were derived from a farm model that evaluates the change in cow profit per unit change of the trait, after accounting for changes in milk and beef revenues, and feed and farm costs. This approach is similar to that presented by Rovere et al. (2014). The economic values for the other traits were estimated using desired relative economic weights indicated by the owner of the herd. The relative emphasis of each trait was calculated as the economic value of the trait times standard deviation (SD) divided by the sum of the absolute values of these products, then multiplied by 100 (Van Raden 2002).

Milk income per cow was estimated using the current payment for the milk, (\$NZ 2.762×FAT) + (\$NZ7.127×PROTEIN) – (\$NZ0.037×MILK). Beef income was calculated from the sum of: sale of male calves (\$NZ 35/head), surplus female calves (\$NZ 159/head) and culled culls (\$NZ 1.29/kg LWT). Main costs were labour \$NZ 117/cow, electricity \$NZ 14.43/cow, health \$NZ 85.14/cow, and breeding \$NZ 78/cow. Feed costs were pasture \$NZ 0.09/kg DM, sorghum silage \$NZ 0.13/kg DM. and concentrate \$NZ 0.44/kg DM.

Results

Descriptive statistics for the animal traits considered for genetic evaluation in this commercial herd are presented in Table 2. The coefficients of variation for SCS and SMCO were greater than those for production traits. The coefficient of variation for conformation traits were similar to the coefficient of variation for production traits.

Table 1 Genetic parameters estimates[1] for traits[2] considered in the genetic evaluation of a commercial dairy herd in Uruguay.

Trait	h^2	σ_g	MY	FY	PY	LWT	SMCO	SCS	UD	US	FT	RT
MY	0.32	450.5		0.51	0.89	0.50	0.04	–0.04	–0.07	0.17	0.11	-0.01
FY	0.26	14.5	0.61		0.64	0.16	–0.08	–0.03	0.06	0.08	0.02	0.01
PY	0.26	12.7	0.88	0.77		0.43	0.00	–0.04	–0.10	0.12	0.09	0.00
LWT	0.24	24.6	0.54	0.45	0.55		0.14	0.24	–0.28	0.05	0.05	–0.13
SMCO	0.04	3.88	0.04	–0.08	0.00	0.14		0.19	0.00	0.02	–0.02	–0.06
SCS	0.14	0.45	–0.04	–0.03	–0.04	0.24	0.19		–0.21	0.15	0.17	0.21
UD	0.29	0.45	–0.07	0.06	–0.10	–0.28	0.00	–0.21		0.13	0.16	0.21
US	0.25	0.68	0.36	0.36	0.36	0.12	0.02	0.15	0.21		0.43	0.45
FT	0.27	0.64	0.51	0.51	0.51	0.01	–0.02	0.17	0.06	0.53		0.44
RT	0.29	0.66	0.51	0.51	0.51	0.01	–0.06	0.21	0.12	0.28	0.59	

[1]Phenotypic (above diagonal) and genetic correlations (below diagonal), h^2 = heritability, σ_g = genetic standard deviation, MY = milk yield, FY = fat yield, PY = protein yield, LWT = live weight, SMCO = start of mating to conception, SCS = somatic cell score calculated as $Log_2(SCC/100{,}000)+3$, UD = udder depth, US = udder support, FT=front-teat placement, RT = rear-teat placement.

[2]Estimates of heritabilities and genetic correlations were from the literature, estimates of phenotypic correlations were estimated using the data set of this study, estimates of genetic standard deviation were derived from estimates of heritabilities from literature (see text) and phenotypic variances estimated using the data set of this study.

Table 2 Descriptive statistics of milk production, live weight, fertility and udder traits considered for genetic evaluation of grazing dairy cows in a commercial dairy herd in Uruguay.

Trait	N	Mean	SD	CV	Min	Max
Lactation number	5,854	2.63	1.56	59	1	9
Lactation length, days	5,594	274	57	21	51	305
Milk, kg	5,347	5,659	1,463	26	160	12,230
Fat, kg	5,332	212	56	26	9	409
Protein, kg	5,332	211	51	24	9	384
Somatic cell score[1]	5,330	2.89	1.51	52	0.16	8.51
Live weight, kg	4,053	470	61	13	239	728
Start of mating to conception, d	5,105	67	64	96	1	180
Udder depth	5,465	5.3	1.0	19	1	8
Udder support	5,466	4.8	1.4	29	1	8
Front teat	5,466	3.9	1.3	33	1	7
Rear teat	5,466	4.5	1.2	27	1	9

[1]Somatic cell score calculated as $Log_2(SCC/100{,}000)+3$.

The effects of lactation number on productive and reproductive performance and type traits of dairy cows in this commercial herd are shown in Table 3. Lactation number had a significant effect ($P<0.05$) on all traits. Production of milk, fat and protein increased up to the third, fourth and fifth lactations and then declined. Cows in third lactation had similar production levels as cows in fifth lactation. Live weight and SCS increased almost linearly from the first lactation to the sixth lactation. Start of mating to conception was significantly ($P<0.05$) shorter in second lactation cows compared to cows of other lactation numbers. Udder-depth score significantly ($P<0.05$) decreased from first to sixth lactation cows. Udder support of fourth lactation cows was significantly ($P<0.05$) better than udder support of first lactation cows.

Economic values and relative emphases for the traits included in the selection index are presented in Table 3. The economic values for MILK, SCS, LWT and SMCO were negative. The overall contribution all udder traits was 20% with positive economic values. Estimated BVs for PROTEIN has the greatest relative emphasis in the selection index.

Productive performance and genetic evaluation of the top (high genetic merit) and bottom 10% (low genetic merit) of the cows that produced milk in 2018 ranked on the economic selection index are show in Table 4. The genetic superiority for farm profit of the top 10% of the cows was $NZ 192/cow and -$NZ 104/cow for the 10% bottom cows. High-genetic merit cows for farm profit had greater productive performance for milk, fat and protein with a lower live weight, produced milk with less somatic cell counts and had 31 days shorter interval from start of mating to conception than did low-genetic-merit cows. The udder scores for high-genetic-merit cows had greater scores for US, FT and RT, but not for UD than low-genetic-merit cows.

Discussion

The level of production per cow of this commercial herd (5,659 L milk and 423 kg milksolids) is slightly lower than the average production reported by Fariña & Chilibroste et al. (2019) for a case study of 256 dairy farms of Uruguay (5,842 kg ECM and 475 kg milksolids).

Effects of lactation number on milk production are widely reported (Macdonald et al. 2008; Lembeye et al. 2016), and as found in this study, lactation yields per cow for milk, fat and protein increased from lactation one to four and fifth and then a decreased was observed. The study reported by Rocha et al. (2017) showed that an overall decrease in the scores for most udder traits was observed for increasing lactation number. This trend was observed only for UD as US scores were higher in older cows than in first-lactation cows in the present study. The reasons for this

Table 3 Least-squares means and standard errors (SE) of milk production, live weight, fertility and udder traits of grazing dairy cows of different lactation numbers in a commercial herd of Uruguay.

	Lactation number											
	1		2		3		4		5		6	
Trait[1]	Mean	SE	Mean	SE	Mean	SE	Mean	SE	Mean	SE	Mean	SE
Milk, kg/cow	4,899d	38	5,758c	38	6,175a	48	6,197a	59	6,071ab	84	5,881bc	90
Fat, kg/cow	201d	1.5	216b	1.5	222a	1.9	214bc	2.3	209c	3.3	195d	3.5
Protein, kg/cow	184d	1.3	217b	1.3	231a	1.7	229a	2.1	225a	2.9	209c	3.1
SCS	2.60e	0.038	2.64e	0.038	3.05d	0.048	3.38c	0.059	3.66b	0.084	3.97a	0.090
LWT, kg/cow	433e	1.4	474d	1.7	509c	2.1	536	2.6	553a	3.7	560a	3.9
SMCO, days	71b	1.7	57c	1.7	64b	2.2	70b	2.7	72ab	4.0	81a	4.3
UD	5.86a	0.02	5.33b	0.02	4.97c	0.03	4.83d	0.03	4.70e	0.05	4.59e	0.05
US	4.68c	0.04	4.80b	0.04	4.87ab	0.04	4.99a	0.06	4.91ab	0.08	4.89ab	0.08
FT	3.80b	0.03	3.88ba	0.03	3.94a	0.04	4.02a	0.05	3.95ab	0.07	3.86ab	0.08
RT	4.53a	0.03	4.51a	0.03	4.46ab	0.04	4.48ab	0.05	4.50ab	0.07	4.31b	0.08

[a,b,c,d,e] Means that do not share a letter are significantly different (P<0.05).
[1]SCS=somatic cell score, LWT=live weight, SMCO=days from start of mating to conception, UD=udder depth, US=udder support, FT=front-teat placement, RT=rear-teat placement.

Table 4 Economic values (EV) of traits and relative emphases (RE) included in the selection index for the ranking of grazing dairy cows in a commercial dairy herd in Uruguay.

Trait	EV (NZ$/unit)	RE (%)
Milk, kg	–0.074	12.0
Fat, kg	2.13	11.1
Protein, kg	7.25	33.2
Somatic cell score	–36.84	6.0
Live weight, kg	–1.48	13.1
Start of mating to conception, d	–3.60	5.0
Udder depth	30.86	5.0
Udder support	19.67	4.8
Front-teat placement	21.10	4.9
Rear-teat placement	20.07	4.8

apparent contradiction are that in the study by Rocha et al. (2017) cows were milked once a day whereas in the present study cows have been milked twice a day, which affects less the udder conformation as the cows become older; and in this herd high level of culling for low US score has been exercised for the last five years.

The resulting selection index indicates that protein and fat yields would be expected to increase with less volume, and lighter cows. The relative emphases for MILK, FAT, PROT and LWT in the breeding worth index of New Zealand dairy cattle in February 2019 were 13%, 20%, 18% and 11% (DairyNZ 2020), respectively, whereas the corresponding relative emphases for the index used in this commercial herd were 12%, 11%, 33% and 13%. The greater emphasis on PROT in this index largely due to the different values for protein used in the payment systems of New Zealand and Uruguay. Current New Zealand payment systems place similar values on fat and protein, whereas the payment system of Uruguay places twice the value of fat on protein production. In both selection indexes, the EVs for milk volume and live weight were negative. The negative EV for milk volume reflects the costs associated with processing dairy products rather than a value for fluid milk. The negative EV for LWT reflects the feed cost for maintenance in grazing cows.

Table 5 Means and standard deviations (SD) of milk production, live weight, fertility and udder traits of grazing dairy cows that produced milk in 2018, ranked on the economic selection index in a commercial dairy herd in Uruguay.

	Top 10%		Bottom 10%	
Trait[1]	Mean	SD	Mean	SD
N	155		155	
Index, $NZ/cow	192	33	-104	40
Milk, kg/cow	5,782	1,614	4,475	1,661
Milk BV	136	328	-315	375
Fat, kg/cow	238	68	156	54
Fat BV	20.0	8.3	-17.3	8.6
Protein, kg/cow	226	60	163	58
Protein BV	11.9	7.2	-12.8	8.7
SCS	3.32	1.65	3.92	1.72
SCS BV	-0.06	0.21	0.06	0.22
Live weight, kg/cow	454	33	474	65
Live weight BV	1.2	14.8	-10.6	15.8
SMCO, days	43	41	74	63
SMCO BV	-5.7	2.6	0.4	3.3
UD	4.70	1.06	4.74	1.08
UD BV	0.05	0.20	0.02	0.21
US	5.10	1.14	4.05	1.30
US BV	0.25	0.27	-0.30	0.27
FT	4.17	1.08	3.03	1.16
FT BV	0.36	0.32	-0.47	0.38
RT	4.79	1.02	3.50	1.16
RT BV	0.39	0.32	-0.48	0.39

BV=estimated breeding value, SCS=somatic cell score, SMCO=days from start of mating to conception, UD=udder depth, US=udder support, FT=front-teat placement, RT=rear-teat placement.

The relative emphases in the selection index used the ranking of Holstein bulls and cows of Uruguay are 18.5% for milk yield, 10.1% for fat yield, 36.4% for protein yield, 7.4% for fertility and 27.6% for SCS. Compared to the selection index developed for this commercial herd the relative emphases for protein and fertility are similar, the Uruguayan selection index places a greater relative emphasis on SCS and does not include udder traits or live weight.

The potential use of the selection index is illustrated in Table 4 when the top 10% of the cows that produced milk in 2018 were compared to the bottom 10% of the cows ranked on the selection index. There is a large difference in the index for farm profit per cow, which is reflected in the superiority in BVs for production, SCS, live weight, SMCO and udder traits. This index has been used to select the best cows as mothers of future replacements, cull the cows with the lowest genetic merit, and to determine retention and culling of heifer replacements. These decisions along with the use of bulls selected using this index are expected to produce cows with higher genetic merit for farm profitability.

Further improvement in genetic evaluation will require the estimation of (co)variance components for this population. This is not an easy task in the short term as a large data set is required with a well-structured pedigree file. A current focus is on the determination of breed composition for each animal to include breed and heterosis effects in the animal model.

References

Aguilar I 2016. Experiences in the use of genomics in ruminants in Uruguay. ICAR 2016, Puerto Varas, Chile. https://interbull.org/static/web/6_ICAR_TS1_2016I_AGUILAR.pdf

Berry DP, Buckley F, Dillon P, Evans RD, Rath M, Veerkamp RF 2003. Genetics relationships among body condition score, body weight, milk yield, and fertility in dairy cows. Journal of Dairy Science 86: 2193-2204.

Berry DP, Buckley F, Dillon PG, Evans RD, Veerkamp RF 2004. Genetic relationships among linear type traits, milk yield, body weight, fertility and somatic cell count in primiparous dairy cows. Irish Journal of Agricultural and Food Research 43: 161-176.

Cue RI, Harris BL, Rendel JM 1996. Genetic parameters for traits other than production in purebred and crossbred New Zealand dairy cattle. Livestock Production Science 45: 123-135

DairyNZ 2020. Economic values. https://www.dairynz.co.nz/animal/animal-evaluation/interpreting-the-info/economic-values/ [accessed 27 Feb 2020].

Evaluaciones Genéticas Lecheras 2018. Evaluación Genética Holando Diciembre 2018. https://www.geneticalechera.com.uy/?n&id=18 [accessed 5 Mar 2020].

Fariña SR, Chilibroste P 2019. Opportunities and challenges for the growth of milk production from pasture: The case of farm systems in Uruguay. Agricultural Systems 176: 102631.

Gilmour AR, Gogel BJ, Cullis BR, Thompson R 2009. ASReml User Guide Release 3.0 VSN International Ltd, Hemel Hempstead, HP1 1ES, UK.

Jorjani H, Klei L, Emanuelson U 2003. A simple method for weighted bending of genetic (co) variance matrices. Journal of Dairy Science 86: 677-679.

Lembeye F, Lopez-Villalobos N, Burke JL, Davis SR 2016. Milk production of Holstein-Friesian, Jersey and crossbred cows milked once-a-day or twice-a-day in New Zealand. New Zealand Journal of Agricultural Research 59: 50-64.

Macdonald KA, Verkerk GA, Thorrold BS, Pryce JE, Penno JW, McNaughton LR, Burton LJ, Lancaster JAS, Williamson JH, Holmes CW 2008. A comparison of three strains of Holstein-Friesian grazed on pasture and managed under different feed allowances. Journal of Dairy Science 91: 1693-1707.

Pryce JE, Harris BL 2006. Genetics of body condition score in New Zealand dairy cows. Journal of Dairy Science 89: 4424-4432

Rocha JF, López-Villalobos N, Burke JL, Donaghy DJ 2017. Traits other than production over lactations and production seasons in dairy cows milked once a day in New Zealand. New Zealand Journal of Agricultural Research 60: 386-403

Rovere G, Astigarraga L, Urioste JI 2014. Economic values for production and reproduction traits In Uruguayan pasture based dairy systems. Proceedings of the 10th World Congress on Genetics Applied to Livestock Production, Vancouver, Canada, 17-22 Aug 2014.

Sargent FD, Lytton VH, Wall OGJ 1968. Test interval method of calculating dairy herd improvement association records. Journal of Dairy Science 51: 170-179.

Spelman RJ, Garrick DJ 1997. Effect of live weight and differing economic values on responses to selection for milk fat, protein, volume, and live weight. Journal of Dairy Science 80: 2557-2562

Van Raden PM 2002. Selection of dairy cattle for lifetime profit. Proceedings of the 7th World Congress on Genetics Applied to Livestock Production, Montpellier, France.

A model to assess the impact of potential genetic selection of dairy cows for volume per urination and total urine volume per day on nitrogen leaching

JM Kennett[a]*, A Romera[bc], P Beukes[b] and P Amer[a]

[a]*AbacusBio Limited, PO Box 5585, Dunedin, New Zealand;* [b]*DairyNZ Ltd, Private Bag 3221, Hamilton 3240, New Zealand;* [c]*AgResearch, Private Bag 3123 Hamilton 3240*

**Corresponding author:* Email: jkennett@abacusbio.co.nz

Abstract

The purpose of this paper is to assess the impacts of changes in herd average urine genetic traits on nitrogen (N) leaching per hectare per year. Two potential urine traits being considered for genetic selection are total volume of urine per cow per day (at constant urinary N output), and average volume per urination (at a constant daily urinary volume and N output). To understand the potential reduction in N leaching that would arise if these traits could be changed using genetic selection, a model of urine patches was developed to derive the necessary relationships between urine genetic traits, patch characteristics, and N leaching. To simulate the effect on N leaching of genetic selection the mean for each urine trait was then changed from base model values by ±10%. Increasing total urine volume per cow per day by 10% was more effective (4.5% less N leaching) than decreasing volume per urination by 10% (2.9% less N leaching). Also, selection for urine traits at higher stocking rates (four cows/ha) and higher N intake (650 g/N/day) had a lower impact on N leaching compared with lower stocking rates (two cows/ha) and lower N intakes (450 g N/day). This study showed that genetic selection for urine traits could have a positive, but limited, impact on N leaching and would be a useful tool for New Zealand dairy farmers.

Keywords: Urine traits; urine patches; nitrate leaching

Introduction

A key driver of water-quality degradation caused by dairy farming in New Zealand is the loss of excess nitrogen (N) into water ways. A review by Selbie et al. (2015) reported N-loading rates within urine patches of 200 to 2000 kg N/ha, with a mean of 613 kg N/ha. Those authors concluded that of the total N deposited in urine: 41% is taken up in pasture, 20% is leached, 26% is immobilised, 12% is lost as ammonia through volatilisation, and 2% as nitrous oxide. This N loading is a function of the volume of urine per urination and urinary N concentration. Previous work has looked at the current genetic gain as a result of the national selection index (Breeding Worth, BW) and its impact on N leaching.

A study by Woodward et al. (2011) investigated the impact of selection breeding for a nationally used index called Breeding Worth (BW) on feed conversion efficiency (FCE) and nitrogen use efficiency (NUE) in late lactation. It was reported that high-index cows partitioned 3.5% more feed intake into milk and 6.5% less feed N intake into urine compared to low BW and PW cows. However, such benefits rely on high selection emphasis for productive traits within the BW index. Improving efficiency by encouraging higher per-cow milk production through genetic improvement combined with more-intensive farming approaches is unlikely to lead to improved environmental outcomes at a national level, if the level of total intake remains the same (Zhang et al. 2019).

Therefore, if genetic change in the New Zealand dairy herd is to make a positive contribution to water quality through reduction in N leaching, then new selection criteria and approaches to genetic improvement will be required. Previous attempts to use selection to address N leaching have focused selection of cows for reduced milk urea nitrogen due to its positive correlation with urinary nitrogen (Ciszuk et al. 1994; Jonker et al. 1998; Kauffman et al. 2001; Luo et al. 2010). Here we focus on the potential value that genetic variation in urine attributes might have as an approach to reduce N leaching. Li et al. (2012) reported that N leaching from urine deposition is very sensitive to volume per individual urination event and urinary N concentration. Therefore, by altering urine patch characteristics in particular directions, nitrogen leaching might be reduced. The hypothesis for this study was that selection among cows for greater total urine volume per day and smaller volume per urination could potentially have a meaningful impact on N leaching. A model designed to estimate the effect of urine characteristics on N leaching was used to show the degree to which genetic change in these traits could impact on N leaching. The effect of a change in total urine volume and volume per urination on N leaching from this study can then be used for future development of economic values of urine traits. They can then be weighted in selection indexes which will help determine the optimal balance of selection emphasis across competing traits.

Material and methods

A model was used to estimate annual N leaching per hectare for a farm based on urine characteristics. This method was chosen as no data on the effect of genetic selection for urine traits were available, therefore the impacts must be predicted using causal relationships between urine and N leaching that are already understood. Figure 1 provides an overview of how the model predicts nitrogen leaching per hectare. The dark boxes represent

Figure 1 Summary of the urine patch model which calculates the effect of change in total urine volume and volume per cow urination on N leaching per hectare per year.

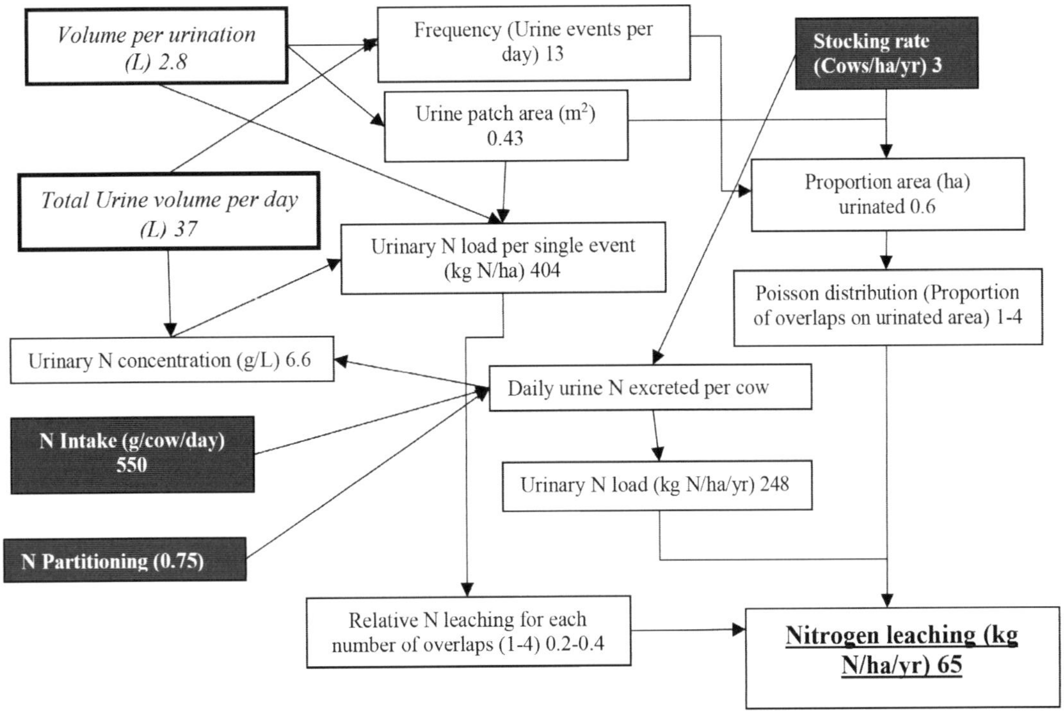

input variables that drive the model, the boxes in italics are the two goal traits and the white boxes are calculated variables that are dependent on the input variables. Each box contains the units and the mean for each variable. The means used for total daily urine volume and volume per urination were derived from research trials in which urine sensors were attached to 300 dairy cows.

The following equations provide a detailed description of how the variables in Figure 1 are calculated. The equations are described from the output (N leaching) back to the inputs. With the equation for N leaching per hectare per year as follows.

$$NLHA = UNload(PoissonDist\ total\ urine\ area \times RelNLOverlaps),$$

where UNload is the total N load per hectare, PoissonDist total urine area is the proportion of the total urinated area with one, two, three and four urine-patch overlaps calculated using a Poisson distribution and relative N leaching (RelNLOverlaps) is the N that is lost from the soil profile as a proportion of the urinary-N load deposited in urine patches accounting for one to four urine-patch overlaps.

$$Total\ urine\ area = SR \times Urine\ Area \times Frequency \times \frac{365}{10000}$$

where *SR* is stocking rate, *Urine Area* is the area covered by a single urination event, *Frequency* is the number of urination events per day, 365 is the number of days in a year and 10,000 is the m² in a hectare.

Relative N leaching (RelNL) was computed as a function of urinary-N load (UNLoadSingle) in a single urine patch;

$$RelNL = 0.4811e^{(-295.6963/UNLoadSingle \times overlaps)}$$

where 0.4811 and 295.6963 are empirical constants calculated by simulating urine patches using the APSIM model, run over 10 climatic years and two dates of deposition per month, and a range on UN loads (0 to 1000 kg/ha) (Keating et al. 2003; Romera et al. 2017).

Urine-N load expressed per hectare (*UNload*) is derived from grams of urine N excreted per cow per day (*UNex*) by multiplying by stocking rate (*SR*) and days in the year as follows;

$$UNload = UNex/1000 \times SR \times 365.$$

Urine-nitrogen load per urination is computed using urine-nitrogen concentration, volume per urination and area per urination as shown in the following equation.

$$UNLoadSingle = \frac{UNconc \times VolperUr}{AUr}/1000 \times 10000,$$

where *UNconc* is the Urinary-N concentration, *VolperUr* is the volume per urination and *AUr* is the urine-patch area.

The number of urinations per cow per day *(Frequency)* is calculated by dividing total urine volume (*UrVol*) by volume per urination event (*VolperUr*).

Note: *UrVol* and *VolperUr* are the two genetic driving variables for which we wish to understand what might change with genetic selection of urination traits.

Area per urination (AUr) is calculated using a quadratic approximation (Li et al. 2012);

$$AUr = -0.0064 \times VolPerUr^2 + 0.0998 \times VolPerUr + 0.1948.$$

Urine-nitrogen concentration is calculated by dividing nitrogen excreted per cow (UNex) by total urine volume per cow, as in the following equation,

$$UNconc = \frac{UNex}{UrVol}$$

where, UrVol is the total urine volume per cow per day. Urinary Nitrogen excreted per cow (UNex) is the weight (g) of nitrogen that is excreted in urine per cow per day as shown in the following equation,

$$UNex = Nin \times 0.75 \times UNpart,$$

where, Nin is the weight (g) of nitrogen consumed in feed per cow per day, 0.75 is the proportion of feed nitrogen that is excreted by the cow and UNpart is the proportion of nitrogen excreted that is partitioned to urine, and was set at 0.55 (Selbie et al. 2015). Nitrogen intake was set at 550 grams per day (Selbie et al. 2015).

This leaves the key variables that simulate genetic change and predict N leaching per hectare to be volume per urination (L) and urination volume per cow (L/d). Nitrogen intake (Nin, g/d) and urine partitioning (UNpart, %N excreted in urine) also have a large influence on the prediction of N leaching, however these are not variables that are changing as a result of genetic selection.

To simulate the effect of genetic selection of urine traits on nitrogen leaching, the mean of each trait was changed by ±10%. At this stage of the research it is unknown how much genetic gain in the two urine traits can be made. Thus, a ±10% change in the traits is assumed. This was done for each possible combination of trait change for each of the urine traits (Table 1). The impact of selection for urine traits on N leaching was also assessed for different stocking rates and N intakes.

Results

The potential effect of genetic selection of urine traits is shown in Table 1. As expected, the model predicted that N leaching would decrease when total urine volume increases or when volume per urination decreases. When the mean for total urine volume changed by -10% and +10%, leaching changed by 5.0% and -4.5%, and for volume per urination, leaching changed by -2.9% and 2.6% respectively. Both average N intake and average N output in urine were kept constant for each ±10% change in trait shown (Table 1). The results in Table 1 show that a change in total urine volume had a greater effect on N leaching than did an equivalent percentage change in volume per urination.

Another finding was that the impact of genetic selection for urine traits that resulted in a decrease in N leaching had less of an impact on nitrogen leaching at higher N intakes and higher stocking rates. Figure 2 shows the impact of stocking rate on the effectiveness of trait change on N leaching. The Y axis is the percentage reduction in N leaching as a result of selection for urine traits and the X axis is the change in stocking rate. The impact of stocking rate was only modelled for the selection of traits that resulted in a reduction in N leaching as shown in the legend of Figure 2. At a stocking rate of two cows/ha/yr, the reduction in N leaching for a +10% change in total urine volume was 5.3%, and 3.4% for a -10% change in volume per urination. When the stocking rate was doubled

Table 1 The mean percentage change in nitrogen leaching per hectare per 10% increase or decrease in each trait and each trait combination.

	Total urine volume per day		
Volume per urination	-10%	0%	10%
-10%	2.1%	-2.9%	-7.4%
0%	5.0%	0.0%	-4.5%
10%	7.6%	2.6%	-1.9%

Figure 2 The predicted impact of stocking rate on the effectiveness of increasing total urine volume by 10% (◆–) and decreasing volume per urination by 10% (■–)to reduce nitrogen leaching per hectare.

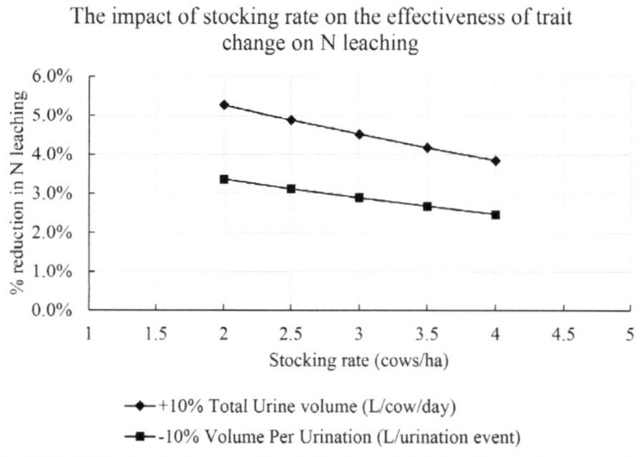

Figure 3 The predicted impact of nitrogen intake on the effectiveness of increasing total urine volume by 10% (◆–) and decreasing volume per urination by 10% (■–)to reduce nitrogen leaching per hectare.

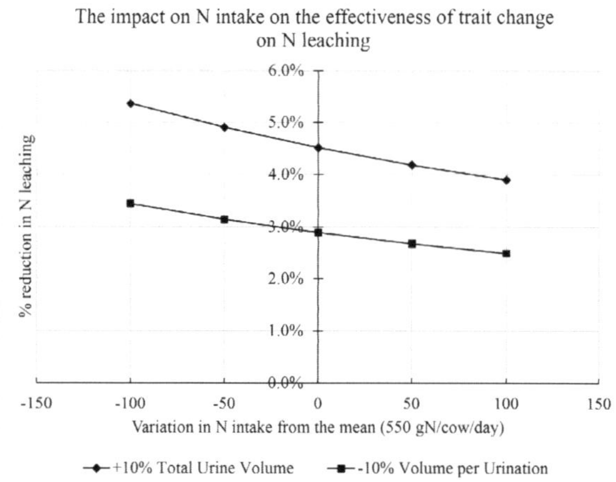

to four cows/ha/yr the reduction in N leaching decreased to 3.8% and 2.5% for total urine volume and volume per urination, respectively.

The same trend was observed for a change in N intakes as shown in Figure 3. The axes are the same as in Figure 2, however the change in stocking rate has been replaced with a change in N intake for the X axis. The mean N intake used in the model was 550 grams/cow/day with variations modelled from the mean in 50-gram increments. As for the stocking-rate simulation, only trait changes that resulted in a reduction in N leaching were modelled. When the mean for N intake was decreased by 100 g/N/day the reduction in N leaching increased to 5.4% and 3.4% for total urine volume and volume per urination, respectively. When N intake was increased by 100 grams, the reduction in N leaching decreased to 3.9% and 2.5% for total urine volume and volume per urination, respectively.

Discussion

This study predicts that genetic selection for urine traits could result in a 3 - 5% reduction in N leaching. The realisation of this potential is dependent on further genetic analyses of phenotype and genotype data to determine how much genetic change can be achieved through selection for urine traits. As such, the results of this study are preliminary in terms of estimating the reduction in N leaching possible through genetics, however the results align with other studies. Ledgard et al. (2015) reported significant reductions in N leaching of 65% when cows were supplemented with salt. The salt caused water intake of cows to increase resulting in a greater total daily urine volume and increased urination frequencies. Although the effects of selecting for urine patch traits is not of the same magnitude, the mechanism to reduce N leaching is consistent.

The purpose of the model is to quantify the impact of changing herd average total urine volume and volume per urination on N leaching. While the model itself has not been validated, the key causal relationships and underlying principles are well established, based on data from other studies (Selbie et al. 2015). Based on the outputs of the model, cows that would have the greatest positive effect on N leaching would have a high volume per day and/or a low volume per urination, at a fixed urinary N output. This is due to the three key factors that determine the nitrogen load of urine patches; being, urinary N concentration, the urine volume per event and the surface area receiving urine (Haynes & Williams, 1993). Therefore, when cows have a high total urine volume at a fixed N output, urinary N concentration decreases due to the dilution effect. Furthermore, when urinary N output and total urine volume are fixed, but volume per urination is decreased (which is the same an increase in urination frequency), urinary N load of urine patches also decreases. This is because less urine is being deposited onto the same area of soil. It also reduces the infiltration depth of urine patches, which means a greater proportion of urinary N remains in the root zone for plant uptake (Li et al. 2012).

It was found that variation in total urine volume had a greater impact on N leaching than did variation in volume per urination. This can be simply explained by the fact that the 10% increase in urine volume has the greatest effect on N loading in single urine patches (9.1% reduction in UNloadSingle) compared with 10% decrease the volume per urination (5.9% reduction in UNloadSingle) (Li et al. 2012). As such, increasing total urine volume, while keeping UN output constant, reduces nitrogen concentration, and thus, N leaching. This means that selection pressure toward increasing total urine volume would (provided that total UN does not increase concomitantly) provide greater value when reducing N leaching per hectare compared to selecting for cows with lower volumes per urination event.

The impact of genetic selection for urine traits is reduced when stocking rate and N intake are increased. The probability of urine-patch overlaps is greater at higher stocking rates. This increases the coverage of urine-patch overlaps, which results in an increase in the weighted average urinary-N loading of the area covered in urine patches (Haynes et al. 1993; Pleasants et al. 2007). The increase in N intake reduces the impact of genetic selection for urine patch traits. This is a result of increased urinary N concentration, which increases urinary-N load and N leaching. Therefore, diluting urine by increasing total urine volume is less effective. These results would indicate that urine traits would have a greater positive impact on N leaching on farms that have low stocking rates and low N intakes per cow. However, dairy systems in New Zealand that have high N leaching generally have high stocking rates and per-cow N intakes. Genetics that reduce N leaching would potentially have the greatest value for these more-intensive farms. This paper provides a basis for further research on the genetic parameters of urine patch traits such as heritability, reliability and genetic variation to determine how much genetic progress can be made in each trait.

Acknowledgments

Low N Livestock is a DairyNZ-led collaborative research programme delivering science for better farming and environmental outcomes. The main funders are DairyNZ and the Ministry of Business, Innovation and Employment, with co-funding from CRV-Ambreed and Fonterra.

References

Ciszuk P, Gebregziabher T 1994. Milk urea as an estimate of urine nitrogen of dairy cows and goats, Acta Agriculturae Scandinavica A: Animal Sciences, 44(2): 87-95. doi: 10.1080/09064709409410187.

Haynes RJ: Williams PH 1993. Nutrient cycling and soil fertility in the grazed pasture ecosystem. Advances in agronomy (USA), 49: 119-199.

Jonker JS, Kohn RA, Erdman RA 1998. Using Milk Urea Nitrogen to Predict Nitrogen Excretion and Utilization Efficiency in Lactating Dairy Cows. Journal of Dairy Science. 81(10): 2681-2692. doi: 10.3168/jds.S0022-0302(98)75825-4.

Kauffman AJ, St-Pierre NR 2001. The relationship of milk urea nitrogen to urine nitrogen excretion in holstein and jersey cows. Journal of Dairy Science. 84(10): 2284-2294. doi: 10.3168/jds.S0022-0302(01)74675-9.

Keating B, Carberry P, Hammer G, Probert M, Robertson M, Holzworth D, Huth N, Hargreaves J, Meinke H, Hochman Z, Mclean G, Verburg K, Snow V, Dimes J, Silburn M, Wang E, Brown S, Bristow K, Asseng S, Chapman S, McCown R, Freebairn D, Smith C 2003. An overview of APSIM, a model designed for farming systems simulation. European Journal of Agronomy. Elsevier, 18(3-4): 267-288. doi: 10.1016/S1161-0301(02)00108-9.

Ledgard SF, Welton B, Betteridge K. 2015. Salt as a mitigation option for decreasing nitrogen leaching losses from grazed pastures. Journal of the Science of Food and Agriculture. 95: 3033-3040.

Li FY, Betteridge K, Cichota R, Hoogendoorn C, Jolly B 2012. Effects of nitrogen load variation in animal urination events on nitrogen leaching from grazed pasture. Agriculture. Ecosystems & Environment. 159: 81–89. doi: 10.1016/J.AGEE.2012.07.003.

Luo J, Kelliher F 2010. Partitioning of animal excreta N into urine and dung and developing the N2O inventory. Available at: http://www.mpi.govt.nz/news-resources/publications.aspx (Accessed: 5 February 2020).

Pleasants AB, Shorten PR, Wake GC 2007. The distribution of urine deposited on a pasture from grazing animals. The Journal of Agricultural Science. 145(1): 81-86. doi: 10.1017/S0021859606006563.

Romera AJ, Cichota R, Beukes P, Gregorini P, Snow Val O, Vogeler I 2017. Combining restricted grazing and nitrification inhibitors to reduce nitrogen leaching on New Zealand dairy farms. Journal of Environmental Quality. Wiley, 46(1): 72-79. doi: 10.2134/jeq2016.08.0325.

Selbie DR, Buckthought LE, Shepherd MA 2015. The challenge of the urine patch for managing nitrogen in grazed pasture systems. Advances in Agronomy. 129: 229-292. doi: 10.1016/bs.agron.2014.09.004.

Woodward SL, Waghorn GC, Bryant MA, Mandok C 2011. Are high breeding worth index cows more feed conversion efficient and nitrogen use efficient? Proceedings of the New Zealand Society of Animal Production, 71: 109-113.

Zhang X, Amer PR, Jenkins GM, Sise JA, Santos B, Quinton CD 2019. Prediction of effects of dairy selection indexes on methane emissions. Journal of Dairy Science 102(12): 11153-11168. doi. org/10.3168/jds.2019-16943.

Effect of simulated spot-sampling duration and timing on the precision of methane estimation from cattle using respiration chambers

AA Biswas[ab]* and A Jonker[a]

[a]*Grasslands Research Centre, AgResearch Ltd., Private Bag 11008, Palmerston North 4442, New Zealand;* [b]*Department of Animal Science and Nutrition, Chattogram Veterinary and Animal Science University, Khulshi-4225, Chattogram, Bangladesh.*

**Corresponding author.* Email: Ashraf.Biswas@agresearch.co.nz

Abstract

The objective of the current study was to determine the precision of CH_4 emission estimates from simulated spot-samples of variable time length (0.25 to 3.0 h) and over time compared to 24-h measured CH_4 emissions, both based on respiration chamber data of the same day within cattle. Respiration chamber methane data, recorded approximately every 3 min, from two experiments were used, each with 12 growing beef cattle measured over two or three consecutive days. The ~3 min CH_4 emissions during 24 h per animal per day were averaged in time intervals (bins; i.e. simulated spot-sample duration) of 0.25, 0.5, 1.0 and 3.0 h (expressed as g/d) from morning and from afternoon feeding. Precision of each time bin was evaluated by determining between-animal coefficient of variation (CV) and Pearson correlation (r) with 24-h measured emissions. In general, the average CV increased and the CV became more variable over time when the bin duration decreased from 3 h to 0.25 h. The correlation was low (r of approximately 0.1 to 0.5) in the first 0.5 to 2 h after the start of a feeding, after which the correlations increased (r of approximately 0.5 to 0.9) and remained relatively constant up to about 8 h after feeding. The overall trends observed suggest that the precision of a CH_4 measurement improved with increasing simulated spot-sample (bin) duration from 0.25 to 3 h and the best time to take a spot-sample (based on any of the bin durations) would be between approximately 1 to 6-8 h after feeding. However, the best timing to perform spot-sampling was not fully consistent between the experiments and between emissions after morning and afternoon feeding, which warrants further investigation.

Keywords: Spot-sampling; enteric methane; precision; time bin; variation

Introduction

Several methods to estimate methane (CH_4) emitted by cattle based on short-term sampling have been developed in the last decade (Hammond et al. 2016). These methods estimate daily CH_4 emissions by averaging CH_4 emissions from multiple breath spot-samples (two to hundreds per animal) lasting from 3 to 60 minutes, collected over multiple days. These methods have some advantages over the 'gold standard' method, i.e., respiration chambers for measuring CH_4 emissions from ruminants, being that they are generally cheaper, less laborious, have a higher throughput and can be used on-farm (Garnsworthy et al., 2019). However, enteric emissions by cattle during the day are not constant and can vary two to six fold (Biswas & Jonker, 2019; Jonker et al. 2014). Therefore, timing and duration of a spot-sample might affect precision of the CH_4 emission estimate from cattle. Several studies compared emissions from cattle estimated using spot-sampling methods with those of respiration chambers, but measurements cannot be performed simultaneously (e.g., Difford et al. 2018; Jonker et al. 2016). Measurements have, therefore, been performed sequentially with different methods on different days. The actual emissions on those specific days might be quite different, which complicates comparison of methods. Furthermore, a 24-h CH_4 emission estimate (g/d) by multiple spot-samples can be based on as little as 60 min of measurement time per animal. The objective of the current study was to determine the precision of CH_4 emission estimates from simulated spot-samples of variable time length (0.25 to 3.0 h) and over time compared to 24-h measured CH_4 emissions, both based on respiration chamber data of the same day within cattle.

Materials and methods

Data of two respiration chamber experiments with growing beef cattle (Hereford × Holstein-Friesian; aged 1.3 and 1.8 years with an average body weight of 327 and 442 kg, respectively) fed cut pasture (twice daily) were used. The two experiments were selected from 15 experiments carried out at AgResearch (Palmerston North) on the basis of having a very small or vary large diurnal variation in emissions (2.5 and 4.4 fold range; Biswas & Jonker, 2019). Both experiments were carried out with 12 animals to measure methane emission over two or three days.

The measurements were performed in four open-circuit respiration chambers (volume of 15.4 m^3) which are linked to one CH_4 analyser via a switching unit that directs the air stream of each chamber to the gas analyser in sequence, which takes approximately three minutes per cycle. Air flow rate through each chamber was 1.8 m^3/min. Doors of chambers were opened twice daily (approx. 20 min) for feed refusal collection, feeding and cleaning, between approximately 0800 and 0900 h in the morning and between 1500 and 1600 h in the afternoon. There was no data recording during these events.

Data processing and analysis

Each respiration chamber recorded data at approximately 3-min intervals. Each ~3-min emissions measurement was expressed as g/d calculated as: CH_4

(g/d) = [CH_4 per ~3 min (g) / time (min) × 60 × 24]. Then all emission measurements within 24 h per animal were averaged to get one daily CH_4 value (g/d). In addition, the ~3 min CH_4 emissions during 24-h per animal per day were averaged at time intervals (bins, i.e. simulated spot-sample duration) of 0.25 (15 min), 0.5 (30 min), 1.0 and 3.0-h from the start of a CH_4 recording period, which started immediately when closing the respiration chamber doors after the morning and the afternoon feeding (separately). Only data of up to 6-h after morning feeding and up to 15-h after afternoon feeding were included to generate time bins. Then the coefficient of variation (CV) was calculated for each time bin (0.25, 0.5, 1 and 3-h) over time within animal measurement day. In addition, Pearson correlations (precision of a relationship) of each time bin over time with 24-h measured CH_4 was generated using the "cor.test" function in R version 3.6.1 (R Core Team, 2019) and 95% confidence intervals extracted for the correlations between total and periodic methane emissions.

Results

Methane production over 24 h averaged 107 and 148 g/d in Exp. 1 and 2, respectively, and the between-animal CV was 7.9% and 7.3%, respectively. The 24-h CH_4 production was previously reported to be (mean±CV) 106±6.6 and 147±7.5 g/d for Exp. 1 and 2, respectively (Jonker et al. 2017), which includes interpolation of data when the chamber doors were open. This is very similar to the values in the current analysis where 24-h emissions were defined by averaging all ~3-min measurements during the day (each first converted to g/d).

In general, CV increased (on average 9.2-13.3 to 12.5-16.7; Table 1) and became more variable over time (range, 7.5-13.8 to 7.1-22.8; Fig. 1) when the binning duration decreased from 3-h bins to 0.25-h bins, which was more pronounced after the morning feeding in Exp.1 and after the afternoon feeding in Exp. 2 (Table 1). The CV was relatively constant over time after afternoon feeding in Exp. 1 and after morning feeding in Exp. 2, while in Exp. 1 the CV increased between about 1.5 and 4.5 h after morning feeding and in Exp. 2 the CV steadily increased from about 5 h after the afternoon feeding (Fig. 1).

Pearson correlation of a CH_4 time bin with 24-h measured CH_4 decreased (on average 0.67-0.78 to 0.55-0.61) and became more variable (range, 0.62-0.81 to 0.55-0.61; Fig. 2) when the binning duration decreased from 3-h bins to 0.25-h bins (Table 1). In general, the correlation was low in the first 0.5 to 2-h after the start of a feeding (*r* of approximately 0.1 to 0.5), after which the correlations increased to a plateau (*r* of approximately 0.5 to 0.9), which remained relatively constant after the morning feeding of both experiments. However, the correlation apparently decreased after about 8 h after feeding in the afternoon of Exp. 1. In Exp. 2, the correlation increased and decreased three times from 2 to 14 h after the afternoon feeding (Fig. 2). In the latter case, 3-h bins resulted in more-constant correlations over time compared to the 0.25-1.0-h bins.

Table 1 Average and range of between-animal coefficient of variation (CV) and Pearson correlation of each time bin over time (after morning and after afternoon feeding) with 24-h measured emissions in two experiments with growing beef cattle fed ryegrass-based pasture in respiration chambers

	Exp. 1		Exp. 2	
	AM	PM	AM	PM
CV, average (min–max)				
24-h	7.9		7.3	
3-h bins	13.3	9.2	10.2	10.8
	(12.8-13.8)	(8.5-10.3)	(9.8-10.7)	(7.5-13.6)
1-h bins	15.0	10.1	11.2	12.2
	(10.7-19.1)	(7.6-12.8)	(10.5-12.6)	(7.7-17.9)
0.5-h bins	15.5	11.1	11.8	13.1
	(9.9-19.8)	(8.4-13.7)	(9.9-13.7)	(7.1-19.4)
0.25-h bins	16.7	12.5	12.5	14.4
	(11.6-21.7)	(9.2-18.1)	(10.0 – 16.4)	(7.1-22.8)
Correlation (*r*) of time bin with 24 h CH_4, (lower – upper 95% confidence interval)				
3-h bins	0.78	0.78	0.67	0.75
	(0.60-0.95)	(0.61-0.95)	(0.45-0.89)	(0.57-0.93)
1-h bins	0.68	0.71	0.61	0.68
	(0.45-0.91)	(0.50-0.92)	(0.36-0.86)	(0.47- 0.89)
0.5-h bins	0.65	0.63	0.58	0.62
	(0.41-0.89)	(0.38-0.88)	(0.33-0.83)	(0.38-0.86)
0.25-h bins	0.61	0.57	0.56	0.55
	(0.35-0.87)	(0.29-0.85)	(0.30-0.82)	(0.28-0.82)

Discussion

The main findings of the current analysis were that the precision (both CV and correlation) of a CH_4 measurement improved with increasing simulated spot-sampling duration (time bin) from 0.25 to 3 h and the best time to take a spot-sample would be between approximately 1 to 6-8 h after feeding. However, the best timing to perform spot-sampling was not fully consistent between the experiments and between emissions after morning and afternoon feeding. The two experiments (selected from 15 experiments; Biswas & Jonker, 2019) used for the current analysis were selected on the basis of having a very small or large diurnal variation in emissions (2.5 and 4.4 fold range for Exp. 1 and 2, respectively). Our thought was that this might affect the precision of a spot-sampling method at different times in the day, but it did not appear that there was a clear difference in precision for estimating CH_4 emissions between Exp. 1 and 2.

Unlike in the current study, Robinson et al. (2019) observed relatively little variation in CV for 40-min CH_4 spot samples over time (0930 to 1400-h; new feed offered at 0800 h) for sheep immediately off feed (CV of 22 to 27%) or taken off feed at one hour before the CH_4 measurement (CV of 23 to 28%). Gunter and Bradford (2015) also found

Figure 1 Between-animal coefficient of variation (CV) of diurnal methane emissions averaged in 0.25-, 0.5-, 1.0- and 3.0-h time bins, which started immediately after closing the respiration chamber doors after the morning (at approximately 0800 to 0900 h) and the afternoon (at approximately 1500 to 1600 h) feeding, in two experiments with growing beef cattle fed ryegrass-based pasture in respiration chambers. The symbols indicate the mid-point of each time bin.

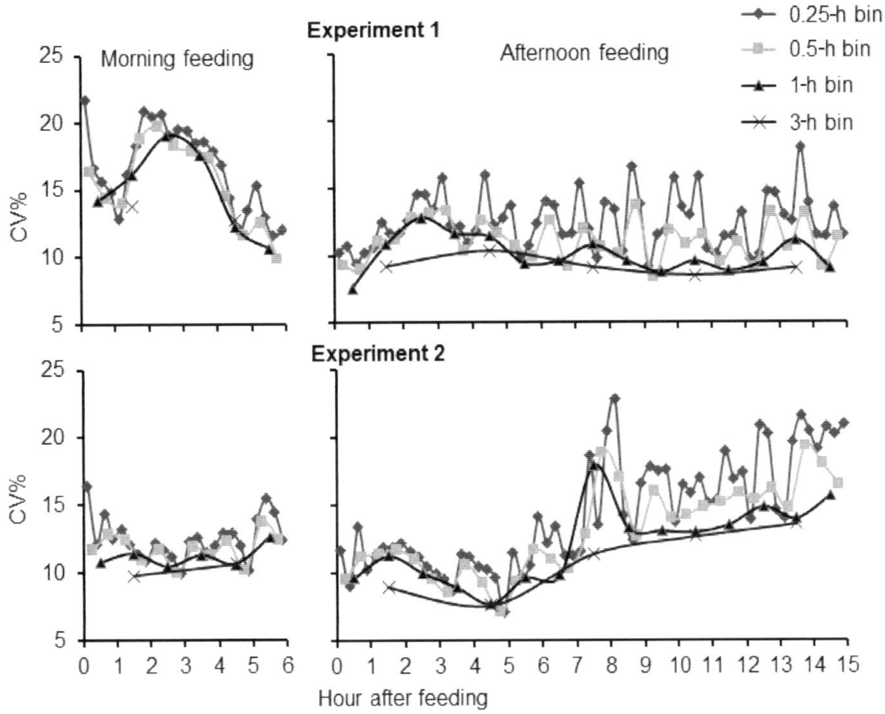

Figure 2 Correlation of each time bin over time (0.25-, 0.5-, 1.0- and 3.0-h time bins) after the morning (at approximately 0800 to 0900 h) and the afternoon (at approximately 1500 to 1600 h) feeding with 24-h measured methane in two experiments with growing beef cattle fed ryegrass-based pasture in respiration chambers. The symbols indicate the mid-point of each time bin and error bars indicate half 95% confidence interval.

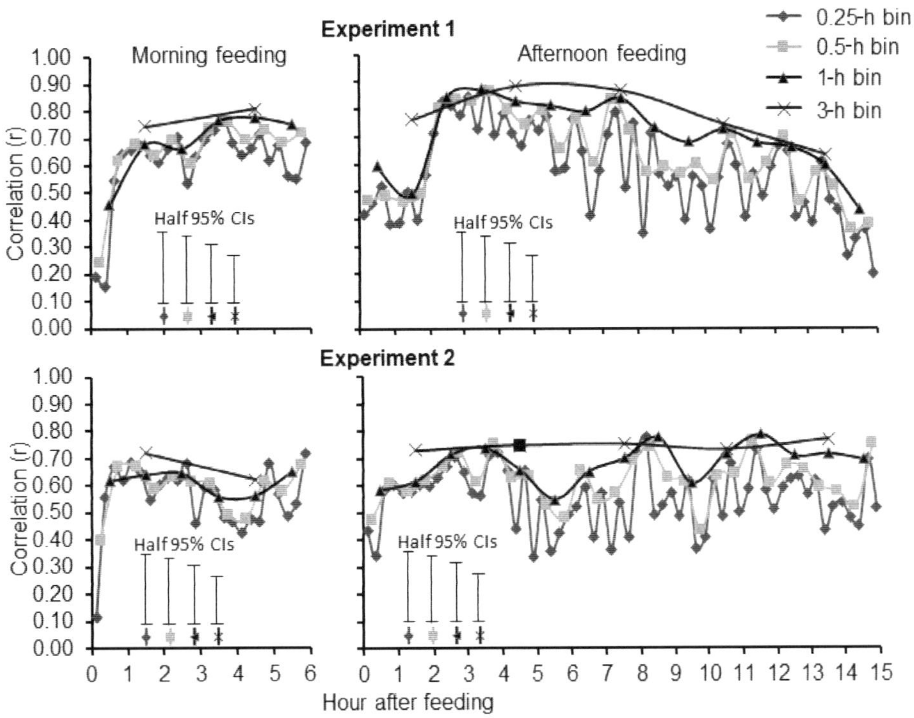

little variation in standard error (SE) when 24 h CH_4 data of growing cattle was summarised in six-hour time bins. Therefore, timing of taking a CH_4 spot-sample did not appear to be very important in the studies of Robinson et al. (2019) and Gunter and Bradford (2015).

As in the current analysis, McEwan et al. (2012) also observed that correlation was lower for CH_4 measurements in approximately the first 0.5 h compared to daily CH_4 in sheep in respiration chambers, after which it increased and stabilised. This knowledge was implemented in the measurement protocol with 1-h CH_4 measurements of sheep in portable accumulation chambers (PAC) with sheep being taken off feed at least 0.5 h before the first measurements began (Jonker et al. 2018).

To our knowledge, little information is available in the literature on the effect of spot-sampling duration on the precision of a CH_4 estimate from ruminants. The precision of a CH_4 measurement improved with increasing simulated spot-sampling duration (time bin) from 0.25 to 3 h in the current study. However, an evaluation in Australia found that 1- and 2-h CH_4 measurements using PAC resulted in similar precision (Goopy et al. 2011). Furthermore, Robinson et al. (2015) reported similar precision of CH_4 estimates from 1-h and 40-min PAC measurements. In the current analysis, however, 3-h bins appeared more precise than did 1-h bins, which in turn were more precise than 0.5-h bins and 0.25-h bins. In general, methane data of PAC had a greater CV than of respiration chamber data (Jonker et al. 2018; Robinson et al. 2019) and this greater variance will make it less likely that different sampling durations can be distinguished. On the other hand, using GreenFeed automated emissions monitoring systems, Arthur et al. (2017) found that precision of ranking beef cattle for CH_4 improved when spot-sample measurements shorter than three min were excluded from their analysis. However, in the latter case, many more spot samples were taken, randomly spread over the day, which would also be an effective strategy to improve the measurement precision.

Altogether, the current analysis indicates that the precision of a CH_4 measurement improved with increasing simulated spot-sampling duration from 0.25- to 3-h bins, while the best timing to perform spot sampling was not fully consistent between the experiments and between emissions after morning and afternoon feeding, which warrants further investigation.

Acknowledgements

Ashraf Biswas was funded by the New Zealand Government through the Global Research Alliance Livestock Emissions and Abatement Research Network (LEARN) awards programme. The authors acknowledge Paul MacLean (AgResearch, Palmerston North) for his help with the statistical analysis.

References

Arthur PF, Barchia IM, Weber C, Bird-Gardiner T, Donoghue KA, Herd RM, Hegarty RS 2017. Optimizing test procedures for estimating daily methane and carbon dioxide emissions in cattle using short-term breath measures. Journal of Animal Science 95: 645-656.

Biswas AA, Jonker A 2019. Circadian variation in methane emissions by cattle and correlation with level and composition of ryegrass-based pasture eaten. New Zealand Journal of Animal Science and Production 79: 61-64.

Difford GF, Olijhoek DW, Hellwing ALF, Lund P, Bjerring MA, De Haas Y, Lassen J, Løvendahl P 2018. Ranking cows' methane emissions under commercial conditions with sniffers versus respiration chambers. Acta Agriculturae Scandinavica, Section A — Animal Science 68: 25-32.

Garnsworthy P, Difford G, Bell M, Bayat A, Huhtanen P, Kuhla B, Lassen J, Peiren N, Pszczola M, Sorg D, Viskers M, Yan T 2019. Comparison of methods to measure methane for use in genetic evaluation of dairy cattle. Animals 9: 837.

Goopy JP, Hegarty RS, Robinson DL 2009 Two hour chamber measurements provide a reliable estimate of daily methane production in sheep. In Ed. Chilliard Y. Proceedings of the 11th International Symposium on Ruminant Physiology Clermont-Ferrand, France 6-9 September 2009. Pg. 190-191.

Gunter SA, Bradford JA 2015. Influence of sampling time on carbon dioxide and methane emissions by grazing cattle. American Society of Animal Science Proceedings 66: 201-203.

Hammond KJ, Crompton LA, Bannink A, Dijkstra J, Yáñez-Ruiz DR, O'kiely P, Kebreab E, Eugène MA, Yu Z, Shingfield KJ, Schwarm A, Hristov AN, Reynolds CK 2016. Review of current in vivo measurement techniques for quantifying enteric methane emission from ruminants. Animal Feed Science and Technology 219: 13-30.

Jonker A, Molano G, Antwi C, Waghorn GC 2014. Feeding lucerne silage to beef cattle at three allowances and four feeding frequencies affects circadian patterns of methane emissions, but not emissions per unit of intake. Animal Production Science 54: 1350-1353.

Jonker A, Molano G, Antwi C, Waghorn GC 2016. Enteric methane and carbon dioxide emissions measured using respiration chambers, the sulfur hexafluoride tracer technique, and a GreenFeed head-chamber system from beef heifers fed alfalfa silage at three allowances and four feeding frequencies. Journal of Animal Science 94: 4326-4337.

Jonker A, Molano G, Koolaard J, Muetzel S 2017. Methane emissions from lactating and non-lactating dairy cows and growing cattle fed fresh pasture. Animal Production Science 57: 643-648.

Jonker A, Hickey SM, Rowe SJ, Janssen PH, Shackell GH, Elmes S, Bain WE, Wing J, Greer GJ, Bryson B, Maclean S, Dodds KG, Pinares-Patiño CS, Young EA, Knowler K, Pickering NK, Mcewan JC 2018. Genetic parameters of methane emissions determined using portable accumulation chambers in lambs and ewes grazing pasture and genetic correlations with emissions determined in respiration chambers. Journal of Animal Science 96: 3031-3042.

McEwan J, Hickey SM, Young EA, Dodds KG, Mclean S, Molano G, Sandoval E, Kjestrup H, Hunt C, Pinares-Patino CS 2012. Heritability estimates for hourly measures of methane emissions. 33rd International Society for Animal Genetics Conference. Cairns, Australia 15-20 July 2012.

R Core Team 2019. R: A language and environment for statistical computing. R Foundation for Statistical Computing, Vienna, Austria. URL: http://www.R-project.org/.

Robinson DL, Goopy JP, Hegarty RS, Oddy VH 2015. Comparison of repeated measurements of methane production in sheep over 5 years and a range of measurement protocols. Journal of Animal Science 93: 4637-4650.

Robinson DL, Dominik S, Donaldson A, Oddy H 2019. Repeatabilities, heritabilities and correlations of methane and feed intake of sheep in respiration and portable chambers Animal Production Science https://doi.org/10.1071/AN18383.

Liveweight gain and urinary nitrogen excretion of lambs grazing diverse (plantain, Italian ryegrass and red clover) or ryegrass-white clover pasture in autumn

O Al-Marashdeh, GA Cook, FC Anderson, JPH Meyer, CM Logan, GR Edwards and TMR Maxwell

Faculty of Agriculture and Life Sciences, Lincoln University, Canterbury, New Zealand

Corresponding author. Email: Omar.Al-Marashdeh@lincoln.ac.nz; Tom.Maxwell@lincoln.ac.nz

Abstract

The objective of this study was to investigate the effect of grazing a diverse pasture of plantain, Italian ryegrass, and red clover versus a ryegrass-white clover pasture on the liveweight gain (LWG) and urinary nitrogen (N) excretion of ram lambs over an 82-day experimental period in autumn. Eighty Coopworth ram lambs (8 months old) were allocated to two replicates of two pasture treatments (n = 20), a diverse pasture containing plantain, Italian ryegrass, and red clover (Diverse) and conventional ryegrass-white clover pasture (RGWC). Unfasted live weight (LWT) of lambs was recorded on seven occasions during the autumn experimental period. Apparent dry matter intake (DMI) was estimated as the difference between pre- and post-grazing herbage mass plus daily herbage growth. On two occasions, urine and blood samples were collected from each lamb to determine concentration of urinary N and plasma urea N (PUN). Liveweight gain (P=0.008) and feed conversion efficiency (P=0.022) were greater in Diverse than RGWC treatment (240 vs 160 g/day and 111 vs 86 g LWT per kg DMI, respectively). Urinary N and PUN concentration were similar between treatments; however, when urinary N excretion (g/d) was estimated as a function of PUN, lambs grazing Diverse pasture excreted less (P=0.003) urinary N per 100 g LWG than those grazing RGWC pasture. The proportion of N intake retained in LWG was greater (P=0.008) for lambs grazing Diverse (11.0%) than those grazing RGWC (9.0%). The results indicate that there is a potential to achieve target LWT of lambs in a shorter time and with less N loss to the environment by using a diverse mix containing plantain, Italian ryegrass and red clover in comparison to ryegrass-white clover mix in autumn.

Keywords: Growing lambs; liveweight gain; urinary nitrogen; diverse pasture; ryegrass

Introduction

The New Zealand pastoral farming system is primarily based on grazed pastures comprising perennial ryegrass (*Lolium perenne* L.) and white clover (*Trifolium repens* L.). However, such swards have seasonal variations in production and nutrient composition, limiting animal production during summer and autumn (Burke et al. 2002). A diverse sward mix that includes legumes and herbs has been reported to provide a more-even distribution of dry matter (DM) production and feed quality throughout the grazing season than the conventional ryegrass-white clover sward (Sanderson et al. 2007; Nobilly et al. 2013). Therefore, diverse swards are known for better supporting high rates of animal production, particularly under dryland systems during summer and autumn, compared to ryegrass-white clover (Cranston et al. 2015). For example, average liveweight gain (LWG) was 50% and 40% greater for weaned lambs grazing on a diverse mix sward than those grazing ryegrass-white clover sward in summer (Somasiri et al. 2015) and autumn (Somasiri 2014), respectively. However, most of the studies comparing performance of lambs grazing diverse versus conventional sward mixes were conducted under a dryland North Island system, and whether any production benefits are expected under an irrigated Canterbury system is unclear.

The pastoral livestock system in New Zealand has been linked to adverse environmental impact due to ongoing intensification (Di & Cameron 2002). The environmental impact mainly includes the contamination of ground waters and surface waterways as a result of nitrate leaching and global warming as a result of greenhouse gas emissions. The urine patch of grazing ruminants is the major source of nitrate leaching, which occurs as a result of imbalance between the nitrogen (N) load per urine patch and herbage capability for N uptake (Di & Cameron 2007). Establishing a pasture sward comprised of plant species varying in functional traits such as growth activity during the season (i.e., Italian ryegrass *Lolium multiflorum* Lam. with greater growth at low temperatures), rooting depth, and profile of bioactive components (i.e., plantain *Plantago lanceolata* L. as a deeper rooted forage with N availability-altering compounds) could be used as a strategy to reduce nitrate leaching. The mechanisms to achieve reduced nitrate leaching from diversified pasture include increasing the uptake of N from the root zone (Moir et al. 2013; Woods et al. 2016; Maxwell et al. 2019) and reducing urinary N excretion, as observed from dairy cattle (Totty et al. 2013; Box et al. 2017; Cheng et al. 2017) and sheep (Al-Mamun et al. 2008) fed a forage-based diet with or without plantain. Therefore, we hypothesised that feeding lambs on a diverse pasture sward of plantain, Italian ryegrass and red clover during autumn would improve live weight (LWT) performance and reduce urinary N excretion per kg LWG compared to lambs fed a perennial ryegrass-white clover pasture sward. The objective of this study was to thus, evaluate LWT performance and urinary N excretion of ram lambs grazing either plantain, Italian ryegrass and red clover (Diverse) pasture or perennial ryegrass-white clover (RGWC) pasture.

Materials and methods

This is part of a longer-term study established in 2016 at Lincoln University's Ashley Dene Research and Development Station, located near Burnham, New Zealand

(−43.65 °N, 172.33 °E) with the approval of the Lincoln University Animal Ethics Committee (AEC application # 2017-05). This manuscript presents data collected during the autumn experimental period from 07 March to 28 May 2019.

Experimental design and management

The 3.6 ha experiment site was comprised of twelve 0.3-ha rectangular paddocks, split into two blocks of six paddocks in a randomised complete block design. Each block contained three paddocks of Diverse pasture and three paddocks of RGWC pasture. Swards were regularly irrigated under a lateral irrigator from November to March, however, no irrigation was applied to these paddocks during the autumn experimental period reported on here.

The 80 ram lambs used in this experiment lineate from the Lincoln University Coopworth flock. From twin-bearing and mixed-age Coopworth ewes, 60 ram lambs were born on the Diverse and RGWC pasture paddocks, and 20 others were born on non-experiment paddocks in Spring (September) 2018 at Ashley Dene. Ewes and lambs continuously grazed each of the 12 paddocks, stocked with 4 – 6 ewes and their twin lambs per paddock, until weaning. After weaning, ram lambs were allocated into four groups of 20 lambs based on LWT (34.6±5.40 kg; mean ± SD) and previous exposure to herbage type; ram lambs born and reared on Diverse or RGWC pasture remained on this pasture type post-weaning. Each grazing block of six paddocks had two lamb groups (n = 20 lambs), with each group rotationally grazing three paddocks of Diverse pasture or three paddocks of RGWC pasture. Lambs were shifted to the next paddock within the three paddock rotation, when the post-grazing residual target range (900 – 1200 kg DM/ha) was met. During the current autumn study, each lamb group grazed one paddock for an average of 12.3±0.81 days before being shifted to the next paddock. At the start of the current autumn study on 7th March 2019, all lambs were weighed and LWT was similar between lambs on Diverse (44.2±6.21 kg) and RGWC (43.2±5.80 kg) pasture. The similar LWT for lambs at weaning, and at the start of this study, suggest that the pre-weaning exposure of lambs to forage type had no effect on LWG of lambs during this study. On 3rd May, due to reduction in herbage growth and subsequent feed availability, each pasture treatment was destocked by reducing the number of lambs in each group from 20 down to 12 lambs. Removed lambs were selected by LWT, with the heaviest lambs taken off the trial.

Pasture establishment

The two pasture sward types were established in October 2016: Diverse pasture (plantain *Plantago lanceolata* L. cv. Tonic, Italian ryegrass *Lolium multiflorum* Lam. cv. Asset, red clover *Trifolium pratense* L. cv. Relish) and RGWC pasture (perennial ryegrass *Lolium perenne* L. Prospect, white clover *Trifolium repens* L. cv. Tribute). Prior to establishment, the twelve paddocks were sprayed out with glyphosate-based herbicide and then cultivated in early October 2016. In late October 2016, paddocks were heavy rolled, seed mixtures were broadcast over sown, chain harrowed and heavy rolled again. Italian ryegrass, plantain and red clover were each sown at 10, 5 and 6 kg/ha respectively for the six paddocks sown in the diverse sward mix. The ryegrass-white clover mix was sown at rates of 20 and 5 kg/ha respectively.

Herbage measurements

Pre- and post-grazing herbage mass in each paddock were assessed 1-2 days before grazing and immediately after grazing respectively, using an electronic rising-plate meter (RPM; Jenquip F150 Electronic Pasture Meter, Fielding, New Zealand). An average of 50 random RPM readings were recorded by walking along a zig-zag transect through the paddock. The RPM measurements were then calibrated against a total of 21 pre-grazing (3-4 per paddock) and 14 post-grazing (2-3 per paddock) 0.2 m^2 quadrat cut to ground level from each sward site. The cut herbage was dried at 60°C for 48 hours to quantify DM weight per quadrat. To measure regrowth of herbage during period of grazing per paddock, two 0.5-m^2 cages were pegged down in two representative areas of each paddock, and herbage regrowth (kg DM/day) was measured as the difference between herbage mass readings taken before and after grazing events, divided by number of grazing days.

Herbage samples were collected from each paddock before grazing to determine chemical and botanical composition for each sward. The herbage (bite size) was cut with clippers above grazing height (2-3 cm above ground) along a diagonal line across the paddock. Approximately six to seven pluck samples were collected per paddock, grouped and subsampled. One subsample was separated into each herbage species, dried at 60°C for 48 hours, dry weight of each component was recorded and proportion of each species was determined as a % of the whole sward DM. A second subsample was dried at 60°C for 48 hours, ground to 1 mm, and analysed for the chemical compositions using near-infrared spectrophotometry (Foss NIRSystems 5000, FOSS NIRSystemsInc, USA). Metabolisable energy (ME) of feed was estimated based on the equation [ME (MJ/kg) = digestible OM content × 0.016 (g/kg of DM)]. Herbage N (%) was calculated by dividing the crude protein content by 6.25.

Animal measurement

Apparent dry matter intake (DMI) was calculated per lamb group using the following equation:

Apparent DMI (kg/day) =
[(Pre-grazing herbage mass – post-grazing herbage mass) + herbage growth during grazing]/ number of grazing days

Lamb apparent DMI (kg/lamb/day) was then calculated by dividing group DMI by number of lambs grazed per paddock.

During the current autumn experimental period, unfasted LWT of lambs was recorded on seven occasions (7th of March, 4th and 17th of April, and 3rd, 14th, 24th and 28th of May), before lambs were shifted to graze the next paddock. All lambs were grouped in a portable yard located on the laneways adjacent to the paddocks and were individually weighed using Prattley scale crate and a Tru-test ID3000 scale head and matching wand (Bluetooth ID reader).

On two occasions (17th April and 28th May) lambs from each treatment were grouped in a portable yard located on the laneways adjacent to the paddocks and were individually sampled for urine and blood. The lamb's nasal and oral passages were obstructed by holding a plastic cup tightly over the restrained animal's mouth and nose. A urine sample was generally produced within 5-10 s of airway obstruction. Obstruction of the lamb's airways was halted as soon as approximately 10-20 ml of mid-stream urine was obtained. Urine was acidified to a pH <4 to minimise volatilisation. All samples were then frozen to -20°C until analysis. Blood samples were collected from the jugular vein using 10-ml EDTA Vacuette tubes. Blood samples were placed on ice immediately after collection and later centrifuged at 3,000 × g for 15 min at 4°C. Plasma was collected into clean tubes, frozen to -20°C until analysis. Urine was analysed for N concentration using a Variomax CN Analyser (Elementar Analysensysteme GmbH, Germany). Plasma urea and urine urea concentration were determined using a kinetic UV and colorimetric assay (RX Daytona Randox, Antrim, Northern Ireland). Urinary N excretion (g/day) was estimated using the following equation: Urinary N (g/day) = 1.2 × PUN (g/l) × LWT (kg), was reported for sheep in the study of Kohn et al. (2005). The N retained in LWG was calculated assuming 1 kg of LWG contains 29 g of N as reported for sheep in the study of Kohn et al. (2005).

Statistical analysis

GenStat 18th Edition was used for analysis. All animal measurements were analysed using one-way ANOVA with sward type as treatment and the mean value averaged across lambs in each group/replicate being the experimental unit (two experimental units per treatment). Paddock was used as the replicate for the analysis of herbage chemical composition. Results were declared significant at P<0.05, and tendency was declared at P<0.1.

Results

Pre- and post-grazing herbage mass and chemical composition of the Diverse and RGWC pasture swards are presented in Table 1. Herbage contents of neutral (P<0.001) and acid (P=0.002) detergent fibre were lower in Diverse than RGWC (35.8 vs 46.3 and 23.9 vs 27.0 % of DM, respectively). High quality herbage was maintained during this study with an average ME content of 11.4 MJ/kg DM (11.3 and 11.6 MJ/kg DM for RGWC and Diverse respectively). The Diverse pasture sward comprised 17.1±5.1% plantain, 41.6±6.7% Italian ryegrass and 15.3±4.2% red clover (26% weeds), while the RGWC sward comprised 63.2±6.6% ryegrass, 11.8±3.9% clover (25% weeds).

Table 1 Pre- and post-grazing herbage mass (kg DM/ha), chemical composition (% of DM) and metabolisable energy content (MJ/kg DM) of RGWC (perennial ryegrass-white clover) and Diverse (plantain, red clover, and Italian ryegrass) swards in autumn at Ashley Dene Research and Development Station, Canterbury, New Zealand.

	RGWC	Diverse	SEM	P value
Pre-grazing mass	2063	1877	211.9	0.597
Post-grazing mass	1235	938	145.9	0.287
Neutral detergent fibre	46.3	35.8	0.93	<0.001
Acid detergent fibre	27.0	23.9	0.54	0.002
Water soluble carbohydrate	13.8	14.6	1.00	0.576
Nitrogen	3.1	3.2	0.15	0.498
Metabolisable energy	11.3	11.6	0.12	0.132

Table 2 Apparent intake, initial and final live weight, liveweight gain, and feed conversion efficiency (FCE) of lambs grazing RGWC (perennial ryegrass-white clover) and Diverse (plantain, red clover, and Italian ryegrass) swards in autumn at Ashley Dene Research and Development Station, Canterbury, New Zealand.

	RGWC	Diverse	SEM	P value
Dry matter intake (kg DM/lamb/day)	1.8	2.1	0.09	0.155
Metabolisable energy intake (MJ/lamb/day)	20.7	24.6	0.89	0.089
Nitrogen intake (g/lamb/day)	56.3	68.4	1.36	0.024
Initial live weight (kg)	43.2	44.2	0.41	0.224
Final live weight (kg)	55.8	63.0	0.69	0.017
Liveweight gain (kg/lamb/day)	0.16	0.24	0.010	0.008
FCE (g live weight/kg DM intake)	86.0	111.0	2.69	0.022

Apparent DMI of both pasture types was similar (P=0.155; average 1.9 kg DM/lamb/day; Table 2). However, ME intake tended to be greater (P=0.089) and N intake was greater (P=0.024) for lambs grazing Diverse pasture compared to those grazing RGWC pasture (Table 2). Change in lamb LWT over the current autumn experimental period is presented in Figure 1.

Initial LWT was similar (P=0.224) between treatments, but final LWT was greater (P=0.017) for lambs grazing the Diverse sward compared to those grazing the RGWC sward (Table 2). The LWG (P=0.008) and feed conversion efficiency (FCE; P=0.022) were greater for lambs on Diverse pasture than those on RGWC pasture (Table 2).

Pasture type did not affect lamb urinary concentration of N, urea, or concentration of plasma urea N (Table 3). Similarly, estimated urinary N excretion (g/day) was similar

Figure 1 Liveweight change of lambs grazing RGWC (--•--; perennial ryegrass-white clover) and Diverse (-■-; plantain, red clover, and Italian ryegrass) pasture in autumn at Ashley Dene Research and Development Station, Canterbury, New Zealand. Bars indicate SEM.

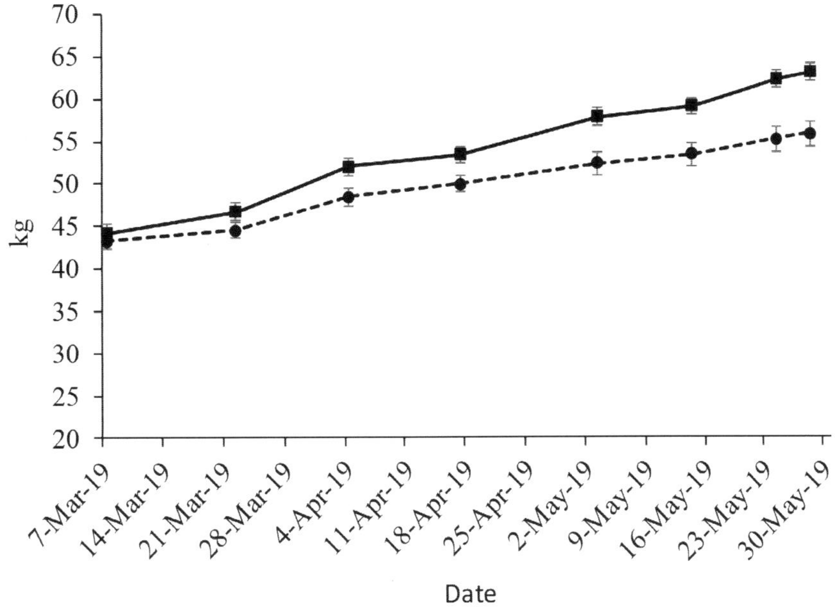

Table 3 Blood and urine metabolites, urinary nitrogen (N) excretion, and N retained in liveweight gain (LWG) of lambs grazing RGWC (perennial ryegrass-white clover) and Diverse (plantain, red clover, and Italian ryegrass) swards in autumn at Ashley Dene Research and Development Station, Canterbury, New Zealand.

	RGWC	Diverse	SEM	P value
Plasma urea N concentration (mmol/l)	20.0	19.9	0.62	0.94
Urine N concentration (%)	0.61	0.57	0.086	0.709
Urine urea concentration (mmol/l)	178	194	25.8	0.687
Urinary N excretion (g/day)	17.8	19.7	0.68	0.193
Urinary N (% of N intake)	31.7	28.7	0.46	0.046
Urinary N (g/100 g LWG)	11.3	8.3	0.11	0.003
Retained N (g/day)	5.0	7.5	0.16	0.008
Retained N (% of N intake)	9.0	11.0	0.06	0.002

(P=0.193) between treatments (Table 3). However, urinary N as % of N intake (P=0.046) and urinary N excreted per 100 g LWG (P=0.003) were both lower for lambs grazing Diverse pasture compared to lambs grazing RGWC pasture (Table 3). The N retained in LWG (g/day; P=0.008) and proportion of N intake retained in LWG (P=0.008) were both greater for lambs grazing Diverse pasture compared to lambs grazing RGWC pasture (Table 3).

Discussion

The objective of this study was to quantify LWG and urinary N excretion of ram lambs grazing either a diverse pasture sward of plantain, Italian ryegrass, and red clover or a perennial ryegrass-white clover pasture sward during the time of decreasing herbage supply and increased risk of nitrate leaching (i.e., autumn) in Canterbury.

The average LWG that accumulated over the autumn period of this study was approximately 50% greater for lambs grazing Diverse pasture compared to lambs grazing the ryegrass-white clover sward (240 vs 160 g LWG/day for Diverse and RGWC respectively). This result is comparable to the 40% increase in LWG reported by Somasiri (2014) for lambs grazing a mixed sward of herbs and clover (chicory, plantain, red clover and white clover) in comparison to ryegrass-white clover during autumn, but less than the >100% increase in LWG reported by Golding et al. (2011) for post-weaning lambs grazing a herbs-clover mix sward compared to lambs grazing ryegrass-white clover. The differences in the magnitude of effect of diverse sward versus a conventional ryegrass-white clover sward on lamb LWG between studies could be attributed to the differences in sward quality between pasture types in each study. The herbs-clover mix sward grazed by lambs in the study of Golding et al. (2011) contained 28% more ME than did the ryegrass-white clover (11.4 vs 8.9 MJ of ME/kg DM for herbs-clover mix and ryegrass-white clover mix respectively), while the ME content of Diverse and RGWC swards in this study was similar (average 11.4 ±0.12 MJ of ME/kg DM).

Despite the ME content of herbage and apparent DMI being similar between pasture treatments in this study, apparent ME intake tended to be greater for lambs on Diverse than those on RGWC pasture, which may partially explain the greater LWG observed in Diverse compared to RGW treatment. Italian ryegrass was reported to contain higher levels of water-soluble carbohydrate and lower levels of neutral detergent fibre than perennial ryegrass (King et al. 2012). Intake or grazing selectivity of lambs for individual pasture species were not measured in this study; however, there is a possibility that the lambs on the Diverse pasture were more selective to the highly digestible pasture species than were their counterparts in the RGWC pasture. The apparent N intake was also greater for lambs in Diverse compared to RGWC treatments (68 and 56 g N/day, respectively); however, the apparent N intake observed was unlikely to be limiting performance of lambs grazing RGWC compared to Diverse pasture. Apparent N intake in both treatments was well above the requirements of weaned lamb (43 g N/day) grazing good-quality pasture (ME = 11.6 MJ/kg DM) for 320 g LWG per day (AA Council 1990). Therefore, the difference in apparent N intake observed between the treatments in this study is unlikely to explain the greater LWG observed in Diverse compared to RGWC treatment.

Sorbitol, a sugar alcohol molecule with six carbons derived from glucose present in plantain herbage, which comprised 17% of Diverse pasture treatment, may have influenced the ability of lambs to gain weight. Sorbitol was reported to alter *in vitro* fermentation pattern (increase propionate concentration and reduce acetate to propionate ratio) and improve LWG and FCE of bulls when fed at 50 g per day (Geay et al. 1992). Plantain contains a greater proportion of sorbitol than does ryegrass herbage (42.1 vs 0% of water-soluble carbohydrate respectively; Jiang et al. 2019), suggesting that lambs on Diverse pasture may have ingested larger quantities of sorbitol than did their counterparts on RGWC pasture. This may explain the greater FCE observed from Diverse compared to RGWC pasture. More work is required to investigate the effect of sorbitol from plantain on LWG and rumen function of lambs.

Nitrogen intake was reported as the major driver for urinary N output in ruminants; both have been positively correlated with each other (Castillo et al. 2000; Kebreab et al. 2009). In this study, however, estimated urinary N excretion was similar between the treatments (average 18.8 g N/day), despite N intake being greater in lambs from Diverse than those from RGWC treatment. The similar urinary N output observed was supported by similar urinary N concentration, urinary urea concentration and PUN concentration results between treatments. This suggests that lambs grazing Diverse pasture containing plantain were more efficient in utilising N compared to those grazing RGWC pasture. Proportion of N intake retained in LWG was greater, and proportion of N intake excreted in urine and urinary N excreted per 100 g of LWG were lower for lambs grazing Diverse compared to those grazing RGWC pasture. Several studies have reported the role plantain has in reducing urinary N excretion (g/day) and concentration, in cattle (Totty et al. 2013; Box et al. 2017; Cheng et al. 2017) and sheep (Al-Mamun et al. 2008), with New Zealand research suggesting plantain as an alternative forage species to ryegrass to mitigate on-farm N loss to water (Totty et al. 2013; Box et al. 2017; Cheng et al. 2017). Furthermore, the greater LWG, FCE and N utilisation observed in lambs grazing Diverse compared to RGWC pasture may also be attributable to both the Italian ryegrass and red clover components which comprised 42% and 15% of the Diverse pasture respectively. Italian ryegrass has higher WSC levels than perennial ryegrass (King et al. 2012), and red clover contains polyphenol oxidase (PPO) which protects plant protein from degradation in the rumen by protecting leaf proteins in the form of protein-bound polyphenols (PBP) (Lee 2014).

It was important in this study to estimate urinary N excretion (g/day) of lambs as a function of physiological factor (i.e., PUN) rather than N intake, to reflect the expected effect of the Diverse pasture on N digestion and utilisation. However, it is worth noting that the estimation of urinary N excretion in this study was based on one PUN spot sample taken per day which may have not covered the expected diurnal variation in the PUN concentration of lambs. This may have affected the accuracy of PUN to give a quantitative reference measure for urinary N excretion, but could be used to rank the treatments (Al-marashdeh et al. 2015). Further research is required to investigate the N balance in sheep fed diverse pasture containing plantain cultivars similar to that used in this study (cv. Tonic).

Conclusion

The results of this study indicated that under a Canterbury irrigated farming system, offering ram lambs a diverse pasture mix containing plantain, Italian ryegrass and red clover in autumn is effective for improving LWG and FCE, and reducing urinary N excreted per unit of LWG in comparison to a ryegrass-white clover mix sward.

References

Al-Mamun M, Hanai Y, Tanaka C, Tamura Y, Sano H 2008. Responses of whole body protein synthesis and degradation to plantain herb in sheep exposed to heat. Archives Animal Nutrition 62: 219-29.

Al-marashdeh O, Greenwood S, Hodge S, Edwards G 2015. The effects of feeding maize silage at different times prior to a herbage meal on dry matter intake, milksolids production and nitrogen excretion in late-lactation dairy cows. Proceedings of the New Zealand Society of Animal Production 75: 140-144.

Box LA, Edwards GR, Bryant RH 2017. Milk production and urinary nitrogen excretion of dairy cows grazing plantain in early and late lactation. New Zealand Journal of Agricultural Research 60: 470-482.

Burke J, Waghorn G, Chaves A 2002. Improving animal performance using forage-based diets. Proceedings of the New Zealand Society of Animal Production 62: 267-272.

Castillo AR, Kebreab E, Beever DE, France J 2000. A review of efficiency of nitrogen utilisation in lactating dairy cows and its relationship with environmental pollution. Journal of Animal and Feed Sciences 9: 1-32.

Cheng L, Judson HG, Bryant RH, Mowat H, Guinot L, Hague H, Taylor S, Edwards GR 2017. The effects of feeding cut plantain and perennial ryegrass-white clover pasture on dairy heifer feed and water intake, apparent nutrient digestibility and nitrogen excretion in urine. Animal Feed Science and Technology 229: 43-46.

Council AA 1990. Feeding Standards for Australian Livestock. Ruminants, Standing Committee on Agriculture Ruminants Subcommittee.

Cranston L, Kenyon P, Morris S, Kemp P 2015. A review of the use of chicory, plantain, red clover and white clover in a sward mix for increased sheep and beef production. Journal of New Zealand Grasslands 77: 89-94.

Di HJ, Cameron KC 2002. Nitrate leaching in temperate agroecosystems: sources, factors and mitigating strategies. Nutrient Cycling in Agroecosystems 64: 237-256.

Di HJ, Cameron KC 2007. Nitrate leaching losses and pasture yields as affected by different rates of animal urine nitrogen returns and application of a nitrification inhibitor—a lysimeter study. Nutrient Cycling in Agroecosystems 79: 281-290.

Geay Y, Richet E, Ba S, Thivend P 1992. Effects of feeding sorbitol associated with different sources and amounts of nitrogen on growth, digestion and metabolism in young bulls. Animal Feed Science and Technology 36: 255-273.

Golding KP, Wilson ED, Kemp PD, Pain SJ, Kenyon PR, Morris ST, Hutton PG 2011. Mixed herb and legume pasture improves the growth of lambs post-weaning. Animal Production Science 51: 717-723.

Jiang S, Bryant R, Jiao J, Tung R 2019. BRIEF COMMUNICATION: Investigation of the water-soluble carbohydrates content of Plantain (Plantago Lanceolata L.). New Zealand Journal of Animal Science and Production 79: 174-176.

Kebreab E, Dijkstra J, Bannink A, France J 2009. Recent advances in modeling nutrient utilization in ruminants. Journal of Animal Science 87: E111-E122.

King C, McEniry J, Richardson M, O'Kiely P 2012. Yield and chemical composition of five common grassland species in response to nitrogen fertiliser application and phenological growth stage. Acta Agriculturae Scandinavica, Section B — Soil & Plant Science 62: 644-658.

Kohn R, Dinneen M, Russek-Cohen E 2005. Using blood urea nitrogen to predict nitrogen excretion and efficiency of nitrogen utilization in cattle, sheep, goats, horses, pigs, and rats. Journal of Animal Science 83: 879-889.

Lee MR 2014. Forage polyphenol oxidase and ruminant livestock nutrition. Frontiers in Plant Science 5: 694.

Maxwell TM, McLenaghen RD, Edwards GR, Di HJ, Cameron KC 2019. Italian ryegrass swards reduce N leaching via greater N uptake and lower drainage over perennial ryegrass cultivars varying in cool season growth rates. New Zealand Journal of Agricultural Research 62: 69-82.

Moir JL, Edwards GR, Berry LN 2013. Nitrogen uptake and leaching loss of thirteen temperate grass species under high N loading. Grass and Forage Science 68: 313-325.

Nobilly F, Bryant R, McKenzie B, Edwards G 2013. Productivity of rotationally grazed simple and diverse pasture mixtures under irrigation in Canterbury. Proceedings of the New Zealand Grassland Association. pp. 165-172.

Sanderson M, Goslee S, Soder K, Skinner R, Tracy B, Deak A 2007. Plant species diversity, ecosystem function, and pasture management—a perspective. Canadian Journal of Plant Science 87: 479-487.

Somasiri S, Kenyon P, Kemp P, Morel P, Morris S 2015. Growth performance and carcass characteristics of lambs grazing forage mixes inclusive of plantain (Plantago lanceolata L.) and chicory (Cichorium intybus L.). Small Ruminant Research 127: 20-27.

Somasiri SC 2014. Effect of herb-clover mixes on weaned lamb growth : a thesis presented in partial fulfilment of the requirements for the degree of Doctor of Philosophy in Animal Science at Massey University, Palmerston North, New Zealand. Unpublished Doctoral thesis, Massey University.

Totty V, Greenwood S, Bryant R, Edwards G 2013. Nitrogen partitioning and milk production of dairy cows grazing simple and diverse pastures. Journal of Dairy Science 96: 141-149.

Woods RR, Cameron KC, Edwards GR, Di HJ, Clough TJ 2016. Effects of forage type and gibberellic acid on nitrate leaching losses. Soil Use and Management 32: 565-572.

Impact of trait genetic gains on methane emissions from NZ beef and dairy farms

LE Proctor*, JA Archer, JA Sise, X Zhang, JJ Crowley and PR Amer

AbacusBio Ltd, PO Box 5585, Dunedin, NZ, 9058

**Corresponding author:* Email: lproctor@abacusbio.co.nz

Abstract

The objective of this study was to provide estimates of the impact of trait genetic gains on methane emissions from NZ dairy and beef farms. The effect of each trait on gross emissions (GE) and emissions intensity (EI) was modelled by estimating effects of trait changes on per-animal feed consumption and the associated methane production, per-animal production and numbers of animals in the system. In dairy, the annual gross emissions per breeding cow associated with genetic change were estimated to increase for all traits except Residual Survival and Fertility. Conversely, emission intensity values were estimated to decrease for Milk Fat, Milk Protein, Milk Solids, Residual Survival, Fertility and Body-condition Score (BCS) as genetic merit improves. In beef production, increases in genetic merit for cow mature weight, cow BCS, cow calving ease and heifer pregnancy were estimated to increase the annual gross emissions per breeding cow. Conversely, an increase in merit associated with stayability and gestation length reduced annual gross emissions per breeding cow. The effect of increasing carcase weight on gross emissions depended on whether the faster growth performance was used to slaughter the animal earlier, or to take the animal through to heavier finishing weights.

Keywords: methane; emissions intensity; gross emissions; dairy; beef

Introduction

Climate change is a pressing global crisis that is already having an impact both in New Zealand (NZ) and internationally. Although New Zealand accounts for a fraction of the world's greenhouse gas emissions, on a per-capita basis it has an over-sized carbon footprint, emitting 18 tonnes of greenhouse gasses per person, per year (OECD 2016). The high per-capita footprint is largely from agricultural sources, which make up close to half of the country's gross emissions (Ministry for the Environment 2019). Within agriculture, dairy cattle are responsible for 47% of emissions, while beef cattle are responsible for 17% (Ministry for the Environment 2019). Methane is generated through ruminant digestion, and the amount of emissions are largely a function of total feed consumed (Fennessy et al. 2019).

Research has demonstrated that genetic gains in livestock production efficiency traits can drive improvements in GHG emissions when expressed on a per-animal or intensity basis (i.e., CO_2 equivalent emissions per unit of product, (Pickering et al. 2015; Quinton et al. 2018; Zhang et al. 2019). Understanding how performance traits that impact on feed intake estimates for dairy and beef cattle will affect our national GHG inventory may help refine the national inventory calculations, and how they should be modified over time to account for genetic and other management changes.

The objective of this study was to provide estimates of the impact of changes in trait-performance values on enteric methane emissions from NZ beef and dairy farms.

Materials and methods

For this study we assumed that the amount of enteric methane emitted by an animal is proportional to the energy consumed by that animal in its feed (Fennessy et al. 2019). Therefore, the methods used here investigate the relationship between genetic gain in each trait and the associated changes in feed-energy requirements. The methane emissions can then be estimated, as carbon dioxide equivalents, (CO_2-eq) as a direct conversion from feed-intake energy, assuming that 21.6 grams of methane is eructated per kg of DM consumed, and that the global warming potential for methane is 25 (1 kg methane = 25 kg CO_2-eq) resulting in a conversion factor of 0.540 kg CO_2-eq/kg DM, as used in the NZ national livestock GHG inventory (Ministry for the Environment 2019).

We are presenting two different measurement definitions to describe the impact of genetic-trait changes on enteric methane emissions as follows:

Gross methane emissions. The gross enteric methane emissions (GME) as CO_2-eq emitted by a breeding cow in a year prior to genetic change (E) was estimated as a product of the number of animals, feed intake, and the conversion coefficient described above.

Methane intensity on an animal-product basis. The emission intensity (EI) was calculated as a ratio of E to total number of product outputs per cow.

The changes in gross emissions and intensity due to genetic improvement were calculated following the methodology set out by Zhang et al. (2019), Amer et al. (2018) and Quinton et al. (2017).

Dairy

The parameters used to estimate gross emissions are summarised in Table 1. For every lactating cow, emissions were aggregated for the cow herself, and the replacements required to maintain the milking herd (Zhang et al. 2019). The feed requirements for each class of animal were calculated using equations developed by Quinton et al. (2018). Briefly, these describe the nutrient requirements of a cow or replacement heifer based on live weight (maintenance), milk production, liveweight gain, mobilisation of body reserves, and stage of gestation. For each of these traits, additional energy may be required to enable a one-unit increase in the trait. For example, the amount of energy required to produce an additional one litre of milk per cow was calculated as the equivalence of the energy required to produce an additional 1 kg of lactose multiplied by the lactose composition of one litre of milk (4.9%).

To calculate emission intensities, total emissions per cow were expressed as a ratio of the total number of product output equivalents per cow. Milk protein was used as the animal product standard with other products converted to protein equivalents using a revenue ratio as described by Zhang et al. (2019). The breeding cow was assumed to be the only stock class that produces milk and meat, with all other products generated through the sale of surplus calves and replacement heifers excluded from the intensity calculations.

To align with the national inventory methodology, gross methane emissions and emissions-intensity values have been calculated using the conversion factor of 0.540 kg CO_2-eq/kg DM instead of 0.583 kg CO_2-eq/kg DM that was used by Zhang et al. (2019). This has caused a slight decrease in both the gross and intensity methane estimates compared to those presented by Zhang et al. (2019).

Beef

The parameters used to estimate gross methane emissions and meat output per breeding cow in a New Zealand beef system are summarised in Table 2. The average number of slaughtered offspring (0.62/cow per year), was based on 0.8 calves/breeding cow/year, of which all males and close to half of females are slaughtered. The average number of replacements reared was 0.18 replacements per breeding cow per year. Average gross methane emissions were calculated from feed intake. Average feed intake for slaughtered offspring was 4,223 kg DM/animal, based on 65% steers each fed 4,291 kg DM to 20 months of age, plus 35% heifers each fed 4,097 kg DM to 26 months of age. Average intake per breeding cow was 4,479 kg DM/year, with each replacement heifer consuming 4,096 kg DM/year. Applying the conversion of 0.540 kg CO_2-eq/kg DM, then emissions per offspring were 2,280 kg CO_2-eq per slaughtered offspring, per replacement is 2,212 kg CO_2-eq per replacement and per cow is 1,462 kg CO_2-eq per breeding cow per year. Therefore, average total system-wide gross emissions (based on 0.62 offspring slaughtered, and 0.18 replacements) were 3,276 kg CO_2-eq per breeding cow per year.

Average product output per slaughtered offspring was calculated from an average carcase weight of 287 kg, assuming 0.686 kg meat/kg carcase; therefore producing 197 kg meat/offspring. Average product output per breeding cow was calculated from average cull cow carcase weight of 270 kg, assuming 0.6 kg meat/kg carcase and that 18% of cows are culled per year resulting in 29.2 kg meat per breeding cow per year. Applying the above values, total system-wide meat product per average breeding female was 152 kg meat/breeding cow/year and average system-wide emissions intensity of 27.8 kg CO_2-eq/kg meat per breeding cow per year.

Table 1 Key assumptions used in the calculations of methane emissions intensity weightings for the New Zealand dairy industry (Zhang et al. 2019).

Variable	Unit	Value
Energy/kg of DM	MJ of ME	11.26
Average cow annual milk yield	kg	3,897
Average cow live weight	kg	450
Milk components		
Protein	%	3.91
Fat	%	4.85
Lactose	%	4.90
Solid	%	8.68
Herd replacement rate	%	22
Cows wintered off platform	%	35.8
Cows wintered on platform	%	64.2

Table 2 Key assumptions in the calculation of methane intensity weightings for the New Zealand beef industry.

Variable	Unit	Value
Energy/kg of DM	MJ of ME	10.05
Pregnancy rate	%	85
Pre-wean survival	%	95
Replacement rate	%	18
Proportion daughters retained	%	45
Proportion of slaughters which are female	%	35
Proportion of slaughters which are male	%	65
Average cow live weight	kg	550
Average weaning weight	kg	243
Dressing proportion (prime)	%	56
Dressing proportion (cow)	%	49

Results

Dairy

The emission values for each of the traits within the national breeding objective are presented in Table 3. When genetic merit increases by one unit, the annual gross emissions per breeding cow associated with genetic change were estimated to increase for all traits except Residual Survival and Fertility. Conversely, emission intensity values were estimated to decrease for Milk Fat, Milk Protein, Milk Solids, Residual Survival, Fertility and Body Condition Score (BCS) as genetic merit improves. Live-weight and Milk Volume emissions-intensity values were estimated to be positive but on a much smaller scale compared to other traits. High somatic cell scores (SCS) result in discarded milk, with no effect on methane, so SCS had a small unfavourable emissions-intensity value.

From the milk component figures presented by Zhang et al. (2019), we calculated that to increase total milk solids by one kilogram requires 6.52 kg of dry matter, which equates to an increase of 3.52 kg CO_2-eq emission/breeding cow/year.

Table 3 Trait-specific estimated effects of a one-unit trait change in gross methane emissions (kg CO_2-eq emission/breeding cow/year, GE) and emission intensity (kg CO_2-eq emission/kg milk protein-eq, EI) for NZ dairy cows.

Trait	Unit	GE	EI
Milk fat	kg	3.31	-0.015
Milk protein	kg	2.03	-0.015
Milk volume	L	0.07	0.0003
Milk solids	kg	3.52	-0.013
Liveweight	kg	2.22	0.005
Residual survival	day	-0.22	-0.0006
Somatic cell score	score	0	0.03
Fertility	%	-5.81	-0.03
Body-condition score	score	20.4	-0.24

A negative emissions-intensity value for any trait indicates that the increase in gross emissions associated with that trait is proportionally smaller than the increase in output of animal product.

Beef

The gross emission (GE) and emissions-intensity (EI) values for a range of traits used in the NZ beef industry are presented in Table 4. A one-unit increase in genetic value for cow mature weight, cow BCS, cow-calving ease and heifer pregnancy was estimated to increase the annual gross emissions per breeding cow. Conversely, an increase in merit associated with stayability and gestation length reduced annual gross emissions per breeding cow. The level of gross emissions associated with changes in genetic merit for carcase weight and weaning weight depended on whether the faster growth performance was used to slaughter the animal earlier (by 1.8 days per kg of carcase weight), and therefore, save feed and the corresponding emissions, or if the animal is taken through to a heavier slaughter weight, which increases the level of feed needed.

Increasing the carcase weight of offspring and increasing cow mature weight by a one-unit trait change were predicted to increase system CO_2-eq/kg meat per breeding cow per year. This was also the case for heifer pregnancy and cow BCS. Conversely, increasing carcase weight for early slaughter animals, decreasing gestation length and increasing stayability and calving ease had negative relationships with system-emissions intensity, meaning that increasing values for these traits were predicted to reduce system kg CO_2-eq/kg meat per breeding cow per year.

Table 4 Trait-specific estimated effects of a one-unit trait change in gross methane emissions (kg CO_2-eq emission/breeding cow/year, GE) and emission intensity (kg CO_2-eq emission/kg meat produced/year, EI) for NZ beef cattle.

Trait	GE	EI
Carcase weight		
Early slaughter steers	-4.21	-0.010
Heavier slaughter steers	8.49	0.003
Early slaughter heifers	-3.04	-0.007
Heavier slaughter heifers	9.28	0.004
Cow mature weight		
Maintenance energy	1.99	0.003
Replacement growth	6.92	0.0004
Weaning weight		
Slaughtered (Maternal)	4.18	0.009
Stores (Mat. & Term.)	-1.09	-0.002
Heifer pregnancy	84.06	0.005
Gestation length	-3.98	-0.005
Cow BCS	14.47	0.018
Stayability	-9.81	-0.026
Calving ease		
Maternal bull - direct	4.01	-0.002
Mat bull - descendants of daughters	3.62	-0.0006
Terminal bull	3.62	-0.002

Discussion

In 2019, the Climate Change Response (Zero Carbon) Amendment Act set into law a new domestic target of 24 to 47 per cent below 2017 biogenic methane emissions by 2050, including 10 per cent below 2017 biogenic methane emissions by 2030. These targets focus solely on reducing gross emissions, however, emissions intensity is a more informative measurement of the effect of genetic improvement of dairy and beef cattle compared with gross emissions, as it considers both improved feed utilisation of individual animals and improved total system efficiency. In contrast, focusing on a reduction in gross emissions can encourage decreasing per-animal production outputs and, consequently, decrease efficiency of production, which is highly counterintuitive (Quinton et al. 2018; Fennessy et al. 2019). The development of emissions-mitigation strategies that do not negatively affect productivity is recognised as a major challenge for ruminant nutritionists and geneticists (Cottle et al. 2011). New selection criteria will be required to reduce both gross emissions and emissions intensity. Herd et al. (2014) suggested that methane emissions could be presented as methane yield (methane production per unit of feed intake), or residual methane (observed methane production less the expected methane production at that level of feed intake). There still will be a trade-off with the inclusion of these criteria, however, as selection effort targeted at this new methane-per-unit feed criterion will draw selection emphasis and effort away from existing traits, which will reduce ongoing profitability gains from genetic improvement, in the absence of a market mechanism to incentivise reductions in emissions. New data and recording systems that facilitate accurate predictions in changes in animal feed consumption at animal and herd level, will be required so that gains from this new trait can be captured in the inventory, and to incentivise farmers to adopt breeding and other practices that reduce farm emissions.

Acknowledgements

Funded by the New Zealand Government to support the objectives of the Livestock Research Group of the Global Research Alliance on Agricultural Greenhouse Gases.

References

Amer PR, Hely FS, Quinton CD, Cromie AR 2018. A methodology framework for weighting genetic traits that impact greenhouse gas emission intensities in selection indexes. Animal 12(1): 5-11. doi.org/10.1017/S1751731117001549.

Cottle DJ, Nolan JV, Wiedemann SG 2011. Ruminant enteric methane mitigation: A review. Animal Production Science 51(6): 491-514. doi.org/10.1071/AN10163.

Fennessy PF, Byrne TJ, Proctor LE, Amer PR 2019. The potential impact of breeding strategies to reduce methane output from beef cattle. Animal Production Science 59(9): 1598. doi.org/10.1071/AN18186.

Herd RM, Arthur PF, Donoghue KA, Bird SH, Bird-Gardiner T, Hegarty RS 2014. Measures of methane production and their phenotypic relationships with dry matter intake, growth, and body composition traits in beef cattle. Journal of Animal Science 92(11): 5267-5274. doi.org/10.2527/jas.2014-8273.

Ministry for the Environment 2019. New Zealand's Greenhouse Gas Inventory 1990-2017.

OECD 2016. OECD Environment Statistics: Greenhouse gas emissions by source 2016.

Pickering NK, Oddy VH, Basarab J, Cammack K, Hayes B, Hegarty RS, Lassen J, McEwan JC, Miller S, Pinares-Patino CS, De Haas Y 2015. Animal board invited review: Genetic possibilities to reduce enteric methane emissions from ruminants. Animal 9(9): 1431-1440. doi.org/10.1017/S1751731115000968.

Quinton CD, Hely FS, Amer PR, Byrne TJ, Cromie AR 2018. Prediction of effects of beef selection indexes on greenhouse gas emissions. Animal 12(5): 889-897. doi.org/10.1017/S1751731117002373.

Zhang X, Amer PR, Jenkins GM, Sise JA, Santos B, Quinton CD 2019. Prediction of effects of dairy selection indexes on methane emissions. Journal of Dairy Science 102(12): 11153-11168. doi.org/10.3168/jds.2019-16943.

Kōura: a novel diversified product for a changing primary sector

JW Hollows

KEEWAI, Invermay, 176 Puddle Alley, Mosgiel 9092.

Corresponding author: Email: john.hollows@ernslaw.co.nz

Abstract

Primary sector industries in New Zealand are under increasing pressure from community to produce products with lower environmental impacts, to both air and water. Contrasting these pressures is a growing world-wide demand for protein, which historically required increased intensification and associated negative environmental impacts. One area promoted for environmental mitigation is the fencing of riparian zones along waterways. The practicalities of this can create operational issues and large areas of land can essentially become non-productive for livestock and timber production. Novel solutions could provide commercial benefit from within these riparian zones. Ernslaw One Ltd. have created approximately 20 hectares of ponds along riparian edges in their Otago and Southland forests. These ponds are used to farm freshwater crayfish or kōura (*Paranephrops zealandicus)* in areas that would otherwise be unproductive as production forest can no longer be grown there for environmental reasons. Customers are increasingly looking for niche foods with unique provenance such as kōura. Currently the kōura industry is in its infancy but there are many groups with licence applications underway. Utilisation of these landscape units add scale and speed towards development of a viable industry with domestic and export potential. High-value novel products such as kōura demonstrate that revenue can be obtained with little environmental impact.

Keywords: kōura; aquaculture; diversification; sustainable; freshwater

Introduction

There is a growing world-wide demand for animal-based protein which will require further intensification and place greater pressure on the environment (Henchion et al. 2017). This is true in New Zealand with the increase in intensive agriculture having negative effects on water quality and quantity, despite innovation into better farming practices and technology (Gluckman 2017). The New Zealand Government's National Policy Statement on water (NPS) stated that by 2025 regional government must have in place a series of rules and standards which protect environmental values for water. The rapid intensification that agriculture has experienced has created, in some regions, waterways that are unlikely to meet potential future water-quality standards. This places agriculture in a difficult position, as increasingly tighter restrictions on environment impacts (MFE 2005) will make it challenging to meet the growing demand for protein.

Furthermore, consumers have traditionally purchased foods based on taste, price, and convenience, but this has changed to now include aspects such as nutrition, naturalness, and sustainability (MFE 2001; Deloitte 2016; Department of Agriculture and Water Resources 2019; MPI 2019a). The overarching theme of this purchasing behaviour is transparency, with consumers wanting to understand the origins and impacts of their food and to have certainty that the food they are eating can be trusted (MPI 2019a). This is important to New Zealand primary producers, who will be able to achieve product premiums if they are able to provide a product with the story that consumers want (MPI 2019a). For agriculture in New Zealand "business as usual" is unlikely to continue and the primary sector needs to quickly come up with solutions to mitigate negative impacts on waterways. Mitigation options such as riparian planting and fencing have been promoted (Collier 1995; Collins 2011; Maseyk et al. 2017) and while environmental benefits are likely to accrue for all of New Zealand, these will come at a direct economic cost to the landowner (Daigneult et al. 2017). The challenge to agriculturists is how economic value can be gained from waterways or other areas within their property retired or rehabilitated for environmental purposes, especially as the vegetation that develops in riparian zones can present new management challenges (e.g., become habitat for pest species such as broom (*Cytisus scoparius*) and gorse (*Ulex europaeus*)).

Riparian setbacks of 5 m or greater are required for the forestry industry (MPI 2019b). Ernslaw One Ltd. is using these setbacks to create ponds for the farming of an indigenous freshwater crayfish known as kōura (*Paranephrops zealandicus*) – a species endemic to New Zealand. Ernslaw One Ltd. markets their farmed kōura under the trade name KEEWAI.

Kōura Aquaculture in New Zealand

While aquaculture in New Zealand has a large profile, freshwater aquaculture is not often thought of in the New Zealand setting despite being undertaken in many other countries. This may be partly due to a lack of research funding into freshwater aquaculture in New Zealand (Hammond 2006; Lovett 2014; Hollows 2016). By comparison, Australia has invested heavily into freshwater aquaculture research with significant gains being made with crayfish species such as Redclaw and Marron (Jones 2000; Jones & Valverde 2020; Lawrence 2007; Rigg et al. 2020).

New Zealand kōura farming is in its infancy with around one tonne produced by two South Island farmers annually. Ernslaw One Ltd. is currently the largest farmer with around nine hectares of ponds in production and another 11 hectares awaiting stocking. Kōura, as grown under the KEEWAI model, receive no artificial feeding or chemical use and provide a healthy natural product in a relatively low-input system, which is rare in aquaculture systems. It produces a product sought after by the market with minimal environmental impact. Additionally, it can have conservation and ecological benefits by restoring or creating wetland habitat of a type significantly reduced since European arrival in New Zealand (Robertson et al. 2019). The Ernslaw experience is that the combination of grass species and kōura ponds provide an effective catch mechanism for sediment and associated phosphate. Kōura are like "a canary at the bottom of the mine shaft" and if they are present in your ponds or streams, then typically you are having low environmental impacts on waterways.

At least three other companies have plans for around 100 hectares of ponds on non-forestry land in the North Island. This new development will provide the scale required to allow the kōura industry to achieve the critical mass required to enable development of overseas export market opportunities. Currently there are limited numbers of juveniles available to seed new ventures and an inability to shift stock for new farms between the North and South island. However, these constraints could be alleviated by the development of hatchery technology, where large numbers of juveniles are produced annually to seed new farms. Hatchery technology is being developed in countries such as Australia with reports of significant gains in juvenile production (Jones & Valverde 2020; Rigg et al. 2020).

Habitat Requirements

Kōura farming can be integrated into most primary sector landscapes - in particular, riparian zones along waterways. The key ingredients are water with a lack of ecotoxic chemicals, particularly insecticides and herbicides, and a riparian buffer which traps and reduces sediment. Kōura can be farmed in static ponds (ones with no flowing water in or out) and, having no-consumptive water use, are an option in areas where water availability is limited or seasonally restricted. Permanently damp (i.e., boggy) areas can easily be developed or rehabilitated into open-water wetlands where kōura can be grown.

Minimum pond size of around 100 m^2, approximately 1.2 m deep, and ideally rectangular in shape is recommended (Hollows 2016). A series of small ponds this size along a waterway or gully can be easily managed and treated as one production area (Fig. 1). Larger reservoirs such as livestock water dams, irrigation dams and duck ponds are places where kōura can be successfully farmed under most conditions. Smaller ponds (~60 m^2) which rely on water from seeps or rain can successfully produce kōura in dry areas with annual precipitation as low as 500 mm. Kōura are typically associated with the bank areas of ponds and streams where these solid edges provide refuge for them to lodge, hide and shelter in. A pond with a large refuge to total surface area will generally offer the highest levels of production. The area of refuge can easily be increased by the addition of coarse rocks, woody vegetation or other artificial refugia placed away from the banks.

Figure 1 Ponds created in stream riparian area where trees are unable to be grown for environmental reasons.

Food Sources

Kōura feed at all trophic levels and can maintain or improve water quality by consuming material such as algae, bacteria, fungi, water plants or any other organic material that may degrade water quality as it decomposes (Hollows 1998). Plants such as *Carex* grasses and watercress (*Nasturtium* species) in the riparian areas provide habitat as well as a food source since kōura will eat the plants and smaller invertebrates that live on them. A commercial kōura dietary supplement is not readily available in New Zealand, but salmon pellets are a suitable feed. These are readily eaten by kōura and typically contain an appropriate balance of nutrients and minerals required for growth. In extensive koura aquaculture operations, such as those currently operated by Ernslaw One Ltd., the existing ecosystems provides all the food required, and, while supplementary feeding is possible and would increase production, it has associated increased input costs (including labour).

Sales and Marketing

Kōura are a unique food-product with a sweet-tasting, delicate flesh. When cooked, the carapace (shells) turn bright red making them particularly desirable within the restaurant trade, especially for Asian markets. They are a product that can be sustainably grown without artificial inputs and can co-exist within most current primary industry operations. The limited New Zealand production relative to domestic and global consumer demand suggests that kōura will remain a niche high-value product. Kōura maintain product quality when transported in chilli-boxes packed with wood-shavings and ice packs. They have a shelf life of up to 10 days, which finds favour with restaurants and overseas markets. In the five years Ernslaw One Ltd. have been selling KEEWAI, there has been no fish mortality transporting product to market (New Zealand, Asia, or Canada). In addition, there may be an alternative market for kōura as aquarium pets, as there is strong demand from Asia. This has yet to be explored by KEEWAI but there is a flourishing world-wide market for freshwater crayfish for the aquarium trade (Faulks 2015).

Current productive outputs

Kōura farms are largely extensive at present and the maximum yield is difficult to define. Water temperature and refuge are key factors determining how fast kōura can achieve a market weight (~70 to 100 grams) but two to three years is the norm in Otago and Southland. Further north in New Zealand you would expect faster growth rates, and therefore, better production due to the warmer climate. Productive yields of up to five saleable kōura per m^2 have been achieved in ponds with mixed age classes by Ernslaw One Ltd. while up to eight per m^2 have been recorded in ponds initially stocked with males, all of a similar live weight, by New Zealand Clearwater Crayfish (Hollows 2016). Labour requirement is low; once ponds are developed and stocked it can require as little as a two visits per pond annually to harvest stock for market through to a few hours per week for larger or more intensive farms.

Regulatory considerations

A fish-farm licence from the Ministry of Primary Industries (MPI) is required to commercially farm kōura in New Zealand. As part of the fish-farm application, resource consents from territorial authorities may be required for activities such as land-use consents, and consents to take, use, and discharge to water. This will help reduce the time and cost to obtain the necessary formal permits and consents. Water availability needs thorough investigation with relevant government agencies and other water users early in the aquaculture planning process (e.g., neighbours or irrigation companies). Consultation with affected parties is another component of the licensing process. These parties include local Iwi, the Department of Conservation (DoC), Regional and Territorial authorities and Fish & Game New Zealand. In addition, you may need to discuss your plans with other groups such as adjacent landowners and/or other water users depending on the size and location of your farm.

Figure 2 Annual kōura harvest from an Otago forest pond, 2019.

Identifying a source of kōura is critical, as farmed stocks are limited, and a permit from DoC to transfer kōura into the ponds may also be required. Currently there are four fish-farms with kōura for sale to seed new farms. Alternatively, a permit for wild capture can be applied for from MPI. To sell kōura for human consumption requires a facility to purge the fish prior to sale (this does not apply to sales between fish farms or for the aquarium trade). An animal material depot (AMD) certificate will be required from MPI prior to selling any stock to ensure relevant food safety standards are met. MPI have a good understanding of what is involved with kōura farming and getting the necessary approvals is now much less onerous than it was when KEEWAI was established. Aside from the land and water resource the equipment required is essentially only nets, bait, buckets, a shed, water tanks and a system for keeping water cool, alongside some recording of stocking and production data. A guide to getting started with kōura aquaculture has been produced and provides some good information around regulatory requirements, as well as practical considerations (Hollows 2016).

Conclusions

Kōura are a unique product as, along with commercial value, there are positive environmental and conservation aspects associated with their production. They are a new opportunity for primary production from land unable to be farmed in traditional or intensive methods. In the current environment, do we need to think outside the square and look at new regulatory requirements around the environment as opportunities for diversification rather than as another nail in the coffin to industry?

References

Collier KJ, Copper AB, Davies-Colley RJ, Rutherford JC, Williamson RB 1995. Managing riparian zones: a contribution to protecting New Zealand's rivers and streams. Department of Conservation. https://www.doc.govt.nz/documents/science-and-technical/riparianzones2.pdf (accessed May 2020).

Collins KE 2011. Evaluating the effectiveness of riparian plantings on water quality: a case study of lowland stream in the Lake Ellesmere catchment. Unpublished Master of Science thesis. Lincoln University. https://researcharchive.lincoln.ac.nz/handle/10182/3835 (accessed May 2020).

Daigmeault AJ, Eppink FV, Lee WG 2017. A national restoration pathway programme in New Zealand: is it value for money? Journal of Environmental Management 187: 166-177.

Deloitte 2016. Capitalizing on the shifting consumer food value equation. https://www2.deloitte.com/content/dam/Deloitte/us/Documents/consumer-business/usfmi-gma-report.pdf. (accessed January 2020).

Department of Agriculture and Water Resources 2019. Ensuring Australia's system of food regulation supports growing food export industries. https://haveyoursay.agriculture.gov.au/43504/documents/98716. (accessed January 2020).

Faulks Z 2015. The global trade in crayfish as pets. Crustacean Research 44: 75–92. DOI: 10.18353/crustacea.44.0_75.

Fox R 2020. Taking the story to the chefs. Otago Daily Times Life & Style Article. 29 January 2020.

Gluckman PD 2017. New Zealand's fresh waters: Values, state, trends, and human impact. New Zealand Government's Chief Scientific Advisor Report.

Hammond KS, Hollows JW, Townsend CR, Lokman PM 2006. Effects of temperature and water calcium concentration on growth, survival and moulting of freshwater crayfish, *Paranephrops zealandicus*. Aquaculture 251 (2-4): 271-279.

Henchion M, Hayes M, Mullen AM, Fenelon M, Tiwari B 2017. Future protein supply and demand: strategies and factors influencing a sustainable equilibrium. Foods 6(7): 53.

Hollows JW 1998. Land use effects on the growth and diet of freshwater crayfish (*Paranephrops zealandicus*). Unpublished Master of Science thesis. University of Otago.

Hollows JW 2016. How to farm freshwater crayfish – a guide to getting started. https://www.researchgate.net/publication/305239925_Freshwater_Crayfish_Farming_-_a_guide_to_getting_started (accessed January 2019).

Jones CM 2000. Redclaw Crayfish Aquaculture. Recommended Practices for Redclaw Crayfish Aquaculture based on Research and Development Activities, 1998 through 2000. Queensland Government, Department of Primary Industries and Fisheries

Jones CM and Valverde C 2020. Development of mass production hatchery technology for the redclaw crayfish, *Cherax quadricarinatus*. Freshwater Crayfish 25(1):1-6. DOI: 10.5869/fc.2020.v25-1.001

Klainbaum A 2019. Seeking a sustainable food chain. Food Technology Magazine. October 2019.

Lawrence C 2007. *Improved performance of marron using genetic and pond management strategies*. Fisheries Research Report No. 2000/215. Department of Fisheries, North Beach, Western Australia.

Lovett B 2014. Early development of the New Zealand freshwater crayfish Paranephrops zealandicus (Decapoda: Parasiticide): Implications for Aquaculture. Unpublished Batchelor of Science thesis, University of Otago.

Melay M 2018. https://blog.vision33.co.uk/country-of-origin-effect-why-provenance-matters-for-food-and-beverage-wholesale-distributors/. (accessed April 2019).

Maseyk F, Dominati E, White T, Mackay A 2017. Farmer perspectives of the on-farm and off-farm pros and cons of planted multifunctional riparian margins. Land Use Policy. 61: 160-170. www.doi.org/10.1016/j.landusepol.2016.10.053. (accessed May 2020).

MFE 2001. Our clean green image: What's it worth? Ministry for the Environment Report, www.mpi.govt.nz. Publication Number ME 405.

MFE 2005. Aquaculture reform: an overview. Ministry for the Environment: Wellington.

MPI 2019a. A strategy for New Zealand food safety. Ministry for Primary Industries Consultation Draft. https://www.fisheries.govt.nz/dmsdocument/36705/direct (accessed January 2020).

MPI 2019b. National environmental standards – plantation forestry. https://www.mpi.govt.nz/growing-and-harvesting/forestry/national-environmental-standards-for-plantation-forestry. (accessed May 2020).

Rigg DP, Seymour JE, Courtney RL and Jones CM 2020. A review of juvenile redclaw crayfish Cherax quadricarinatus (von Martens, 1898) production in aquaculture. Freshwater Crayfish 25(1):13-30. DOI: 10.5869/fc.2020.v25-1.013

Robertson HA, Ausseil A, Rance B, Betts H, Pomeroy E 2019. Loss of wetlands since 1990 in southland New Zealand. New Zealand Journal of Ecology. 43(1): 5p.

The management of Standardbred breeding stock on commercial properties

CW Rogers[a,b*], A Herbst[c], K Langhans[c], R Stone[a], R Hirst[a], EK Gee[a] and PJ Back[a,b]

[a]School of Veterinary Science, Massey University, New Zealand, [b]School of Agriculture and Environment, Massey University, New Zealand, [c]Hochschule für Wirtschaft und Umwelt, University of Nürtingen-Geislingen, Germany

**Corresponding author:* Email: c.w.rogers@massey.ac.nz

Abstract

This paper describes the on-farm pasture management of Standardbred broodmares on commercial breeding farms in New Zealand using data collected from three studies. The pasture on offer was typically ryegrass (70% (IQR 50-70), clover (15% (IQR 15-22), and fescue (12% IQR 6-22). Other species present included cocksfoot and plantain (10% on one farm). Weed content was low at 5% (IQR 4-8). During winter, on two farms mares were break-fed on crops of kale, standing oats and Italian ryegrass. Through the year there was limited variation in the nutritive composition of the pasture with a DM of 17±0.3%, ME of 11±0.1 MJ/kg DM and crude protein of 23±0.5%. Horses were managed using a semi-set-stocked pattern (1.7 mares/ha; 2.6 weanlings/ha). Pasture DM on offer for mares ranged from 1700-2500 kg DM/ha and 2500-3000 kg DM/ha for weanlings, which were also offered ~1.5 kg/day (as fed) of pre-mixed concentrates. To manage pasture quality and minimise the establishment of lawns and roughs, paddocks on all farms were harrowed and cross-grazed with sheep or cattle. The management system described, while similar to that of Thoroughbreds, differs with the offering of crops to mares during winter and a higher BCS of mares.

Keywords: horse; pasture; Standardbred; management; mare

Introduction

At present, most regional councils require large-scale farming operations to work within a regional nutrient management plan. Traditionally, application of such plans has focused on ruminant-based farming systems and has not included smaller scale lifestyle blocks or equine properties. Recently, the Waikato Regional Council's Plan Change 1 examined whether equine properties should also be included and, therefore, be required to calculate a nitrogen-loss baseline using Overseer™. For this to be possible there is a requirement for documentation of current equine farming practices, animal-level technical data and generation of best management practices against which farms could be benchmarked (Chin et al. 2019a; Chin et al. 2019b).

New Zealand equine systems are unique in being pasture-based and this restricts the direct utilisation of production data from overseas production systems. Breeding stock, in particular, have pasture as the major, or only component, of the diet (Rogers et al. 2017b). Seasonal supply of pasture and fluctuations in stock numbers during the breeding season can dramatically alter feed supply for empty and in-foal, foal-at-foot mares, which may alter N loss at both an animal and farm level (Bengtsson et al. 2018). Deterministic modelling of pasture supply and N loss has emphasised the role pasture plays in N loss under New Zealand pasture-based management systems and the need for robust understanding of the production system (Chin et al. 2019a; Chin et al. 2019b).

To date, the Thoroughbred production system, from breeding through to sport, has received the most attention within the literature. This focus is possibly due to the high level of organisation and regulation within this industry and its numerical and financial domination of the equine sector (Bolwell et al. 2017). The Standardbred (harness-racing) industry is approximately half the size of the Thoroughbred industry, in both breeding and sport numbers (Tanner et al. 2012). In contrast to the Thoroughbred production system with a clear commercial supply chain from breeders through yearling sales to racing, the Standardbred industry has a large number of participants that are termed breeder-owner-trainers. This group of breeder-owner-trainers breed horses which they subsequently train and race themselves (Legg et al. 2020).

It is believed that, with a lower proportion of horses bred and grown for sale as yearlings in the Standardbred industry there will be differences in production practices compared to the Thoroughbred system. Differences in industry-level reproductive parameters have been reported between the two production systems (Standardbred vs Thoroughbred) (Rogers et al. 2009). However, at present within the literature, there are limited production data, and limited mention of pasture management and pasture supply within Standardbred production systems (Stowers et al. 2010). These animal-level data, as well as pasture- and management-level data are required as key input parameters within the nutrient-management software (Overseer™). This paper collates data from three separate studies to provide some descriptive data on the pasture composition and management on commercial Standardbred breeding farms in New Zealand.

Materials and methods

The data collated and presented in this paper were collected from three separate experiments described below.

Study 1: A cross-sectional survey of Standardbred mare and farm management

Data were collected via a face-to-face cross sectional survey of six commercial Standardbred breeding farms in August 2015 (four in the South Island and two in the North Island). Data were collected on the number of horses in the different stock classes and the management of the broodmares during the previous breeding season (2014/2015 season).

Study 2: Prospective monitoring of a standardbred case farm

Detailed stock- and pasture-management data were collected prospectively during 2015/16 breeding season the from one commercial breeding farm located in South Auckland. The total effective farm area was 200 ha with 36 ha of the operation devoted to the management of the horses. During the observation period, feed supply and demand were modelled using pasture data from nine representative paddocks ranging in size from 1.3 to 2.25 ha, every two weeks, with a rising-plate meter (total area pasture plated 15.6 ha). Data were collected for total pasture cover as well as lawns (areas intensively grazed and free of faeces), and roughs (longer sections of pasture identified as latrine areas) (Bengtsson et al. 2018). On-farm pasture supply and demand was modelled using a customised feed budget with the assumption that pasture ME remained at 10 MJ/kg DM throughout the year. Any supplementary feed provided was included in the feed budget.

Study 3: Prospective monitoring of botanical and chemical pasture composition on commercial equine stud farms

A full description of the cross-sectional survey methods was reported by Hirst (2011). In brief, botanical composition and nutrient composition of pasture samples (three representative paddocks per farm) were collected across one breeding season (2009-2010) from four commercial Standardbred stud farms distributed across New Zealand (three South Island and one North Island). Samples were collected on four occasions (spring, summer, autumn, winter). Seasonal pasture botanical composition was estimated for each of the three paddocks on each farm using a representative sample (~1 kg wet weight) and sorted into the categories of grasses, clover, dead matter and weeds. Pasture samples were weighed fresh (wet weight) and stored frozen (-20°C) until drying at 75°C for 24 hours and weighed again to estimate percentage DM. Metabolisable energy values were estimated using a subsample (100 g) of the pasture samples using Near–Infrared-Spectroscopy (NIRS) analysis (Feedtech laboratory, AgResearch, Palmerston North, New Zealand). Differences among seasons was tested using an ANOVA within Stata version 12 (StataCorp LP, College Station, TX, USA).

Table 1 Overview of the type of data collected from each of the three studies reported in this manuscript.

	Study 1	Study 2	Study 3
Study type	Cross sectional	Prospective	Prospective
Number of farms	6	1	4
Farm management	x	x	
Stock numbers	x	x	x
Body condition score	x	x	
Feeding	x	x	
Pasture mass	x	x	x
Chemical composition			x
Botanical composition			x

Results

Study 1: Cross-sectional survey

Data were collected from the six largest commercial Standardbred stud farms in New Zealand. The median farm size was 201 ha (IQR 130-210). Data were collected on the management of 833 mares (~30% of the Standardbred national mare herd) of which 70% (585/833) were reported in-foal at the end of the breeding season. The median number of mares and mares in foal per farm were 140 (IQR 140-150) and 104 (IQR 80-113). Based on resident mare numbers, the farms had a large range in off-season mare density median 0.75 (IQR 0.6-1.1) mares/ha, approximately half the mare density during the breeding season (median 1.7 (IQR 1.3 – 2.1) mares /ha). The age distribution of the mares was 17% (IQR 10-20) 3–5 year olds, 57% (IQR 55-60) were 6-12 year olds, and 29% (IQR 27-36) ≥13 years old. The median frequency of anthelminthic drench administration was 11 weeks (IQR 8-20). However, two farms commented that this was only an estimate as they attempted to move away from a set drench frequency and would only drench when the mares looked like they needed it, rather than routine schedule.

None of the farms used weigh scales to monitor the body weight of the mares or the youngstock. Informal body condition scoring (BCS) was the primary method of monitoring adequate energy balance. Based on the method of Henneke et al. (1983) for assessing BCS (scale 1-9), the stud masters indicated based on group estimates for the different mare categories that prior to foaling, mares had a median BCS of 6.5/9 (IQR 6-7.5), at breeding mares with foals at foot had a median BCS 5.5/9 (IQR 5.5-6.5) and empty mares 5.0/9 (IQR 5-5.5).

The stud masters estimated that typical pasture composition during the breeding season was 70% (IQR 45-70) perennial ryegrass (*Lolium perenne*) and 15% (IQR 10-25)% white clover (*Trifolium repens*). Three farms reported having tall fescue (*Festuca arundinacea*) present in low

Table 2 Key production values for production data during the 2014/15 breeding season collated from six commercial Standardbred stud farms in New Zealand.

Mean farm size (ha)		201 (IQR 130-210)
Number of resident mares	Total	833
	Median (IQR)	140 (IQR 140-150)
Mares in foal	Total	585
	Median (IQR)	104 (IQR 80-113)
% mares "in- foal" / resident mares (mean ±SEM)		88±4%
Percentage mares in-foal producing viable foal (mean ±SEM)		90±4%

Figure 1 Average farm pasture cover estimated from nine paddocks (15.6 ha) set stocked with horses on a commercial Standardbred breeding farm.

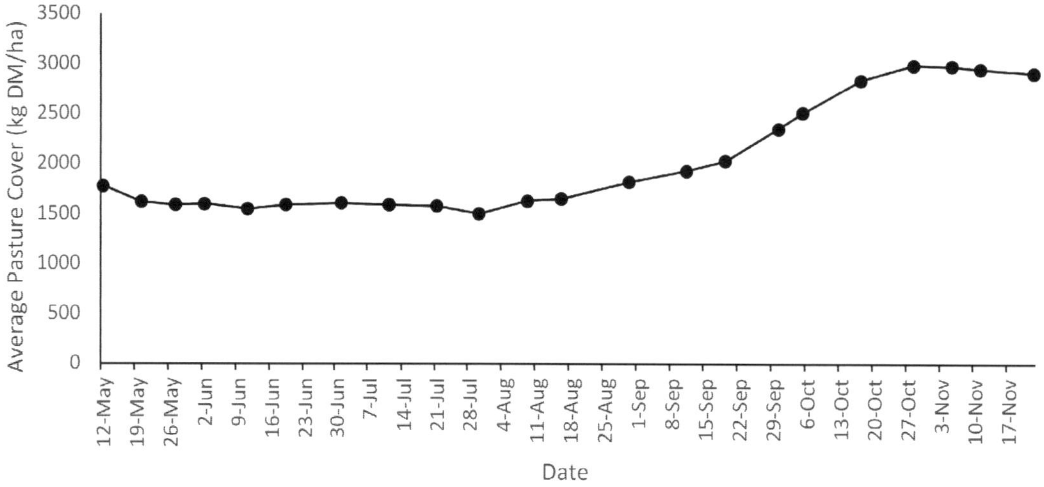

Figure 2 Average pasture cover in the lawns and roughs in nine paddocks (15.6 ha) set stocked with horses on a commercial Standardbred breeding farm.

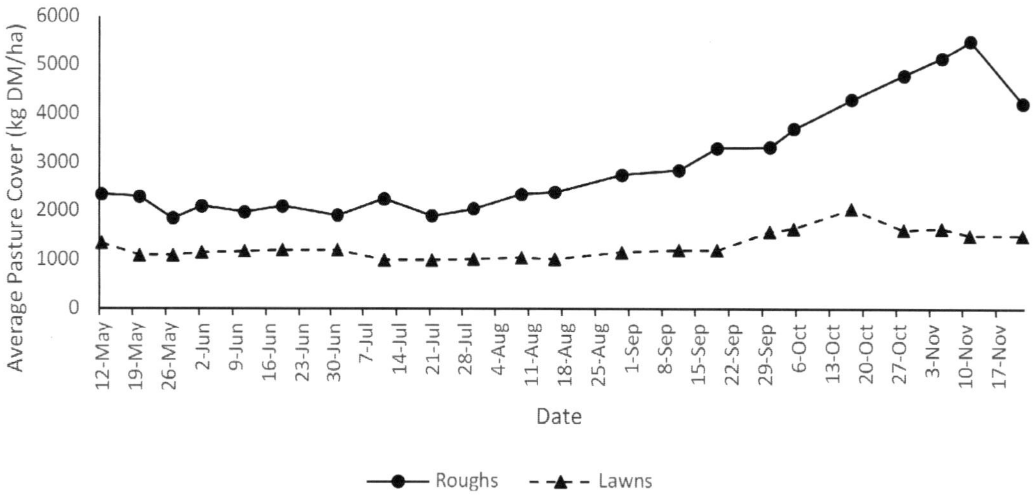

Figure 3 Pasture supply and demand modelled using feed budget data derived from pasture measurements from nine paddocks on a commercial Standardbred breeding farm.

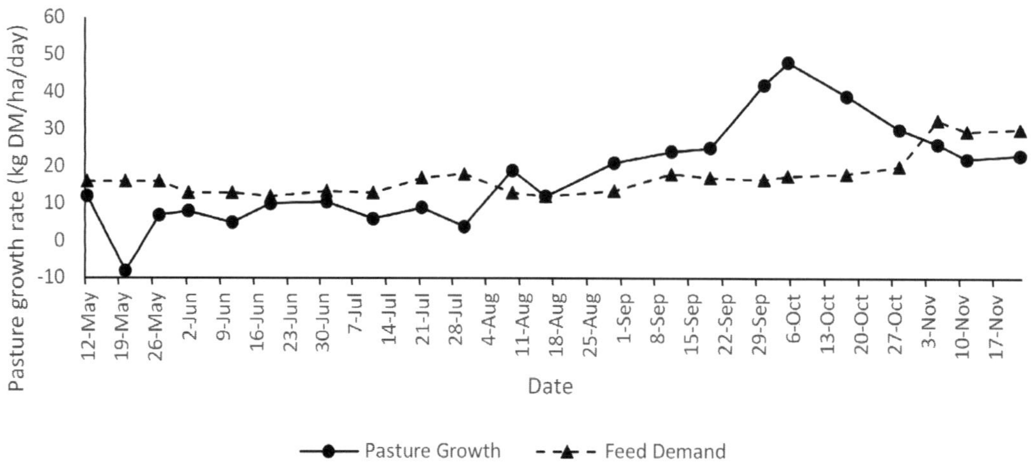

proportions 12% (IQR 6-30) within the sward and one North Island farm reported that some pasture contained up to of 50% Kikuyu (*Cenchrus clandestinus*). One Southland farm had intentionally sown 10% cocksfoot and plantain within the pasture. The proportion of weed content reported (dock (*Rumex obtusifolius),* buttercup *(Ranunculus repens)*) was generally low 5% (IQR 3-10). All farms reported cross grazing with ruminants (sheep and cattle) and occasional harrowing. During winter, on two farms, the mares were also break-fed on crops of kale (*Brassica oleracea*), standing oats (*Avena sativa*) and Italian ryegrass *(Lolium multiflorum)*.

During winter, five farms provided grass baleage in addition to pasture (quantities not recorded). One farm only provided grass hay as conserved forage during winter (quantities not recorded). Mares on 5/6 farms were provided with additional concentrate feed during winter (crushed barley or commercial premix) at a moderate rate of 0.5 -0.8 kg/mare/day as feed (~4-7 MJ ME, ~ 5-9% of maintenance requirement). These farms also provided a mineral supplement (mare balancer pellets) to the mares during the third trimester of pregnancy. Weanlings were provided with a median 1.55 (IQR: 1.82-1.2) kg DM/day of concentrates at weaning and at a rate of 2.5 kg (IQR: 2.1-3.2) kg DM/day during winter.

Study 2: Prospective monitoring on a case farm

The effective farm area devoted to the horses was 36 ha subdivided into 24 paddocks ranging in size from 0.73 to 2.25 ha. There were 57 horses from May to August and 43 horses from August to November, provide a stocking density of 1.5 horses/ha to 1.2 horses/ha. During the observation period, the horses were set stocked in each paddock (4-6 horses/paddock). The pasture was described as perennial ryegrass/white clover mix, with some of the paddocks having an Italian ryegrass/white clover mix. The soil type was described as loam with some areas of silty loam over clay.

Average farm pasture cover remained between 1,400 to 1,600 kg DM/ha up to September when there was a reduction in the number of horses (from 57 to 43 horses), as some mares went to another farm to foal down and be bred. The effect of the destocking can be observed in Fig. 1 (pasture supply vs. pasture demand). Feed demand remained relatively constant throughout the observation period, in part due to the provision of supplementary feed of baleage (at a rate of 2 kg DM/mare/day). Pasture growth (based on the total pasture values) was estimated to be approximately 10 kg/ha/day up to the start of August and continued to increase in spring up to 48 kg DM/ha. The higher pasture mass of the roughs relative to the lawns, demonstrated preferential grazing of the lawns and the contribution of "non-utilised" roughs to the increase in total farm pasture cover modelled. The relative percentage area of pasture in each paddock as either lawns or roughs was not estimated.

Study 3: Prospective pasture composition

Table 3 Seasonal botanical and chemical composition of equine pastures on four commercial Standardbred stud farms (values % of total sample DM) and metabolisable energy estimates (MJ) (mean ± SEM) collected from commercial Standardbred stud farms in New Zealand (n=4) during the 2009/10 to 2010/11 season.

Botanical Composition	Spring	Summer	Autumn	Winter	P value
Ryegrass	67±4%^{a}	45±4%^{b}	61±5%^{ab}	69±7%^{a}	P<0.001
Other grass species	21±4%	17±5%	20±5%	15±4%	ns
Total clover	8±1%^{a}	18±4%^{b}	14±2%^{b}	2±1%^{a}	P<0.001
Weeds	2±1%^{ab}	5±1%^{a}	3±1%^{ab}	1±1%^{b}	P<0.001
Dead matter	2±1%^{a}	15±5%^{b}	2±1%^{a}	13±5%^{b}	P<0.001
Chemical composition					
Dry matter %	18.5±0.5^{a}	15.1±0.7^{b}	17.9±0.6^{a}	15.2±0.5^{b}	P<0.001
Metabolisable energy (MJ)	12.3±0.1^{a}	10.7±0.3^{b}	11.6±0.2^{c}	10.4±0.3^{b}	P<0.001
Crude protein (%)	24.6±0.7^{a}	21.4±0.9^{b}	23.6±0.8^{ab}	21.6±1.0^{b}	P<0.05
ADF (%)	23.3±0.4^{a}	25.4±0.9^{ab}	24.6±0.5^{ab}	26.1±0.8^{b}	P<0.001
NDF (%)	41.4±0.8^{a}	50.8±1.6^{b}	42.1±1.2^{a}	46.1±0.8^{a}	P<0.001
Soluble carbohydrate %	11.1±0.5^{a}	7.2±1.1^{bc}	11.3±0.4^{b}	8.5±0.5^{c}	P<0.001

Different superscript within a row are significantly different P<0.05

Discussion

To date there have been few data published on Standardbred production in New Zealand compared to the Thoroughbred industry. The Standardbred industry structure, with a significant bias towards breeder-owner-trainers, alters the primary production focus away from the production of yearlings to sell to that of supply of product for breeders to race themselves. One of the effects of this industry focus is that there are fewer large-scale breeding operations (stud farms) within the standardbred industry compared to that observed in the Thoroughbred industry (six farms *vs.* >26 farms) (Rogers et al. 2018). The use of artificial insemination in the Standardbred industry also reduces the seasonal movement of mares among farms and helps explain why many of the farms in this study would be categorised as medium sized based on the Thoroughbred scale, even though several of the farms were standing 2–4 stallions.

The across-farm stocking density reported here during the off-season was low or moderate at 0.75 mares/ha (~356 kg LWT/ha), during the breeding season this value increased to 2 mares/ha which was similar to values reported for Thoroughbreds on commercial farms (Rogers et al. 2007). These values as a per farm basis can be a misleading as they do not represent the true stocking density during a rotation. Data from Thoroughbred farms indicates that the management of mares during the breeding season provides an effective stocking density of 4–6 mares/ha

(2000–3000 kg LWT/ha) and, thus, a daily feed demand of 24-32 kg pasture DM/day/ mob of mares. Given that mares are usually managed on a semi-set-stocked pattern, with a sustained period of grazing of 2 to 4 weeks, sustainability after utilisation of the stored pasture mass, therefore, relies on adequate daily pasture growth to meet this feed demand. The data from the case farm and regional averages during the breeding season, indicate that this may be possible during the breeding season due to adequate daily pasture growth. However, as the length of sustained period of grazing increases there will be an accumulation of faecal matter and expansion or density of faecal piles within the latrine areas, which may provide some moderation of this possibility. Previous modelling has indicated that these latrine areas effectively limit pasture availability to 70% of the total pasture mass measured (Rogers et al. 2017a). Thus for accurate estimation of true pasture mass on offer for horses either the total pasture mass estimate should be moderated to 70% of the measured value, or the signals for the end of the sustained period of grazing should be reduction in the pasture mass of the lawns to less than 1500 kg DM/ha (Rogers et al. 2018).

The botanical and chemical composition of the pasture on Standardbred farms was similar to data collected on Thoroughbred farms collected during the same season (Hirst 2011). Somewhat surprisingly, the estimates by stud masters of the pasture composition were in close agreement with the actual botanical composition data from selected paddocks. This may indicate a reasonable holistic awareness among stud masters of pasture supply and demand, even without the collection of quantifiable metrics and feed budgeting.

Horses are selective grazers and, therefore, provide some challenges for pasture management, particularly persistence of desired species and the development of focal areas of faecal material and weeds. Feed budgeting on the case farm (study 2) demonstrated an increasing average farm pasture cover and a feed supply surplus during spring. Measurement of pasture mass via pasture plating of the lawns and roughs demonstrated that this increasing pasture cover was being driven by increasing pasture mass in the "roughs", which may not be fully utilisable by the horses due to faecal avoidance. Previous monitoring of commercial Thoroughbred stud farms also reported this observation with preferential grazing of lawns and accumulation of pasture mass in roughs. At present the best estimates to correct for this in feed budgeting is to assume 70% pasture availability by horses (Rogers et al. 2017a). This 70% utilisation of pasture mass provides the unique situation where farms could increase the ruminant numbers to consume the non-utilised 30% and increase pasture productivity. Most equine stud farms utilise cross grazing with ruminants, but may not be aware of the relative stocking ratio possible without restricting or compromising feed supply for horses. Cross grazing with ruminants may help reduce the need for frequent interval drenching and may explain the moderately longer drench interval reported here 11 (IQR 8-20) compared to a recent survey of Thoroughbred and Standardbred farms in Australia (~8 weeks) (Wilkes et al. 2019). Two of the farms reported they were attempting to move away from interval drenching and utilise a targeted strategy for drenching mares. Similar to the Australian Thoroughbred and Standardbred farms, none of the farms weighed mares and this may provide an opportunity for under-dosing mares with anthelminthic drenches.

On the Standardbred farms the pasture mass on offer ranged from 1,700 to 2,500 kg DM/ha. Estimates from surveys on Thoroughbred stud farms has indicated a greater pre-grazing mass (~3,500 kg DM/ha), though observational trials have indicated that on some Thoroughbred farms during the breeding season that empty mares were managed at levels similar to that reported here for Standardbreds (Rogers et al. 2007; Bengtsson et al. 2018). A possible explanation for the lower pasture mass estimated for Standardbreds may be associated with the common perception that Standardbreds are of a thriftier phenotype than are Thoroughbreds and, thus, may be able to maintain weight and body condition when provided lower levels of feed on offer. This thriftier phenotype of the Standardbred may have been reflected in the moderately higher BCS reported by stud masters (6 to 7.5/10) than reported in the Thoroughbred industry (median 6/10) (Gee et al. 2017).

While the Standardbred mares may have been provided with less pasture mass than that observed on Thoroughbred farms, the weanlings were provided pasture mass at a level comparable to that offered to Thoroughbreds. Total pasture mass of 2,500-3,000 kg DM/ha should, at least at the start of the rotation, provide lawns with a pasture mass >1,500 kg DM/ha, which appears to be the threshold level for weanlings to start to graze in the roughs and may be associated with reduced volutary feed intake. The provision of ~2.5 kg of concentrates to the weanlings would equate to ~25 MJ DE or 40 to 30% of estimated daily requiement from 5 months old to 12 months. This level of concentrate feeding was lower than that observed on commerical Thoroughbred farms (50- 80% DE requirement from concentrates) and may reflect the differences in the short-term production focus, with Thoroughbred breeders accutely aware of the need to optimise growth rate to maximise size at the time of the yearling sales (Stowers et al. 2009).

While there were some geographical drivers for seasonal changes in pasture botanical and chemical composition (i.e., Southland *vs.* Canterbury *vs.* South Auckland) they did not differ from those generated from Thoroughbred farms and indicates that these data may provide suitable reference points for understanding the basics of pasture production on commercial equine properties in New Zealand. These pasture data, in association with seasonal production data, are increasingly needed if equine properties become included in the nutrient-management schemes operated by regional councils.

Acknowledgements

Funding for components of the studies in this manuscript were provided by the New Zealand Equine Trust 2/2008 and 2/2014

References

Bengtsson J, Rogers CW, Back PJ, Emanuelson U, Roca J, Gee EK, Bolwell CF 2018. Characteristics of the grazing and farm management of broodmares on commercial Thoroughbred stud farms during spring New Zealand Journal of Animal Science and Production 78: 88-91

Bolwell CF, Rogers CW, Gee EK, Rosanowski SM 2017. Commercial equine production in New Zealand 3: The racing and sport industries. Animal Production Science http://dx.doi.org/10.1071/AN16753.

Chin YY, Back PJ, Gee EK, Rogers CW 2019a. Deterministic modelling of nitrogen utilisation by horses managed under pasture-based, intensive and semi-intensive systems with different levels of pasture intake. New Zealand Journal of Animal Science and Production 79: 1-7.

Chin YY, Back PJ, Gee EK, Rogers CW 2019b. Livestock and pasture management on commercial Thoroughbred breeding farms: implications for estimating nitrogen loss. New Zealand Journal of Animal Science and Production 79: 65-70.

Gee EK, Rogers CW, Bolwell CF 2017. Commerical equine production in New Zealand 1:Reproduction and breeding. Animal Production Science http://dx.doi.org/10.1071/AN16728.

Henneke DR, Potter GD, Kreider JL, Yeates BF 1983. Relationship between condition score, physical measurements and body-fat percentages in mares. Equine Veterinary Journal 15: 371-372.

Hirst RL. 2011. Seasonal variation of pasture quality on commerical equine farms in New Zealand. M.AgriScience Thesis, Massey University.

Legg K, Gee EK, Bolwell CF, Bridges J, Rogers CW 2020. A Cross-Sectional Survey of the Training and Management of a Cohort of 2-Year-Old Standardbred Racehorses in New Zealand. Journal of Equine Veterinary Science 87: https://doi.org/10.1016/j.jevs.2020.102936.

Rogers CW, Gee EK, Back PJ 2017a. Pastures and supplements in New Zealand commercial equine production systems. In: Rattray PV, Brookes IM & Nicol AM (eds). Pasture and supplements for grazing animals. New Zealand Society of Animal Production.

Rogers CW, Gee EK, Back PJ, van Son S, Hirst RJ, Pomroy WE 2018. Pasture use and management in commercial equine production systems. New Zealand Journal of Animal Science and Production 78: 40-44.

Rogers CW, Gee EK, Bolwell CF, Rosanowski SM 2017b. Commerical equine production in New Zealand 2: Growth and development of the equine athlete. Animal Production Science. https://doi.org/10.1071/AN16752.

Rogers CW, Gee EK, Firth EC 2007. A cross-sectional survey of Thoroughbred stud farm management in the North Island of New Zealand. New Zealand Veterinary Journal 55: 302-307.

Rogers CW, Gee EK,Vermeij E 2009. Retrospective examination of the breeding efficiency of the New Zealand Thoroughbred and Standardbred. Proceedings of the New Zealand Society of Animal Production 69: 126-131.

Stowers NL, ErdtsieckB, Rogers CW, Taylor TB, Firth EC 2010. The prevelance of limb deformities in New Zealand Standardbred foals and their influence on racing sucess – A preliminary investigation. Proceedings New Zealand Society of Animal Production 70: 140-142.

Stowers NL, Rogers CW, Hoskin SO 2009. Management of weanlings on commercial Thoroughbred stud farms in the North Island of New Zealand. Proceedings of the New Zealand Society of Animal Production 69: 4-9.

Tanner JC, Rogers CW, Bolwell CF, Gee EK 2012. Preliminary examination of wastage in Thoroughbred and Standardbred horses in New Zealand using training milestones. Proceedings of the New Zealand Society of Animal Production 72:172-174.

Wilkes E, Heller J, Raidal S, Woodgate R, Hughes K 2019. A questionnaire study of parasite control in Thoroughbred and Standardbred horses in Australia. Equine Veterinary Journal 00: 1-9. https://doi.org/10.1111/evj.13207

Trainers perceptions of the impact of different feeding and management practices on racehorses they identified displaying symptoms of recurrent exertional rhabdomyolysis

LJ Wood[a], BE Lancaster[b], MR Breheny[cd] and CW Rogers[cd]

[a]*NRM and McMillan Equine, 9 Link Dr, Rolleston, Christchurch 7614, New Zealand;* [b]*The Royal (Dick) School of Veterinary Studies and Roslin Institute, The University of Edinburgh, Easter Bush Campus, Midlothian, UK;* [c]*School of Agriculture and Environment, Massey University, Private Bag 11-222, 4442, Palmerston North;* [d]*School of Veterinary Science, Massey University, Private Bag 11-222, 4442, Palmerston North*

Corresponding author: Email: luisa.wood@mcmillanequine.co.nz

Abstract

Data on the feeding and management of racehorses and the practices perceived to benefit horses displaying signs of recurrent exertional rhabdomyolysis (RER) were collected via a cross-sectional face-to-face survey of 100 registered Thoroughbred and Standardbred trainers in New Zealand (n=1,771 horses). In addition to quantitative data on feeding practices, qualitative data on trainers' perceptions and motivations for the different feeding and management practices were also collected. Few trainers recognised that starch in the diet was associated with increased clinical signs of RER (26% of Standardbred and 13% of Thoroughbred trainers). One third of trainers (39% of SB and 34% of TB) stated that oats contributed to RER. Most trainers with RER horses (96% TB and 84% SB) provided a day off (day with no training) to these horses. Half of the trainers with RER horses (SB and TB) decreased concentrate feeds on days off for all horses and few trainers (12.5% SB and 8% TB) only decreased concentrate on days off if the horse displayed signs of RER. Most trainers had sought advice about RER management from a veterinarian or feed representative (63% SB and 78% TB). However, despite this, many of the responses indicated a lack of clarity on the feed and management factors that contribute to the risk of clinical signs of RER.

Keywords: horse; feeding; Thoroughbred; Standardbred; recurrent exertional rhabdomyolysis

Introduction

The Thoroughbred and Standardbred racing industries have long-standing reputations for feeding and management strategies that are based on traditional methods. This is further enforced by strong family ties and generational influences. While younger generations are becoming successful trainers, management strategies are strongly influenced by their predecessors and there is often little room for evolving feeding and management techniques that are in line with the latest research on equine health and performance.

Exertional rhabdomyolysis (ER) is the overarching term for the various disorders causing muscle pain and stiffness that are triggered by exercise (Harris & Rivero 2017) and is the most common equine myopathy (MacLeay et al. 1999b) that affects most athletic breeds (Harris & Rivero 2017). Chronic and recurrent exertional rhabdomyolysis (RER) represent a syndrome of repeated exercise-associated muscle damage (McKenzie & Firshman 2009) accompanied by increased muscle enzyme activity, often with mild exertion at lower training intensity levels below the anaerobic threshold (Valberg 2005). While each type of exertional rhabdomyolysis has been known to occur in a variety of different breeds (Valberg 2010; Harris & Rivero 2017), there is potential economic loss to the racing industries with a high prevalence of RER (5-10%) reported in Thoroughbreds (MacLeay et al. 1999a,b).

The late nineties saw a surge in research focussing on enhancing performance, improving equine health, and reducing the risk of performance associated conditions such as RER. Research in these areas has continued in recent years, and knowledge around techniques to improve RER is constantly evolving. Previous associations with muscle calcium regulation abnormalities in the occurrence of RER (Lentz et al. 1999) have since been questioned (Piercy & Rivero 2014; Mickelson & Valberg 2015; Harris & Rivero 2017) and more recent work has shown the condition has a strong genetic component (Valberg 2006; Mickelson & Valberg 2015; Harris & Rivero 2017).

This research indicates that causes of RER are multi-factorial and management requires attention to both diet and exercise components. Changes in exercise management are thought to improve symptoms of the condition by moderating behaviour and/or excitability (Harris & Rivero 2017). Regular daily exercise is important in managing the condition and it is recommended that days off are minimised (Valberg 2010). Dietary management has been shown to mitigate symptoms, as diets with too-little fibre combined with too-much non-structural carbohydrates contribute to RER. Daily energy-source manipulation has been successful, with the current dietary recommendations being to limit starch sources to less than 20% of daily energy and include at least 20% of energy requirements as fat for horses in intense work (McKenzie & Firshman 2009; Valberg 2010; Harris & Rivero 2017).

Although there is research-based consensus on the treatment of RER, the traditional nature of the Thoroughbred and Standardbred racing industries means that management and feeding practices are not synchronised with research. Recent research has shown that current New Zealand feeding practices for RER horses are not in alignment with current recommendations. The average concentrate-to-roughage ratios in Thoroughbreds and Standardbreds were found to be 5.6±0.15:4.8±0.2 and 4.12±0.16:3.46±0.2 respectively (Wood et al. 2019). The average starch levels as a percentage of total DE offered to horses displaying signs of RER in New Zealand was 33.4±1.1%. Only 7% (11/149) of horses displaying signs of RER were provided with dietary starch levels at the current best-management practice level of < 20% of total DE (Wood et al. 2019). Despite the availability of information around correct feeding practices for RER horses, these practices are not currently being applied in the Thoroughbred and Standardbred industries.

Despite an estimated RER prevalence of 8.4% (Wood et al. 2019), and ongoing research regarding risk factors and appropriate management of horses with RER, industry knowledge and the application of correct feeding and management factors in New Zealand appears limited. Information about current best practice for management of RER affected horses is readily available through qualified veterinarians and nutritionists. However, the data on current feeding practices displays a disconnect between this information and how it is disseminated to trainers (Wood et al. 2019). To remedy this situation, there is a need to examine why there is a gap between established veterinary guidelines and management practices. Further, improving management requires identifying whether the gap arises from the ways the information is delivered to trainers, or if traditional practices limit implementation of the best practice. To understand the driving factors behind feeding and management factors of horses with RER in New Zealand, this study reports on a cross-sectional survey of New Zealand Thoroughbred and Standardbred trainers and examines the rationale behind their selective feeding practices.

Materials and methods

The sample frame consisted of a convenience sample of registered Thoroughbred and Standardbred racehorse trainers with at least one horse currently in full race work. The trainers were selected from the major training tracks throughout the North and the South Islands. Trainers were initially selected through direct contact. Further trainers were then recruited at the same training venue, or area, using a snowball sampling technique beginning with a referral from the initial trainer contacted. This process was repeated until 100 trainers were recruited.

The survey was developed using a number of iterations and tested using racing industry personnel (none of which were included in the subsequent survey). The survey was then pilot tested on one trainer with < 10 horses and one trainer with > 20 horses in-work.

Prior to recruitment, the trainers were provided with a one-page summary and overview of the study. The symptoms of the condition (RER) were described in detail by the interviewer to each trainer. If they were not aware of "tying up" and how to identify the symptoms, they were excluded from the study (n=0 trainers). The survey consisted of a section of closed questions followed by a section of open questions. Initially trainers were asked for demographic data on the number of horses in work and the proportion of horses trained that were showing symptoms of RER, before asking for details of diets for horses that were displaying symptoms of RER and horses that were not. This first section contained quantitative questions relating to the current diets and management factors of horses that were and weren't displaying symptoms of RER. The trainers provided a description of the supplementary feed offered to the horses, including brand and/or type of feed offered. All hay, fibre products and concentrate feeds offered in a daily diet for all horses were weighed and expressed as kilograms dry matter offered (Verhaar et al. 2014). Further questions were also asked relating to management, including size of the turnout area each horse had access to.

The second section of the survey consisted of two qualitative questions relating to why the trainer adopted the current feeding practices for the horses with RER, what they believed were the risk factors of the condition, and what measures they thought they should be taking to manage the condition nutritionally. Such questions included "What are the reasons behind your feeding and management practices for your horses with tying up symptoms?" and "How do you believe horses showing symptoms of tying up should be fed and managed?" These questions would often prompt the trainer to continue discussing feeding practices, and lead into other topics of nutrition. As the trainer responded to these open-ended questions, the interviewer wrote notes describing the reasons given for current feeding and management practices. These responses were analysed thematically and coded to understand individual trainer knowledge and management reasoning further. Key words and phrases were used to code answers immediately following the completion of each survey. Where appropriate, differences in responses were examined using chi squared test and differences in means were tested using an ANOVA within Stata 12 (StataCorp LP, College Station, TX, USA).

Results

Data were collected via a cross-sectional face-to-face survey of 100 registered Thoroughbred and Standardbred trainers in New Zealand (n=1,771 horses; 995 Thoroughbreds and 776 Standardbreds). Detailed demographics of the respondents were published previously (Wood et al. 2019).

A consistent theme throughout both the answers to the closed and open-ended questions was a lack of clarity in identifying the major risk factors for clinical signs of RER. In some circumstances there was clear evidence of contradiction in these answers. For example, some trainers acknowledged the role of starch or grain levels as contributing to the risk of RER, whilst also reporting that they added grains to a commercial (low-starch) RER-specific pre-mixed ration.

There was widespread acknowledgement of the role

of diet in RER, with over half of the trainers (56%) making specific reference to starch and/or oats as contributing factors to the clinical symptoms of RER. However, when the analysis focused on the key nutritional component that elevates risk (the starch component of the ration offered), few trainers (19%) mentioned specifically that more starch in the diet was associated with greater risk of clinical signs of the condition. Of these trainers 32% (n=6) also mentioned that oats were associated with a greater risk of clinical signs of the condition. There was a trend for Standardbred trainers to be more likely to mention starch as a risk factor compared to Thoroughbred trainers (26% vs. 13%, p=0.07). However, this was found to be a relatively small proportion of the trainers surveyed.

Despite the moderate prevalence of RER in New Zealand racing stables, and the survey targeting trainers that were aware of the condition, the presence of RER horses in the stable did not alter the odds that the trainer would mention starch, or the relative levels of starch in the diet, and its relationship with clinical signs of RER.

Over one-third of all trainers (37%) specifically mentioned that oats were associated with increased risk of clinical signs of RER, with no difference in responses between Standardbred and Thoroughbred trainers (39% vs. 34%). Only six of these trainers also mentioned starch as a contributing factor towards symptoms of the condition.

Few of the trainers (n= 11) specifically mentioned both starch and oats as being contributing factors to the clinical symptoms of RER.

RER trainers

Most trainers reported they had horses in their stables displaying signs of RER (62/100). In this subset of trainers, 48% (30/62) made specific reference to starch and/or oats as contributing factors to the clinical symptoms of the condition. Over a third of trainers with RER horses specifically mentioned that oats were associated with increased risk of clinical signs of RER (37%; 23/62) but few (13%, n=3) also mentioned that starch was associated with increased risk of clinical signs of the condition. Many (66%) of the trainers of RER horses that identified both starch and oats as contributing to the symptoms of the condition decreased the quantity of concentrate fed to the RER horses on their day off work. One trainer specifically mentioned both oats and starch as increasing the risk of the condition but did not decrease the amount of concentrate feed provided to RER horses on days off. There was no association between mentioning starch or oats and providing a day off for the horses in training. This lack of association indicated that trainers with a more robust nutritional understanding did not complement this with knowledge of recent research-based training strategies for horses at risk of RER.

Most trainers with RER horses provided a day off (no training) to these horses (96% TB and 84% SB). None of the Standardbred trainers kept their RER horses in stables at all times and most (67%) gave them daily turnout in paddocks that were ≥ 0.1 ha. Fewer Thoroughbred trainers provided daily turnout in paddocks ≥ 0.1 ha (49%), and 11% kept their horses with RER symptoms in stables at all times. Average turn-out time given to RER horses was longer than that for non-RER horses for both breeds, with Thoroughbred trainers allowing an average of 13.1 hours per day and Standardbred trainers allowing 15.7 hours per day.

Most trainers had a standardised turnout time for all horses with only 23% providing their horses showing symptoms of RER more time in the paddock than their non-RER horses. Standardbred horses were provided more turnout time than were Thoroughbreds and, if additional turnout was provided for RER horses, they had an additional three hours turnout per day. Most trainers (80%) perceived that there was no benefit of swimming to reduce clinical signs of RER. There was a significant breed bias in this perception, with fewer Standardbred trainers with RER horses reporting any perception of benefit than did Thoroughbred trainers (6% vs. 24% , P<0.05).

Seeking advice about RER management was high, with 63% and 78% of Standardbred and Thoroughbred trainers respectively having sought advice on RER from a veterinarian, feed representative or both. Whether trainers had sought advice regarding management of RER or not did not alter the odds of that trainer mentioning that either oats or starch were contributing factors to the clinical signs of RER.

Discussion

The sample of trainers in this study is believed to be representative of the Thoroughbred and Standardbred racehorse trainer population in New Zealand, as sampling was distributed throughout New Zealand and the distribution of training-establishment size reflected published data on both the Thoroughbred and Standardbred racing industries (Legg et al. 2020; Bolwell et al. 2017). The even split of Thoroughbred (54) and Standardbred (47) trainers, and the even split of small (42) and large (58) trainers ensured a fair representation of training and management practices in both industries (Wood et al. 2019).

Despite various grains including barley, maize and oats provided in the diets of racehorses in New Zealand (Wood et al. 2019), approximately one third of trainers specifically mentioned oats as a contributing factor to the RER condition. However, few of these trainers mentioned excess dietary starch as a contributing factor. The assumption was that these trainers were not making the association that the primary energy source in oats is starch, and thus, by increasing the quantity of oats, they are increasing the percentage of DE that was derived from starch. This assumption is supported by the observation that few trainers specifically mentioned that increased dietary starch was associated with increased risk of clinical signs of RER, and six of these trainers were feeding oats to horses that were displaying clinical signs of RER. Despite maize being higher in starch than are oats, none of the trainers mentioned maize as a contributing factor and oats were the only grain specifically mentioned.

This disassociation between grains and starch as the energy could be occurring through a lack of basic nutritional knowledge (understanding that oats contain starch), or through a disconnect between what the trainers know and what they are applying in everyday feeding practices. There may still exist a common misconception that racehorses can only obtain the DE required by the feeding of cereal grain-based concentrates. Recent work from Sweden has demonstrated that Standardbreds, in race training, can obtain sufficient DE from a predominantly forage / fibre-based diet and that this diet was not associated with any decrease in race performance (Ringmark et al. 2017). This finding is interesting ,as many of the Standardbred trainers that fed a low-starch diet designed for horses with clinical signs of RER added oats or barley to the diet. These cereals were added due to the belief this was necessary to provide sufficient DE to meet the demands of race training and racing. Such a practice shows a disconnect with current best practice and, that there may be significant latency in the dissemination of recent research findings within this group, despite the fact that the majority of trainers had sought advice from either a veterinarian or nutritionist. Translating research findings into daily practice can be problematic across disciplines and industries. Further research to examine in more detail the daily decision-making of trainers will enable greater understanding of the role of tradition and entrenched practice in preventing the uptake of evidence-based advice.

Management of RER and minimising clinical signs requires a multifactorial management and feeding approach. Energy requirements must be balanced with the workload and while days off (days when not worked) are not advised, if given there has to be a reduction in the DE supplied, but also the opportunity for free movement on those days off. Despite that fact that many trainers added a cereal grain to the pre-mixed low-starch RER diets, most trainers with RER horses indicated but they reduced the total volume of concentrates offered to RER horses on days off. Unfortunately, the methodology by which the data were collected did not permit us to identify if this reduction in concentrates offered included both the cereal and the specialist low-starch pre-mix, or just the cereal component of the diet. This type of data should be collected prospectively in association with management practices and documentation of the clinical signs of RER to provide greater clarity on the interaction of feed, management and exercise on RER under typical New Zealand conditions.

An interesting trend within the data was a reduction in the number of trainers keeping horses in stables $\geq$ 12 hours per day compared to an earlier cross-sectional survey (67% vs. 97% Williamson et al. 2007), particularly in Standardbred trainers who provided more turnout in general than Thoroughbred trainers. We were unable to identify the primary reason for this change in management practice. However, we hypothesised that this increased opportunity for exercise may be associated with an increased awareness by trainers of the benefits of free exercise. Reduced time in stables has been demonstrated to reduce the prevalence of stereotypical behaviours (Waters et al. 2010) which in some management systems, can have a high prevalence. While not detrimental to race training or success, stereotypical behaviours can be an indicator that horses are under some degree of stress and not in a positive affective state, and thus, often perceived negatively by industry participants. The limited differentiation of time outside between RER and non-RER horses may simply be a reflection of the difficulty in providing highly individualised management programmes for different horses, given the number of horses and number of different staff involved in their care and management. Greater consistency in management may be made possible by having a standardised time in turn out. Horses are social animals and become stressed when unable to see or touch co-specifics. Given that one of the major precursors for the expression of RER appears to be stress, it may be more efficient to have all horses with the same turnout time and reduce the chance of a horse becoming stressed if in the turnout yards for a longer period of time, but without co-specifics.

Maintenance of exercise load is important in reducing the clinical signs of RER, yet most trainers did not perceive any benefit from using swimming as an alternative exercise in the management of RER horses. This is in line with the cautious observation of Valberg et al. (2006) that swimming should be evaluated and utilised on an individual basis with RER horses, as it can exacerbate the condition. This limited perception of benefit from swimming may also be related to the limited routine use of swimming and access to swimming facilities (Steele et al. 2019).

Despite the availability of current research and professionals willing to assist trainers, there appears to be a struggle to transfer knowledge in the racing industry. The strong traditional ties mean trainers may choose to respect the knowledge of fellow successful trainers or previous trainers in their family rather than that of industry professionals. A probable mechanism for this would be through consistent exposure to other trainers at the track each morning. Seeing fellow trainers each morning but veterinarians or feed professionals only every week, or month, could have an impact on knowledge transfer and retention of information. Veterinarians are usually only utilised in a reactive manner, when an injury or illness has occurred, and are, therefore, providing advice on a more reactive basis rather than in a role providing establishment of best management practices (Meredith et al. 2011). Advice from feed specialists may not be fully utilised due to the trainers questioning possible motives for increased sales. There is also a possibility that failure of trainers to understand and retain correct information from veterinarians and feed specialists is occurring due to poor transfer of information from the industry specialists, and information not explained in a way that trainers can understand.

Resistance to change and the slow uptake of recent research is not unique to the racing industry. Poor information transfer and repeated exposure to fellow trainers are contributing factors, and there are indications of tradition limiting implementation of best practice. However, there is a real need to generate a culture of a proactive management approach to the equine athlete (Meredith et al. 2011). The use of specialist lower-starch feeds is encouraging, but the addition of cereals indicates some limitations in the knowledge of equine nutrition, requiring a greater focus from industry consultants on, not just providing an option to minimise risk (such as low-starch feeds), but on education of the underlying nutrition principles and the benefits they have in managing this condition.

Acknowledgements

With thanks to NRM and McMillan Equine, for providing financial assistance and time-management support for the duration of the data collection and writing of the paper.

References

Bolwell CF, Rogers CW, Gee EK, Rosanowski SM 2017. Commercial equine production in New Zealand 3; The racing and sport industries. Animal Production Science: http://dx.doi.org/10.1071/AN16753.

Harris PA, Rivero JLL 2017. Nutritional considerations for equine rhabdomyolysis syndrome. Equine Veterinary Education 29(8): 459-465.

Legg K, Gee E, Bolwell C, Bridges J, Rogers CW 2020. A cross-sectional survey of the training and management of a cohort of 2-year-old standardbred racehorses in New Zealand. Journal of Equine Veterinary Science 87: 1029-36

Lentz LR, Valberg SJ, Herold LV, Onan GW, Mickelson JR, Gallant EM 2002. Myoplasmic calcium regulation in myotubes from horses with recurrent exertional rhabdomyolysis. American Journal of Veterinary Research 63: 1724-31.

McKenzie EC, Firshman AM 2009. Optimal diet of horses with chronic exertional myopathies. Veterinary Clinics of North America: Equine Practice 25(1): 121-135.

MacLeay JM, Sorum SA, Valberg SJ, Marsh WE, Sorum MD 1999a. Epidemiologic analysis of factors influencing exertional rhabdomyolysis in thoroughbreds. American Journal of Veterinary Research 60(12): 1562-1566.

MacLeay JM, Valberg SJ, Pagan JD, De La Corte, F, Roberts, J, Billstrom J, Miginnity J, Kaese H 1999b. Effect of diet on thoroughbred horses with recurrent exertional rhabdomyolysis performing a standardised exercise test. Equine Veterinary Journal. Supplement 30: 458-462.

Meredith K, Bolwell CF, Rogers CW, Gee EK 2011. The use of allied health therapies on competition horses in the North Island of New Zealand. New Zealand Veterinary Journal 59: 123-127.

Mickelson JR, Valberg SJ 2015. The genetics of skeletal muscle disorders in horses. Annual Review of Animal Biosciences 3: 197-217.

Piercy RJ, Rivero J 2014. Muscle disorders of equine athletes. In: Equine Sports Medicine and Surgery: Basic and Clinical Sciences of the Equine Athlete. 2nd ed. London: W.B. Saunders 109.

Ringmark, S, Roepstorff L, Hedenström U, Lindholm A, Jansson A 2017. Reduced training distance and a forage-only diet did not limit race participation in young standardbred horses. Comparative Exercise Physiology 13: 265-272.

Steele CM, Bond BM, Morrice-West AV 2019. Survey of trainers on the use of swimming exercise for standardbred racehorses in Australia. Australian Veterinary Journal 97(3): 61-67.

Valberg S 2006. Exertional rhabdomyolysis. American Association of Equine Practitioners Proceedings 52: 365-372.

Valberg SJ 2010. The management of tying up in sport horses: challenges and successes. Proceedings of the 2010 Kentucky Equine Research Nutrition Conference, Lexington, Kentucky, United States of America 16-17 April 2010. pp. 82-93.

Verhaar N, Rogers CW, Gee EK, Bolwell CF, Rosanowski SM 2014. The feeding practices and estimated workload in a cohort of New Zealand competition horses. Journal of Equine Veterinary Science 34 (11-12): 1257-1262.

Waters AJ, Nicol NP, French P 2010. Factors influencing the development of stereotypic and redirected behaviours in young horses: findings of a four year prospective epidemiological study. Equine Veterinary Journal 34(6): 572-579.

Williamson A, Rogers CW, Firth EC 2007. A survey of feeding management and faecal pH of Thoroughbred racehorses in the North Island of New Zealand. New Zealand Veterinary Journal 55(6): 337-34.

Wood LJ, Lancaster BE, Rogers CW 2019. The feeding and management of thoroughbred and standardbred racehorses displaying clinical signs of recurrent exertional rhabdomyolysis. New Zealand Journal of Animal Science and Production 79: 26-31.

Factors affecting early concentrate uptake by calves

PD Muir, BC Thomson* and NB Smith

On-Farm Research, PO Box 1142, Hastings

**Corresponding author:* Email: bev@on-farm.co.nz

Abstract

Early solid food intake is key to a successful early rumen development system. In NZ, specialist bull-calf rearers tend to feed four-day-old calves restricted milk, *ad lib* pellets and wean early (5 to 6 weeks). A range of experiments examined the effect of protein %, feed form and the effect of changing protein source in older calves. There was no difference between 16% and 20% protein pellets in the first three weeks but between weeks three and six, feed intakes and liveweight gains were higher on 20% protein pellets ($P<0.05$). Weaning live weights were higher on a customised pellet (51.5% maize, 20.0% peas, 20.0% soy bean extract 48, 5% molasses, 1.5% limestone, 1.0% soybean oil, 0.8% salt, calf vitamin mineral premix (0.01%), Bovatec (0.006%) and Rumasweet palatant (0.00002%)) than on a commercial pellet (68.9 vs 64.8 kg, $P<0.05$). Feeding the customised formulation either in roller-milled, hammer-milled or pelleted form did not affect feed intake or liveweight gain. In weaned calves well-adjusted to consuming concentrates, substituting a commercial meal with palm kernel significantly reduced feed intake when fed at 60% of the ration whilst copra meal substitution significantly reduced intake at 40% in calves accustomed to eating pellets. Pellet composition had a greater impact on feed intakes and growth rate than did the form in which the feed was offered.

Keywords: calf; copra meal; palm kernel; protein content; artificially reared

Introduction

Because of the low margins associated with the rearing of dairy bull calves in New Zealand, low-cost, reduced milk systems along with concentrate feeding and early weaning have become part of specialist bull calf rearing systems. Early intake of calf pellets is critical to the early weaning process involved in these systems due to the nutrient density of these products and the acceleration of rumen development through the intake of solid feeds (Henrichs 2005). Early rumen development enables early weaning onto pasture and since the cost per unit of energy is higher for milk ingredients than pasture, the sooner calves can start consuming pasture and be weaned off milk, the lower the cost of rearing. Calves in early rumen-development systems tend to be purchased at around four-days of age and sold at 100 kg at 12 weeks of age (end of October) and cost reductions need to be balanced with effects on calf growth rate. Calves on a once-a-day early rumen-development system are weaned when intake of solid feed reaches 1 kg/day, usually around six weeks of age (Muir et al. 2002). To achieve these solid feed intakes in young naïve calves, meals need to be highly palatable (Miller-Cushon et al. 2014).

Traditionally, calves raised using New Zealand early rumen-development systems are fed 20% protein calf pellets before weaning, then fed a lower-cost 16% protein pellet after weaning. Anecdotally, some calf rearers are feeding calf meals with 16% crude protein throughout the rearing phase. Whilst dairy farmers rear their heifer replacements on whole milk, most New Zealand bull-calf rearers feed casein-based milk replacer (Thomson et al. 2018). A laboratory analysis of six milk different calf milk replacers brands showed average crude protein contents of 26.4% (Muir, unpublished data). Since milk replacers typically make up a 50% of the diet (on a DM basis) on an early rumen-development system, it is possible that feeding a lower protein content pellet could still provide an average protein content in the diet of 21%. This is still in excess of the 18% dietary protein in pellets suggested by Khan et al. (2016).

Relatively high and consistent intakes of calf pellets were recorded by the authors in previous experiments between 1996 and 2005 but intakes declined by around 50% in a 2007 experiment (Figure 1). Potential reasons for the decline in intakes include change in type of ingredients used, changes in protein and energy content or old, stale and less palatable feed. Unfortunately, labelling on bags of calf pellets is poor, with only minimum specifications for protein content and typically stating that the product could be made from some or all of a long list of ingredients pre-printed on the bags. The lack of detailed information on New Zealand calf pellets makes it difficult for rearers to make an informed purchase decision. Moreover, least-cost formulations and limitations on supplies of ingredients mean that composition of calf meals can vary between batches or across the season as the availability and price of some components change.

Whilst many calf rearers purchase commercial pellets, others mix their own feed and offer it as a loose meal. The pressing of loose ingredients into a pellet is an additional cost (local mills charge $60/tonne) and this increases the overall cost of rearing. There are, however, few data on whether the form (roller-milled, hammer-milled, pelleted) in which feed is presented to calves impacts on voluntary feed intakes and growth rate of calves.

Palm kernel and copra meal have both been utilized as low-cost protein sources in New Zealand and have

Figure 1. Average feed intakes in calves fed commercial pellets from seven trials between 1996 and 2005 compared with feed intakes from a 2007 trial. Dotted lines indicate results from Experiment 2 of the pilot trial comparing commercial pellets with a customised ration.

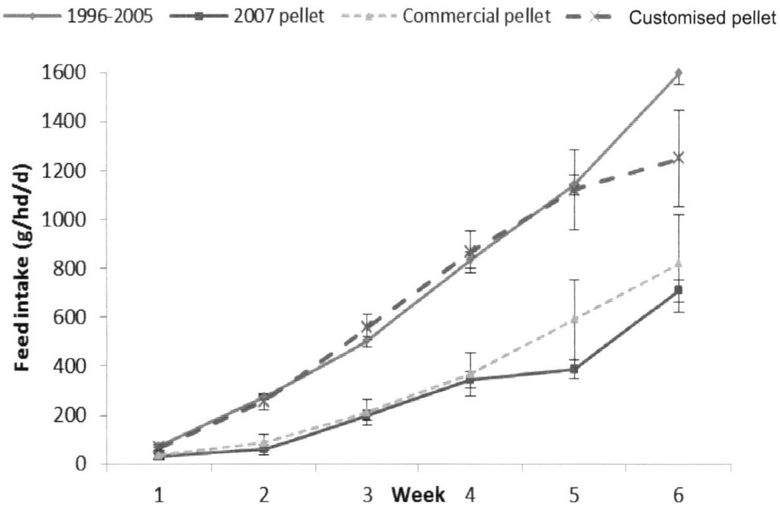

been imported in large quantities for sale especially to the dairy industry. It is possible that these products have been incorporated into calf feeds and may have a role in reduced palatability and decreased feed intakes.

This work reports on a series of experiments which examined the effect of feed type on calf feed intakes and growth rates by comparing:

(1) The growth rate of calves fed 20% or 16% protein pellets pre-weaning
(2) The feeding of a customised pellet with known high-quality ingredients pre-weaning against a commercial pellet which had previously been associated with low feed intakes
(3) The form in which solid feed (roller-milled, hammer-milled, pelleted) is offered to young calves on liveweight gain pre-weaning
(4) The intake of diets containing copra meal or palm kernel on feed intake in weaned calves.

Materials and methods

Calves for Experiment 1-2 were purchased as four-day-old calves from the dairy industry and transported to the Hawkes Bay. They were tagged and weighed on arrival and allocated to treatments. Treatments were balanced by live weight and arrival date. Calves were fed 1 litre of calf milk replacer (CMR 200g/l) twice a day for the first four days and then 2.5 l of CMR (200g/l) in compartmental feeders. Calves were supervised at each feeding to ensure each calf drank its allowance. Clean water was available *ad libitum* in each pen. Calves were weighed prior to weaning. The weaning criterion was that an individual calf had put on at least 20 kg since arrival.

Experiment 1. Feed intake in young calves of pellets containing 20% and 16% crude protein

In this experiment, two groups of 120 Friesian bull calves purchased at four days of age from commercial dairy farms and were offered commercial pelleted rations containing either 20% or 16% protein (Harvey Farms, Wanganui). Pellets were analysed by Hill Laboratories (Hamilton) and found to contain 20.1% and 16.2% crude protein for the 20% and 16% pellets respectively. On arrival, calves were tagged and weighed. Calves were penned in groups of eight, with groups balanced for arrival weight and fed 500 g of a commercial milk replacer (Bounce, Fonterra, Auckland) in 2.5 litres water per head per day. Calves were fed once a day using compartmental feeders and monitored during feeding to ensure each calf drank its full allowance. Calves were checked for scouring and any other health issues at each feed. Pellets were fed *ad libitum* in a group feeder from Day 1. Fresh pellets were added daily and refusals measured weekly to determine pellet intake for each pen. Calves were weighed on arrival (0 weeks) and again at three and six weeks after arrival. Calves that were not weaned at six weeks were re-weighed at eight weeks and all but three were weaned. Weaning criteria were that calves weighed more than 60 kg and had gained at least 20 kg since arrival. Milk feeding was stopped abruptly once individual calves met the weaning criteria. After milk feeding stopped, calves were kept indoors for three days and fed *ad libitum* on the same pellets they had been fed prior to weaning.

Experiment 2. Evaluation of a commercial calf pellet

A customized pelleted calf ration was developed using 51.5% maize, 20.0% peas, 20.0% soy bean extract 48, 5% molasses, 1.5% limestone, 1.0% soybean oil, 0.8% salt plus small amounts of calf vitamin mineral premix (0.01%), Bovatec (0.006%) and palatability enhancer (Rumasweet palatant 0.00002%). This ration was then compared in an on-farm trial against a commercial pelleted ration marketed as containing 20% crude protein and which had been associated with low feed intakes and poor calf growth rates the previous year. Pellets were analysed and found to have 20.6% and 20.4% crude protein (Hill Laboratories, Hamilton), for the formulated and commercial rations respectively. Twenty, four-day old Friesian bull calves were trucked from the Waikato region and tagged and weighed on arrival. Calves were allocated to four pens of five calves and balanced for live weight. Two pens of calves were each fed either the commercial ration or the customised ration. Calves were fed once daily with 500 g of a commercial milk replacer (Ngahiwi Farms, Auckland) in 2.5 litres water per head. Calves were fed using compartmental feeders and monitored during feeding to ensure each calf drank its full allowance. Calves were checked for scouring and any other health issues at each feeding. Pellets were fed *ad libitum* in a single covered feeder per pen from Day 1. Fresh pellets were added daily with feed refusals recorded weekly and intakes calculated. Fresh water was freely available. Calves were weighed on arrival (0 weeks) and at three weeks and six weeks of age. At six weeks, calves which had put on 20 kg live weight were weaned. The remainder remained on milk until they reached the weaning criteria but experimental data were only analysed up to weighing at six weeks of age.

Experiment 3. Effect of meal presentation on feed intake

In this study, 194 four-day-old Friesian heifer and bull calves were sourced from commercial dairy farms, tagged, weighed on arrival and allocated to 15 pens of 12-13 calves. Calves arrived in three batches each a week apart. On arrival, calves were weighed and tagged. Within each batch, pens were randomly allocated to one of three treatment groups with five pens per treatment in total. Treatment groups were balanced for live weight and batch. The same customised feed formulation from Experiment 2 was offered either in pelleted, hammer-milled or roller-milled form. Calves were each fed 3.5 litres fresh transition milk daily in compartment feeders and the concentrate feed was offered *ad libitum* to each pen in a covered feeder from Day 1. Milk feeding was supervised to ensure each calf drank its full milk allowance. Calves were checked for scouring and any other health issues at each feed. Fresh feed was added daily and refusals measured weekly and feed intakes calculated. Fresh water was always available. Calves were weighed on arrival (week 0) and again at six weeks of age and calves that had increased in weight by 20 kg were weaned. After weaning off milk, all calves were run together and offered the pelleted ration.

Experiment 4. Effect of increasing proportion of palm kernel and copra meal on post-weaning feed intakes of calves

This trial used seventy-two weaned Friesian bull calves aged eight weeks and which had been reared on a once-a-day milk feeding system as described in Experiment 1. Calves had been fed on 20% protein pellets (Topcalf, Harvey Farms, Wanganui) and had been kept indoors after weaning. Calves were randomized into four treatment groups and balanced for live weight. Copra meal was substituted into the ration at 0, 20, 40 and 60% of the total feed on offer and feed intake measured every two days over a nine-day period. Calves were then re-randomized into four groups and placed on 20% protein pellets for two days. Palm kernel meal was substituted into the ration at 0, 20, 40 and 60% of the total feed on offer for nine days. Daily feed intake was measured every two days. Straw and fresh water were freely available through both treatment periods, but the amounts were not measured.

Statistical analysis

Experiment 1was analysed using a Generalised Linear Model in Minitab with two treatment levels – 16% and 20% protein pellets. Pen was used as the experimental unit for feed intakes. Experiment 2 was analysed using a Generalised Linear Model in Minitab with two treatment levels – customised formulated versus a commercial 20% protein pellet. Pen was used as the experimental unit for feed intakes and initial live weight fitted as a covariate for the liveweight data. Experiment 3 was analysed using a Generalised Linear Model in Minitab with three treatment levels – pelleted, hammer-milled and roller-milled plus breed and sex of calf. Arrival live weight and batch were fitted as covariates for live weight. Batch was fitted as a covariate for live weight gain and feed intake. Pen was used as the experimental unit for feed intakes. Experiment 4 was analysed using a Generalised Linear Model in Minitab with four treatment levels (0, 20, 40, 60%) and pen used as the experimental unit. The data were analysed both by individual day and as the total amount eaten over the period. Copra meal and palm kernel data were analysed as separate experiments.

This work was approved by the Agresearch Grasslands Animal Ethics Committee (AE 10534,10650 and 11534).

Results

Experiment 1

Calves fed the 20% pellets ate more from weeks three to six and grew faster before weaning than did the calves fed on the 16% protein pellets (Table 1) resulting in more calves weaned at six weeks in the 20% protein pellet treatment (78.8%) than in the 16% protein pellet treatment (52.6%). Calves fed 20% protein pellets ate an average of 184 g/d over the first three weeks and 918 g/d from three to six weeks. Calves fed the 16% protein pellets consumed an average of 164 g/d from zero to three weeks and 738 g/d over the second three weeks.

Experiment 2: Comparison of a customised formulated pellet with a commercially available pellet.

Calves fed the formulated pellets ate 29.3 kg over the six weeks of the experiment, whereas the calves fed the commercial pellet ate 14.8 kg over the same period (Table 2). These means were not significantly different (SEM 1.19 kg P=0.11). Feed intake of the formulated ration was 1.1 kg/head/day at the end of week 5 while on the commercial pellet the intake was only 0.59 kg/day/day (Table 2).

When initial weight was fitted as a covariate, the calves on the formulated pellets were heavier than the calves on the commercial pellets (68.9 vs 64.8 kg, P<0.03).

Experiment 3: Effect of diet form on liveweight gain and feed intake

The form in which the diet was offered to the calves

Table 1 Live weight, weaning percentage and solid food intake of Friesian bull calves fed commercial pellets containing either 20% or 16% protein from four days of age to weaning at six weeks of age.

	20% Protein		16% Protein		
	Mean	SEM	Mean	SEM	P
Number of animals	60		60		
Start weight (kg)	43.1	0.39	43.6	0.41	0.36
3 week weight (kg)	50.6	0.32	49.3	0.32	0.07
6 week weaning weight (kg)	67.4	0.51	63.2	0.51	0.001
Calves not weaned at 6 weeks (%)	21.2		47.4		
Intake (kg/hd/d)					
Week 1	0.066	0.005	0.064	0.005	0.77
Week 2	0.167	0.010	0.160	0.010	0.66
Week 3	0.320	0.020	0.268	0.020	0.07
Week 4	0.680	0.032	0.519	0.032	0.001
Week 5	0.963	0.040	0.779	0.040	0.003
Week 6	1.110	0.050	0.918	0.050	0.01
Total (kg/hd)	23.1	0.89	19.0	0.89	0.003

Table 2 Feed intake of Friesian bull calves fed a customised formulated pellet or a commercial 20% protein calf pellet from four days of age to weaning at six weeks of age.

Week	Formulated		Commercial		P
	Mean	SEM	Mean	SEM	
1	0.069	0.011	0.035	0.011	0.16
2	0.255	0.033	0.0894	0.033	0.08
3	0.557	0.052	0.212	0.052	0.04
4	0.867	0.087	0.367	0.087	0.06
5	1.12	0.165	0.59	0.165	0.15
6	1.32	0.198	0.82	0.198	0.2
Total (kg/calf)	29.3	3.63	14.8	3.63	0.11
Number of animals	10		10		

had no significant effect on feed intake, pre-weaning growth rate (0.55, 0.56 and 0.54 kg/head/day for pelleted, hammer-milled and roller-milled diets respectively P > 0.40) or post-weaning growth rate (0.69, 0.66 and 071 kg/head/day for pelleted, hammer-milled and roller-milled diets respectively P > 0.30). Intakes between pens and batches of calves were highly variable (Table 3).

Experiment 4: Effect of copra meal and palm kernel on the palatability of post-weaning calf diets

From eight weeks of age, intakes rose from 2.72 kg/day to 3.21 kg/day in the group fed entirely on calf pellets (Table 4). Replacing 20% of the calf pellet ration with copra had no effect on calf intake, whereas replacing 40% and 60% of the pellet ration with copra meal decreased calf intake. Palm kernel tended to reduce feed intake, but this was only significant at the 60% substitution level (Table 4).

Discussion

In New Zealand, many specialist bull-calf rearers use a restricted milk system, *ad libitum* pellets and then weaning starting at five weeks of age. Current practice under these restricted milk feeding systems is to feed calves on 18-20% protein meal prior to weaning and then feed 16% protein pellets after weaning which typically occurs at between 5 and 7 weeks of age (Muir et al, 2002). Protein tends to be the most expensive component of the ration here, so rations with lower protein contents are usually cheaper. There is anecdotal evidence that a number of bull-calf rearers are feeding lower-protein calf pellets throughout the rearing phase to reduce costs. However, there are no comparable data on calf liveweight gain. Overseas recommendations suggest that calf diets should contain 18% crude protein on a DM basis (Hill et al. 2005, Khan et al. 2016). Kertz et al. (2017) suggested that 16% crude protein was adequate

Table 3 Daily calf meal intakes (kg/d) of Friesian bull and heifer calves when fed the same diet manufactured in three different forms from four days of age to weaning at six weeks of age.

	Form						
	Pellet		Hammer milled		Roller milled		
	Mean	SEM	Mean	SEM	Mean	SEM	P
Number of calves	65		63		65		
Arrival wt (kg)	36.7	1.87	36.4	1.95	34.8	1.90	0.10
Weaning wt (kg)	65.2	1.69	65.4	1.77	64.9	1.75	0.91
Age weaned (d)	42.4[ab]	0.97	41.4[a]	1.01	42.7[b]	1.00	0.02
Pre-weaning growth (kg/d)	0.55	0.040	0.56	0.041	0.54	0.041	0.42
Final wt (kg)	98.5	3.23	97.2	3.37	97.7	3.33	0.72
Age final (d)	89.1	1.74	89.2	1.82	88.2	1.80	0.54
Post-weaning growth (kg/d)	0.69	0.066	0.66	0.069	0.71	0.069	0.31
Average growth rate (kg/d)	0.63	0.037	0.619	0.039	0.63	0.038	0.75
Intake (kg/hd/d)							
Week 1	0.114	0.028	0.096	0.28	0.136	0.031	0.65
Week 2	0.172	0.028	0.156	0.028	0.190	0.037	0.75
Week 3	0.296	0.036	0.271	0.036	0.295	0.040	0.86
Week 4	0.475	0.037	0.502	0.037	0.530	0.416	0.65
Week 5	0.715	0.051	0.654	0.051	0.803	0.056	0.21
Week 6	0.818	0.073	0.963	0.073	1.052	0.082	0.15
Total (kg/hd)	18.1	1.45	18.5	1.44	21.0	1.84	0.42

Columns with in a row with different superscript (abc) are significantly different ($P < 0.05$)

Table 4 Intake of weaned Friesian bull calves fed concentrate with different proportions of Copra and Palm kernel from eight and ten weeks of age respectively.

	Number	Day 1	3	5	7	9	Total
Copra %							
0	18	2.72	2.59^{b}	2.83^{b}	3.01^{b}	3.21^{b}	16.9^{b}
20	18	2.72	2.42^{b}	2.81^{b}	3.00^{b}	3.11^{ab}	16.4^{b}
40	18	2.28	2.02^{a}	1.94^{a}	2.22^{a}	2.63^{a}	13.4^{a}
60	18	2.13	1.74^{a}	2.12^{a}	2.35^{a}	2.62^{a}	13.4^{a}
SEM		0.218	0.131	0.183	0.136	0.110	0.56
P		0.20	0.007	0.02	0.005	0.009	0.01
Palm kernel %							Total
0	18	3.31	3.73^{b}	4.06^{b}	3.99^{b}	3.91^{b}	19.0^{b}
20	18	3.19	3.58^{ba}	3.53^{ab}	3.57^{ab}	3.54^{ab}	17.4^{ab}
40	18	3.12	3.58^{ba}	3.49^{ab}	3.30^{a}	3.74^{ab}	17.2^{ab}
60	18	2.88	3.23^{a}	3.24^{a}	3.05^{a}	3.33^{a}	15.7^{a}
SEM		0.102	0.101	0.169	0.147	0.121	0.43
P		0.08	0.04	0.05	0.01	0.05	0.02

Different subscripts within the same column within the copra or palm kernel groups indicate significant difference at the 5% level

when whole-milk is being fed. In the current study, feeding of 16% protein feeds had no effect on growth rate over the first three weeks. However, between three and six weeks of age, calves fed the 20% protein pellets ate more and grew faster. The calf pellets in the present study were commercially formulated and information regarding the ingredients was unavailable, so we do not know whether the rations differed in palatability or other components. The source of protein in these diets was unknown and protein type is known to affect feed intake (Kertz et al. 2017) and calf performance (Khan et al. 2016). Thus, we do not know whether the effect observed here was due simply to better palatability leading to higher feed intakes or to the protein content *per se*. However, without further research, it does suggest that specialist bull-calf rearers using a restricted milk and early weaning system should feed 20% protein meals before weaning in order to reach the liveweight targets to enable bull calf sale at 100 kg at 12 weeks of age. Achieving target weights as early as possible is important in a New Zealand context as weaned calves become available in late spring and there is pressure for finishers to obtain calves before the onset of summer and deteriorating feed quality. Feeding a low-protein meal might achieve some modest savings but these are likely to be small when compared to the price drops that can occur within days when calf sales are delayed.

Low feed intakes of commercially purchased calf pellets led us to develop and test our own customized formulation in a small pilot trial. Differences in absolute average feed intake were relatively large (29.3 vs 14.8 kg/head) but were not significant due to the large variation between pens. Under a restricted-milk system, weaning is not recommended until the calves have put on 20 kg of live weight, at which point they are consuming around 1 kg of concentrate per head per day (Muir et al. 2002). In this study, the intake of the customised ration was over 1 kg/day at the end of week 5 meaning weaning off milk could have started. On the other hand, calves on the commercial meal were still only consuming 0.82 kg/head/day at the end of week 6, resulting in delayed weaning and leading to increased milk and labour costs. Although the comparison is across years, calves fed the customised ration had similar feed intakes to those in seven previous experiments (Figure 1) whilst the feed intakes on the commercial ration were dramatically lower and similar to the pellet intakes observed in the same commercial pellets in the previous year (2007). The reason for this is unknown. Commercial diets are based on least cost formulations and in NZ there is no requirement to list the amounts of the component ingredients. Whilst the overall specifications may remain constant the ingredients or proportions may vary and this may change palatability (Miller-Cushon et al. 2013, Tere et al. 2016).

In Experiment 3, the effect of diet form was examined. Typically, calves are fed a pelleted ration which has been hammer milled and then pelletized under pressure. The pelleting process typically adds a cost of approximately $60/Tonne. In this study there was no effect of the form of the ration on intake or live weight, so the more expensive pelleting process does not appear necessary for calf performance. However, pelleting could have advantages for other purposes, e.g., retaining freshness, ease of bulk storage or facilitating ease of feeding. Bach et al. (2007) also compared pelleted *vs* non-pelleted rations and found no effect on liveweight gain. Moreover, feeding a roller-milled loose meal has the added advantage of providing the purchaser a good insight as to the ingredients of the meal they are purchasing, which is otherwise hidden by the hammer milling and pelleting process.

Internationally, soyabean meal is seen as having a high palatability (Miller-Cushon et al. 2014) and is generally regarded as the optimum protein source for solid feeds to be fed to calves (Davis & Drackley 1998; Hill et al. 2005). Comparative studies have shown that both canola meal

(Fiems et al. 1985) and cottonseed meal (Fiems et al. 1986) led to poorer calf performance than when soyabean meal was used as a protein source. All soyabean meal used in New Zealand is imported and, thus, tends to be one of the more expensive protein sources. On the other hand, palm kernel and, to a lesser extent, copra meal are imported in large quantities. In 2009, 1755 tonne of copra meal and 665,000 tonne of palm kernel was used in a range of compound feeds (New Zealand Feed Manufactures Association). It seems reasonable to assume that these lower-cost protein sources may have been incorporated into calf meals. The older calves in this study only rejected the palm kernel and copra meal when they became a significant proportion of the diet. It is worth noting that younger calves or calves that are only just starting to eat concentrates are likely to be even more sensitive to these alternative (cheaper) protein sources and to find them less palatable.

This research has demonstrated that the protein content of the concentrate ration fed to calves can influence growth rate and that some additives at high rates can affect palatability. It is the opinion of the authors that more appropriate labelling of concentrate feeds would assist calf rearers in making better-informed purchasing decisions that would help support their calf-rearing businesses.

Acknowledgements

The authors would like to acknowledge the assistance of John Lane, Stuart MacMillan and Kathleen Ward for running the calf-rearing experiments. This work was funded by M&WNZ (now B+LNZ).

References

Bach A, Gimenez A, Juaristi JL, Ahedo J 2007. Physical form of a starter for dairy replacement calves on feed intake and performance. Journal of Dairy Science 90: 3028-3033.

Davis CL, Drackley JK 1998. The development, nutrition and management of the young calf. Iowa, Iowa State University Press.

Fiems LO, Bouchque CV, Cottyn BG, Bysse FX 1985. Evaluation of rapeseed meal with low and high glucosinolates as a protein source in calf starters. Livestock Production Science 12: 131-143.

Fiems LO, Bouchque CV, Cottyn BG, Bysee FX 1986. Cottonseed meal and maize gluten fed versus soyabean meal as protein supplements in calf starters. Archives of Animal Nutrition 36: 731-740.

Groenendijk ME, Lowe K, Molenaar AJ, McCoard SA, Luo D, Khan MA 2018. Growth performance of crossbred dairy calves fed different milk allowances using an automatic feeding system. New Zealand Journal of Animal Science and Production 78: 21-25.

Heinrichs AJ, Lesmeister KE 2007. Rumen development in the dairy calf. In: Calf and heifer rearing. Garnsworthy PC ed. Nottingham University Press.

Heinrichs AJ 2005. Rumen development in the dairy calf. Advances in Dairy Technology 17:179-87.

Hill TM, Aldrich JM, Schlotterbeck RL 2005. Nutrient sources for solid feeds and factors affecting their intake by calves. In-Calf and heifer rearing. Garnsworthy PC ed. Nottingham University Press.

Kertz AF, Hill TM, Quigley III JD, Heinrichs AJ, Linn JG, Drackley JK,. 2017. A 100-year review: Calf nutrition and management. Journal of Dairy Science 100: 10151-10172

Khan MA, Bach A, Weary DM, von Keyserlink MAG 2016. Invited review. Transitioning from milk to solid feed in dairy heifers. Journal of Dairy Science 99: 885-902.

Miller-Cushon EK, Montoro C, Bach A, DeVries TJ. 2013. Effect of early exposure to mixed rations differing in forage particle size on feed sorting of dairy calves. Journal of Dairy Science 96: 3257-3264

Miller-Cushon EK, Terre M, DeVries TJ, Bach A 2014. The effect of protein source on dietary selection in dairy calves. Journal of Dairy Science 97: 4444-4454.

Mirzaei M, Khorvash M, Ghorbani GR, Kazemi-Bonchenai M, Riasi A, Soltani A, Moshiri B, Ghaffari MH. 2016. Interactions between the physical form of starter (mashed vs textured) and corn silage provision on performance, rumen fermentation and structural growth of Holstein calves. Journal of Animal Science 94: 678-686.

Moran J 2002. Calf rearing. A practical guide. Landlinks Press.

Muir PD, Fugle CJ, Ormond AWA 2002. Calf rearing using a once-a-day milk feeding system: current best practice. Proceedings of the New Zealand Grasslands Association 64: 21-24.

NZ Feed Manufacturers Association www.nzfma.org.nz

Thomson BC, Muir PD, Ward KR 2018. Calf-rearing systems on dairy farms and specialist calf rearing units: results of a New Zealand survey. New Zealand Journal of Animal Science and Production 78: 173-176.

Van Amburgh MV, Drackley J 2005. Current perspectives on the energy and protein requirements of the pre-weaned calf. In Calf and heifer rearing. Garnsworthy PC ed. Nottingham University Press.

A survey of fodder beet use and feeding practices on dairy farms in Canterbury, Otago and Southland

JP Edwards[a], DE Dalley[a], JB Pinxterhuis[a] and RR Woods[a]*

[a]*DairyNZ Ltd, PO Box 85066, Lincoln University, Lincoln 7647, New Zealand.*

**Corresponding author:* Email: Roshean.Woods@dairynz.co.nz

Abstract

High yields, consistent quality and emerging environmental benefits make fodder beet (FB) an important feed in South Island dairy systems. However, these benefits may be negated by animal-health issues associated with some FB-feeding regimes. To quantify the range and prevalence of feeding regimes, a telephone survey focussing on practices in 2018 was conducted in Canterbury, Otago and Southland. Of the farmers surveyed, 69% fed FB, 24% had never fed FB and 8% of farmers had stopped feeding FB. The most frequently cited reasons for having stopped feeding FB were animal-health issues, cost and management challenges. Most (82%) respondents feeding FB determined allocation by yield and break area. Almost all farmers (98%) transitioned cattle on to FB, over an average of three weeks. Of those that fed FB to non-lactating cows in winter, the mean allocation was 10.3 kg DM/cow/day (66% of the diet), and 12% fed FB *ad libitum*. A greater proportion of herds fed FB (41% of herds) reported metabolic issues (>5% of the herd affected) compared with herds not fed FB (23%). This survey is valuable to inform future research and reinforces the need to continue investigating animal-health issues associated with FB-feeding, with an emphasis on metabolic issues.

Keywords: fodder beet; winter crop; animal health

Introduction

Forage crops such as brassicas and fodder beet (FB) are important features of farming in the southern regions of New Zealand, especially during the cool winter months when pasture growth is slow (Dalley & Geddes 2012). Fodder beet is a low nitrogen (N) feed which can be grazed *in situ* or lifted and fed out or stored (DairyNZ 2013). It has a high yield potential with typical target yields of 20 t DM/ha for dryland crops and 25 t DM/ha for irrigated crops (Gibbs 2014). The consistent quality (Gibbs 2011) and high utilisation of FB (Edwards et al. 2014) mean that high energy intakes can be achieved. Feeding FB in the period before calving can help to meet body-condition score targets at calving (Gibbs 2014) of 5 to 5.5 (Roche et al. 2009).

Recent studies have shown that FB may have environmental benefits due to the smaller area of land required for cropping (due to high yields), and lower N leaching losses measured from simulated grazed FB in comparison to other forage crops (Malcolm et al. 2016). Other studies have shown that increasing amounts of FB in the diet reduced urine-N concentration (Dalley et al. 2020, Waghorn et al. 2019) and a lower N intake resulted in lower urine-N excretion (Waghorn et al. 2019). Lower urine-N concentration and N excretion are likely to result in lower N leaching losses due to the relationship between urine-N loading rates and subsequent leaching (Di & Cameron 2007).

The benefits of feeding FB may be negated by increased animal-health and welfare risks associated with some FB-feeding regimes, for example poor yield estimation leading to over allocation and potentially rumen acidosis. A recent study showed that feeding 85% of the diet as FB (with barley straw as the sole fibre source) to non-lactating cattle was unsuitable due to inadequate nutrition, a high incidence of acidosis (Waghorn et al. 2018) and negative effects of FB on rumen function (Pacheco et al. 2020). Similarly, Waghorn et al. (2019) concluded that the risks associated with feeding lactating cows high proportions of FB for extended periods were likely to outweigh benefits associated with reducing N excretion, unless appropriate mineral supplementation is adopted.

The integration of FB into dairy-farm systems saw exponential growth from 2005 until 2018, however the area planted has declined for the last two years. Early research focused on understanding digestive changes during the introduction of livestock to the crop and developing a robust set of transitioning guidelines for farmers to follow to minimise the risk of acidosis and other animal-health issues (Dalley 2016, Gibbs 2011, 2014, Gibbs et al. 2015). More recent studies have investigated dairy-cow-wintering practices in Canterbury (Edwards et al. 2017) where it was shown that a high proportion of cows were wintered on-paddock, off the milking platform, with dairy farmer-owned or -leased support blocks being the most common location. The current study sought to better understand the range of FB use and feeding practices within South Island dairy systems. Information can be used to identify the prevalence of 'high-risk' practices and results will help focus the direction of future research as well as where development and extension efforts should be focussed.

Materials and methods

A telephone survey of 508 dairy farmers was completed between 4 December 2018 and 15 February 2019, when farmers were asked about their FB-feeding practices in winter 2018.

Survey questions

The survey had three sections. The introductory section collected information about the respondent's role on farm, the size and type of farm and what time of year they calve (questions related to spring-calving herds only). The second section asked specific questions about any animal-health or performance issues occurring in the previous 12 months across all animal classes on farm, and the percentage of the group affected. In the third section, farmers were asked questions about their FB-feeding practices (farmers not feeding FB did not complete this section). Questions included whether FB was grazed or lifted, details around feed transitioning, feed allocation, and what supplements or other feeds were offered (and amounts), including mineral supplements. Note that all survey data collected from farmers were self-reported.

Selection criteria

A random sample of dairy farmers from the Canterbury, Otago and Southland regions, with contact details, was sourced from DairyNZ's customer relationships management database. Telephone interviews were conducted by independent interviewers contracted by Cuthbert and Associates in two phases. In the first phase 583 calls were made and 207 farmers who fed FB and 95 farmers who did not feed FB in 2018 completed the survey. A second phase of 401 calls was made to increase responses from farmers who did not feed FB in 2018. An additional 58 farmers who did not feed FB in 2018 completed the survey. The 148 additional farmers contacted who fed FB in 2018 were recorded for the purposes of establishing a population estimate of FB use, but as the required sample number had been met, they were not asked to complete the full survey. Only 2% of a total of 984 farmers called refused to take part, and with 508 interviews completed, the overall response rate was 52%; the remainder had not answered after three attempts, had disconnected numbers or had left dairy farming.

Data analysis

Due to question filtering, number of responses and over-sampling of non-FB users, three distinct segments were represented. Sample sizes, and the associated margins of error at the 95% confidence interval were as follows: 1) the sample size for the FB use/non-use is n=508, which gives a maximum margin of error of ±4%, 2) the sample size for the animal-health section is n=359, which gives a maximum margin of error of ±6.5% for FB users and ±7% for non-FB users, and 3) the sample size for FB feeding practices section is n=207, which gives a maximum margin of error of ±6.5%.

The number of responses (n) can vary slightly between questions where the base n of a sub-group would appear to be the same. This is due to omitting extremes or cleansing of data, e.g., deleting obvious typographical errors from the dataset. The n numbers stated in the results refer to the number of responses to a particular question, not the number that responded with a particular answer. Outliers have not been excluded in most central tendency analyses, with the exception of averages, which are displayed as trimmed means. Except for population estimates of FB use, no weighting has been applied to these data as FB users and non-FB users have been reported separately.

Survey data have been summarised using percentages. Note that not all percentages add up to 100% due to either rounding or respondents having the option of selecting multiple responses for some questions.

Results

Population and demographic

The sample of farmers surveyed represented the population of dairy farmers and farms in Canterbury, Otago and Southland (Table 1) (LIC & DairyNZ 2019). Of the 508 farmers who completed the survey, 69% fed FB in 2018 (5% were feeding FB for the first time), 24% had never fed FB, and 8% of farmers surveyed had stopped feeding FB. The most frequently cited reasons for stopping feeding FB were animal-health issues (34%), not getting value for money (22%) and management challenges (18%). Farmers who fed FB in 2018 (n=207) operated on average 2.3 farms, with 53% operating more than one farm, whereas, farmers who did not feed FB (n=153), operated on average 1.8 farms, and 41% operated more than one farm. They also milked more cows (767 cows; n=196) compared with farmers who did not feed FB (645 cows; n=144). Of the farmers who fed FB in 2018, 19% had been feeding it for 1-2 years, 59% for 3-5 years, 19% for 6-10 years, and 4% had been feeding FB for more than 10 years.

Fodder beet-feeding practices

Of the farmers who fed FB in 2018, many used a combination of sources of FB and feeding practices. The majority (90%) grew FB on farm (milking platform and/ or support block), while some purchased it standing (13%) or lifted (6%), or FB was fed by a grazier (5%). Of those farmers who grew or purchased FB standing, 96% said they left FB in the ground and 32% said they lifted some FB (i.e., many used a combination of both of these practices) (Table 2). The majority of farmers feeding lifted FB said they fed it in the paddock, and 13% said they fed it off paddock, for example, on a feed pad (Table 2).

On average, FB was grown on 5% of the milking platform area and 29% of the support block, which equates to 9.5% of the total area associated with a dairy farm. Caution is advised regarding the reliability of the support-block data due to multiple farms sharing a support block

Table 1 Summary statistics of survey respondents (located in Canterbury, Otago and Southland) and comparative population statistics.

	Survey	Population[1]
Total herds	343	2,630
Total cows	243,435	1,820,411
Total effective hectares	79,172	591,513
Average herd size	715	692
Average effective hectares	225	225
Average cows per hectare	3.2	3.1

[1]New Zealand Dairy Statistics 2018-19 (LIC & DairyNZ 2019)

Table 2 Prevalence of fodder beet (FB) feeding methods from a 2018 survey of farmers in Canterbury, Otago and Southland.

Method of feeding out	% of FB feeders (n=197)[1]	% of sub-group[1]	% of sub-group
Left in the ground and grazed	96		
Quantity to feed estimated by:			
Yield and paddock length		82	
Counting rows		23	
Time in paddock		13	
Other		4	
Lifted then fed to stock	32		
Quantity to feed estimated by:			
Weighing on feed wagon		75	
Amount that fits in a bucket or wagon		29	
Don't know		1	
Where Lifted FB is fed:			
In paddock		94	
Off-paddock		13	
Component fed:			
Bulb & leaf		52	
Length of time stored:			
Within one week[2]			44
Within one month			30
Longer than one month			25
Don't know			1
Bulb only		48	
Length of time stored:			
Within one week[2]			18
Within one month			42
Longer than one month			39
Don't know			0

[1]Adds to more than 100% due to some farmers using multiple methods

[2]Including lifted and fed immediately

and data may be overestimated. Of the farmers who grew FB in 2018 (n=207), more grew FB on the milking platform (83%) than on support blocks (78%), indicating that some farmers might be using FB purely for autumn feed. Many farmers (45%) surveyed did not know their FB cultivar (n=186). For those who answered, the most popular cultivar was Brigadier (Seed Force™ Ltd, Christchurch, New Zealand) followed by Jamon (Agricom Ltd, Christchurch, New Zealand). Fodder beet was followed by permanent pasture in rotation in 45% of responses, with the next frequent being forage crop (23%), then cereal (20%), and short-term pasture (11%) (n=238).

Estimating yield and dry matter (DM)

Seventy-one percent of respondents used a commercial company to assess their FB yield, with an equal percentage using an independent company or the company which supplied the FB seed. Another 21% of farmers cut and weighed FB themselves (81% of these weighing leaf and bulb separately), 8% estimated yield by visual assessment, and 2% did not estimate yield. Of the farmers who grew FB or purchased it standing 84% had dry matter analysed and 12% used a literature value for dry matter (n=180). The mean FB yield achieved was 24 t DM/ha; 7% of respondents did not know their yield (n=196).

Feed allocation

Farmers used a combination of methods to determine how much FB to feed. When FB was grazed *in situ*, 82% of farmers said they used the estimated yield and break-feed face length to determine break width, 23% said they allocated FB by counting rows, and 13% of farmers allocated FB based on time in the paddock (Table 2). Of the 32% of farmers lifting FB, 75% said they weighed the FB to determine allocation before feeding, and 29% said they estimated the amount based on what fitted in a tractor bucket or a wagon. Around half of the farmers feeding lifted FB were feeding both leaf and bulb (52%), while the rest were feeding bulb only and stored them longer (39% longer than a month, compared with 25% for leaf and bulb).

Almost all farmers (98%; n=199) transitioned their cows onto FB, on average taking three weeks to reach maximum allocation.

Fodder beet use by animal class

The use of FB by age class and time of the season are presented in Table 3 with the age class most commonly fed FB being non-lactating cows over winter. Significantly (P=0.01) more farmers fed FB to rising two-year-old heifers (R2) (52% of farmers) and to cows during mid to late lactation (65% of farmers) in Southland and South Otago than in Canterbury and North Otago (32% and 45% of farmers, respectively). However, a significantly (P=0.05) greater proportion of farmers in Canterbury and North Otago wintered non-lactating cows on FB (91%) than in Southland and South Otago (82%). More farmers managed their R2 heifers differently to their non-lactating mixed-age cows (51%) than managed them the same (40%). The average number of weeks each age class was fed FB is presented in Table 3. Young stock tended to be fed FB for longer than mixed-age cows.

Mean maximum allocations of FB fed to cows of different age classes and at different times of the season as well as total allocation of other feeds are presented in Table 3. On average, 12% of FB fed to non-lactating cows during winter was *ad libitum*, otherwise the mean maximum allocation of FB was 10.3 kg DM/cow/day, 66% of the offered diet. Rising two-year-old heifers were fed mean maximum allocations of 9.8 kg DM/cow/day. *Ad libitum* feeding of FB to rising one-year-old heifers (R1) was more common than for other age classes with 23% of farmers saying that they let the R1 heifers eat as much as they want. Greater amounts of other feeds were fed to lactating cows than non-lactating cows (Table 3).

The most common feed offered with FB was pasture silage or baleage, for mixed-age non-lactating cows during winter. This was followed by straw, and maize silage, cereal silage or baleage. Many farmers may have fed a combination of feeds. Cows fed FB during lactation were

Table 3 Percentage of surveyed farmers feeding fodder beet (FB) in Canterbury, Otago and Southland regions in 2018, the average length of time, and the average amount allocated for age classes and seasons.

Total Sample[1]	Non-lactating cows (winter)	Non-lactating pre-calving cows (spring)	Cows in early lactation (spring)	Cows in mid-late lactation (autumn)	Rising 1-year-olds (winter)	Rising 2-year-olds (winter)
Fed FB in 2018 (%)	57	13	24	35	17	27
Sub Sample[2]						
Fed FB in 2018 (%)	87	20	36	53	26	40
Weeks fed FB	8.9	4.3	5.7	5.6	10.9	9
Maximum amount of FB						
Allocation (kg/cow/day)	10.3	5.8	3.4	4.9	5.8	9.8
Eat as much as they want (%)	12	8	3	2	23	13
Other feed						
Allocation (kg/cow/day)	4.9	9.7	12.8	12.5	3.6	5
Eat as much as they want (%)	11	5	18	12	25	11
None, i.e., solely FB (%)[3]	1	0	8	11	23	0
Total diet						
Allocation (kg/cow/day)	16	15	15	16	9	15
Proportion of FB (%)	66	36	33	40	74	66

[1]All farms, i.e. including those that did not feed FB (n=302)
[2]Only those that fed FB in 2018 (n=198)
[3]It is likely that farmers may have misinterpreted this question and not been thinking of pasture as an "other feed"

Table 4 Percentage of farmers surveyed in Canterbury, Otago and Southland regions who experienced animal-health issues in >5% of their herd in 2018, split between those that fed fodder beet (to any stock class) and those that did not feed fodder beet.

	Fodder beet (%) (n=207)	Non-fodder beet (%) (n=153)	
Metabolic issues/milk fever	41	23	**
Mastitis	42	54	*
Rumen acidosis	1	1	
Broken bones	0	0	
Abortions	0	1	

*Significant difference based on two-sided tests assuming equal variances with a confidence level 0.05
**Significant difference based on two-sided tests assuming equal variances with a confidence level 0.01

most likely to be fed the balance of their diet as pasture, followed by pasture silage, and straw.

Use of minerals

The responses indicate that many farmers fed more than one mineral with FB. Dicalcium phosphate (DCP), magnesium oxide, magnesium chloride, or a mix customised for their farm, were the most-common mineral supplements fed to mixed-age non-lactating cows during winter, which was similar for cows in early lactation, except that more farmers also fed lime flour in early lactation. Sixteen percent of farmers who fed FB to non-lactating cows said they did not feed any mineral supplements: this was 10% for non-lactating cows pre-calving, 6% for cows in early lactation, and 8% for cows in mid-late lactation.

Sixty percent of farmers who fed FB to non-lactating cows over winter knew the allocation of phosphate supplement they were feeding. This averaged 71 g of phosphate supplement/cow/day such as DCP, MagPhos, monosodium phosphate, monocalcium phosphate, or soluble phosphate. The most common method of offering phosphate supplements to non-lactating cows during winter was to mix it with silage using a mixer wagon (40%), followed by applying a slurry on supplement or baleage once in the paddock (18%), loose lick or lick block (18%), in-line water dispenser (15%), and 10% said they dusted it onto paddocks (n=53).

Attitude towards fodder beet

Attitude towards FB was generally positive. Of farmers who fed FB in 2018 (n=188), 44% rated FB 8 to 10 out of 10 as a stock feed, 29% rated it 5 to 7, 15% rated it less than 5, and 12% didn't know; where 0 meant "very dissatisfied" and 10 meant "very satisfied".

Animal-health issues

Of the herds fed FB in 2018, a significantly greater proportion (41%) were affected by metabolic issues (>5% of the herd affected), compared with 23% for herds not fed FB (P=0.01; Table 4). In contrast, a greater proportion of non-FB herds were affected by mastitis (54%) compared with those fed FB (42%) (P=0.05; Table 4). On farms where FB was fed, the greatest incidence of both metabolic issues and mastitis occurred when FB had been fed for 3-5 years, the majority reported as occurring when cows were lactating in spring. Around 12% and 20% of mastitis was reported as occurring in non-lactating cows for FB feeders and non-FB feeders, respectively. For metabolic issues the occurrence in non-lactating cows for FB feeders and non-FB feeders was 6% and 3%, respectively. Other performance issues which farmers were concerned about included poor reproductive performance, poor body-condition score, excessive body-condition score and poor production. However, the proportions of farmers concerned with these were similar for those that had fed FB in the last 12 months and those that had not.

Discussion

The 57% of farms feeding FB during the non-lactation winter period (Table 3) aligns with data collected as part of the 2018-19 DairyNZ Animal Husbandry Survey. From the annual DairyNZ Animal Husbandry consults (n=500 nationally) the number of cows fed FB had declined from 87% in 2016-17 to 69% in 2018-19 for Canterbury/North Otago, and from 63% to 46% for Southland/South Otago, respectively. This is represented by the 8% of farmers in the current survey who had previously fed FB but did not feed FB in 2018. The proportion of farms feeding FB on the milking platform (57%) in the current survey was similar to that reported by Edwards et al. (2017) in Canterbury (64%). The current survey delved deeper specifically into FB-feeding practices, age classes of stock, animal-health issues and mineral supplementation than these previous studies.

On average FB made up 66% of the diet of non-lactating cows over winter in this study (Table 3) which is more than the maximum of 60% FB recommended when fed with pasture silage (Pacheco et al. 2020). A study by Waghorn et al. (2018) demonstrated that a diet comprising 85% FB with barley straw was not suitable for non-lactating dairy cows due to the risk of inadequate nutrition and a high incidence of acidosis; lower dry matter intake, poor rumen function and a negative N balance resulted. A diet of 65% FB and 35% pasture silage provided adequate nutrition, however, there was still some risk of acidosis. The high average proportion of FB in the diet of non-lactating cows during winter (of those surveyed), combined with the 16% of farmers not feeding mineral supplements to these animals, should be a focus of future research and extension to ensure diets containing FB supply sufficient minerals to reduce the risk of animal-health issues.

The use of FB in New Zealand has expanded beyond winter feeding to non-lactating cows, with lactation feeding and youngstock rearing on FB proving successful (Gibbs et al. 2015). In the current study, R1 heifers were fed diets of 74% FB on average (n=23), and R2 heifers 66% FB diets (n=55; Table 3). This is similar to the 65% FB diet fed to R2 heifers by Atkins et al. (2018) where this was shown to be a viable alternative to winter housing in high-input total-mixed-ration systems. An integrated heifer-management system using FB fed *ad libitum* from early autumn (after careful transition) has been developed by Gibbs et al. (2015) with suggested intakes of 3-4 kg FB for weaned heifer calves and 9 kg FB for heifers prior to calving. The mean maximum allocations of FB to R1 and R2 animals in the survey were higher than those suggested by Gibbs et al. (2015) at 5.8 and 9.8 kg DM/cow/day, respectively (Table 3). Young stock are not as prone to rumen acidosis as adult cows, as they have different intake patterns (Gibbs et al. 2015), however, they have a higher requirement for protein and minerals to support growth. This indicates that youngstock diets for many of the respondents may be inadequate. Many respondents did not know how their youngstock were being managed with 20% of FB feeders and 27% of non-FB feeders reporting that they did not know what percentage of their youngstock were affected by animal-health issues. This is likely due to youngstock typically being managed separately off farm. A similar observation around uncertainty of management by graziers was made by Edwards et al. (2017) where few farmers answered a question relating to supplement fed to cows by the grazier.

The proportion of FB in the diet fed to cows in early lactation and mid-late lactation of 33% and 40%, respectively (Table 3) is within the maximum amount of FB in the diet of lactating cows recommended by previous studies (Waghorn et al. 2019). A diet comprising 40% FB with pasture resulted in lower milk production than a 25% FB or 25% maize diet; this may have been a result of subclinical acidosis caused by the high sugar content of FB (Dalley et al. 2020). Similarly, Waghorn et al. (2019) reported that a diet of 60% FB was detrimental to lactating cow health due to the occurrence of acidosis. While a diet with 23% FB increased dry matter digestibility, 45% FB reduced N and neutral detergent fibre (aNDF) digestibility, suggesting an alteration in rumen function. The authors warned that care should be taken to ensure diets contain sufficient N, phosphorus and sulphur as FB bulbs are inadequate in these minerals for lactating cows if fed for extended periods.

The survey indicated that farmers generally use recommended yield-estimation practices. Most farmers surveyed were relatively experienced in feeding FB with only 19% having fed FB for less than two years. High-risk practices of feed estimation, such as only visually assessing crop yield or not assessing it at all, not weighing FB bulb and leaf separately, and using a literature value to estimate dry matter, were few within the survey group. These practices lead to poor accuracy of FB allocation. Feeding FB in the paddock using a time-based approach to allocate FB has a higher risk of acidosis if strict guidelines on herd feeding management are not followed, since cows can consume up to 1 kg FB DM/20 minutes.

Conclusion

The survey results demonstrate how widely FB is used and that, despite animal-health challenges, relatively few farmers have stopped feeding FB. However, declining area sown may indicate farmers are reducing the amount they use. In general, farmers are using recommended yield-estimation practices with a low incidence of high-risk practices relating to feeding. The high proportions of FB in the diets of non-lactating cattle and replacement heifers is of concern if sufficient protein and minerals are not supplied to overcome deficiencies and potential animal-health risks. This survey has helped identify gaps for future research priorities and extension: reinforcing the need to continue investigating opportunities for FB diets that meet protein and mineral-requirement targets to minimise animal-health issues associated with FB-feeding.

Acknowledgements

This project was funded by the Sustainable Farming Fund (405512) administered by the Ministry for Primary Industries, Wellington, New Zealand; DairyNZ and PGG Wrightson Seeds. We would like to acknowledge Susan Cuthbert (surveyor) of Cuthbert and Associates for facilitating the survey and the wider project team for their input into survey questions.

References

Atkins NE, Bleach ECL, Sinclair LA 2018. Periparturient and early lactation performance and metabolism of replacement Holstein-Friesian heifers out-wintered on fodder beet or perennial ryegrass compared with winter housing. Grass and Forage Science 73(4): 828-840.

DairyNZ. 2013. Fodder beet - growing a high yielding crop (1-77) [Online]. DairyNZ. Available: https://www.dairynz.co.nz/media/253812/1-77_fodder_beet_growing_a_high_yielding_crop_2013.pdf [Accessed 7 February 2020].

Dalley D, Waugh D, Griffin A, Higham C, de Ruiter J, Malcolm B 2020. Productivity and environmental implications of fodder beet and maize silage as supplements to pasture for late lactation dairy cows. New Zealand Journal of Agricultural Research 63(1): 145-164.

Dalley DE. 2016. The foibles of fodder beet and other forage crops – animal and environmental considerations for successfully feeding forage crops. South Island Dairy Event, Invercargill, New Zealand, 2016.

Dalley DE, Geddes T 2012. Pasture growth and quality on Southland and Otago dairy farms. Proceedings of the New Zealand Grassland Association 74:237-242.

Di HJ, Cameron KC 2007. Nitrate leaching losses and pasture yields as affected by different rates of animal urine nitrogen returns and application of a nitrification inhibitor – a lysimeter study. Nutrient Cycling in Agroecosystems 79(3): 281-290.

Edwards GR, de Ruiter JM, Dalley DE, Pinxterhuis JB, Cameron KC, Bryant RH, Di H, Malcolm BJ, Chapman DF 2014. Dry matter intake and body condition score change of dairy cows grazing fodder beet, kale and kale-oat forage systems in winter. Proceedings of the New Zealand Grassland Association 76: 81-88.

Edwards JP, Mashlan K, Dalley DE, Pinxterhuis JB 2017. A survey of dairy cow wintering practices in Canterbury, New Zealand. Animal Production Science 57(7): 1323-1329.

Gibbs J. 2011. Wintering dairy cows on fodder beet. In: Doig K & Gow N eds. South Island Dairy Event, Lincoln, New Zealand, 2011.

Gibbs J. 2014. Fodder beet in the New Zealand Dairy Industry. In: Doig K ed. South Island Dairy Event, Invercargill, New Zealand, 2014.

Gibbs J, Saldias B, Trotter C. 2015. Feeding fodder beet in lactation and to replacement heifers. In: Doig K ed. South Island Dairy Event, Lincoln, New Zealand, 2015.

LIC, DairyNZ. 2019. New Zealand Dairy Statistics 2018-19 [Online]. Hamilton, New Zealand: Livestock Improvement Corporation Limited & DairyNZ Limited. Available: https://www.dairynz.co.nz/media/5792393/nz-dairy-statistics-2018-19-web.pdf [Accessed 5 February 2020].

Malcolm BJ, Cameron KC, Edwards GR, Di HJ, de Ruiter JM, Dalley DE 2016. Nitrate leaching losses from lysimeters simulating winter grazing of fodder beet by dairy cows. New Zealand Journal of Agricultural Research 59(2): 194-203.

Pacheco D, Muetzel S, Lewis S, Dalley D, Bryant M, Waghorn GC 2020. Rumen digesta and products of fermentation in cows fed varying proportions of fodder beet (*Beta vulgaris*) with fresh pasture or silage or straw. Animal Production Science 60(4): 524-534.

Roche JR, Friggens NC, Kay JK, Fisher MW, Stafford KJ, Berry DP 2009. Invited review: Body condition score and its association with dairy cow productivity, health, and welfare. Journal of Dairy Science 92(12): 5769-5801.

Waghorn G, Collier K, Bryant M, Dalley D 2018. Feeding fodder beet (*Beta vulgaris* L.) with either barley straw or pasture silage to non-lactating dairy cows. New Zealand Veterinary Journal 66(4): 178-185.

Waghorn G, Law N, Bryant M, Pacheco D, Dalley D 2019. Digestion and nitrogen excretion by Holstein–Friesian cows in late lactation offered ryegrass-based pasture supplemented with fodder beet. Animal Production Science 59(7): 1261-1270.

Body condition scoring of sheep: intra- and inter-observer variability

RA Corner-Thomas[a]*, AM Sewell[b], P Kemp[a], BA Wood[a], DI Gray[a], ST Morris[a], HT Blair[a] and PR Kenyon[a]

[a]*School of Agriculture and Environment, Massey University, Palmerston North, New Zealand,* [b]*Institute of Education, Massey University, Palmerston North, New Zealand*

**Corresponding author.* E-mail: r.corner@massey.ac.nz

Abstract

Body condition scoring (BCS) is a hands-on tool that farmers can use to make decisions about their animal feeding and management. BCS, however, is a subjective measure of the muscle and fat cover of the lumbar spine. Observers, therefore, may show variability in scores both across time and from other observers. This study aimed to determine the intra- and inter-observer variation of both farmers and research technicians as part of a learning exercise of a farmer-learning group based at Massey University between 2011 and 2015. Nineteen farmers and three research technicians condition scored 45 mixed-age ewes on two consecutive days. Data from both farmers and technicians were analysed to determine the intra- and inter-observer variability using a weighted kappa. The results indicate that the majority of farmers and technicians had 'excellent' agreement (21 of the 22 observers had kappa values greater than 0.75) between days. Similarly, among pairs of observers the agreement was also 'excellent' (212 of 231 comparisons had kappa values greater than 0.75). The distribution of scores that contributed to each median condition score, however, indicated that lower scores (1, 1.5 and 2) has less variability than did higher scores (2.5 or greater). These results suggest that BCS is a robust farm-management tool that can be used with a high degree of repeatability.

Keywords: body condition scoring; intra-observer variability, inter-observer variability

Introduction

Body condition scoring (BCS) of sheep is a management tool that farmers can use to aid on-farm decision making and optimise animal performance (Kenyon et al. 2014). BCS provides a subjective assessment of the subcutaneous fat and muscle of the lumbar spine (Jefferies 1961). BCS is assessed by the palpation of both the spinous and transverse processes of the lumbar vertebrae and is assessed against a five-point scale which includes either half or, sometimes, quarter scores (Jefferies 1961; Russel 1984). BCS has advantages over the assessment of live weight alone as BCS is not influenced by the stature of the animal nor by its physiological state, fleece weight or gut fill (Jefferies 1961; Sezenler et al. 2011).

Body condition score has a positive relationship with range of reproductive parameters such as ovulation rate, conception rate, pregnancy rate, fecundity, and with lamb birth weight and survival (Kenyon et al. 2014). For most production traits, such as ovulation rate and pregnancy rate, there is a curvilinear relationship among scores with the response plateauing to an optimum usually between 3 and 3.5 (Gunn et al. 1991; Kenyon et al. 2014). Due to this curvilinear relationship selecting ewes with sub-optimal BCS for additional feeding will likely result in a greater production increase for ewes with poor condition compared with greater BCS. The use of BCS is a potentially valuable farm management tool, however, its value is maximised if consistency of scoring within or between assessors can be achieved.

Due to its subjective nature, BCS has the potential to be limited by repeatability, both within and between assessors. In their review, Kenyon et al. (2014) reported that there was inconsistency in the repeatability of BCS technique between and within assessors, which had been attributed to the different experience of the assessors. In general, low reliability was found in studies with inexperienced assessors compared to studies of experienced assessors. The aim of the current study was to determine the intra- and inter-observer repeatability of a group of farmers and research technicians involved in a farmer-learning group at Massey University.

Materials and methods

From 2011 to 2015 a farmer-learning project was conducted at Massey University. The group of 26 farmers worked with an interdisciplinary group of seven University experts (three animal scientists, an agronomist, a farm-management specialist, an educationalist and a sociologist; Blair et al. 2013). The project focused on a University farmlet trial that investigated lamb finishing on herb-mix pastures (clover, chicory and plantain; Kenyon et al. 2017). The participants met four times per year at Massey University during a 24-hour period from noon to noon. Farmer participants were involved in a number of learning experiences. One of the learning experiences was focussed on the technique of sheep BCS.

Of the 26 farmer participants, 23 attended the session during which the BCS activity was conducted. The session began with a presentation by an experienced academic about BCS followed by a discussion about the technique and the potential opportunities that BCS could provide to the farmers. Participants were provided with both a one-page fact sheet on the technique created by the university experts, and a copy of a one-page handout produced by Beef+Lamb NZ (2013). Prior to the session an experienced BCS- technician selected and weighed 45 mixed-age ewes which they assessed to have a BCS between 1.5 and 5 (Jefferies 1961). The experienced technicians in this study regularly BCS sheep as part of their research studies and had worked together for a number of years. The learning group participants (n=23 observers) and technicians experienced in BCS (n=3 observers) were then asked to manually record to 0.5 the BCS of all 45 ewes. The following day the participants and technicians recorded the BCS of the same 45 ewes. No record was made of the previous experience of the observers in this study.

Statistical analysis

All statistical analyses were conducted using SPSS 26.0 (SPSS Inc, 2006). Data from four observers (n=4 farmers) was discarded due to data being recorded for only one of the two observation days. This resulted in data being analysed for a total of 19 farmers and three experienced technicians. Across the two days of observations, nine observers recorded scores for all 45 ewes, 12 observers did not record a BCS for one or two ewes and four observers omitted between eight and ten ewes. Descriptive statistics including mode, minimum, maximum, median, and lower and upper quartiles were computed for BCS data recorded on each day and for the ΔBCS between days. Descriptive statistics were also calculated for each observer. The percentage of exact agreement between and within observers was calculated and the inter- and intra-observer variability was assessed using intra-class correlation coefficients (ICC; Shrout & Fleiss 1979) and weighted kappa coefficients (K_w) (Cohen 1968). BCS is an ordinal measurement and, therefore, the weighted κ was used as it attributed more weight to large measurement differences than to small ones. κ_w was calculated the using quadratic weights for paired intra- and inter-observer assessments. All κ_w results were interpreted according to Fleiss (1981), where values >0.75 suggested 'excellent', 0.4 to 0.75 indicated 'fair-good' and <0.4 indicated 'poor' levels of agreement.

Results

Body condition scores

For the 45 ewes that were observed, a total of 1927 individual BCS were recorded by the 22 observers during two days of observation. Kendall's coefficient of concordance was 0.887, which indicated that for each ewe there was a high level of agreement across all observers and both days of observation. A breakdown of the scores that contributed to each ewe's median BCS is shown in Table 1. The ewe that had a median BCS of 1, was scored 1 in almost 80% of the observations and scored a 1.5 by just over 20% (Table 1). In contrast, the four ewes with a median score of 1.5 were scored a 1, 1.5, 2 and 2.5. The median score with the greatest variability in scores was 3.5 which was given scores ranging from 2 to 5.

Intra-observer variability

The BCS data recorded by each observer on day 1 and 2 are shown in Figure 1. The average exact agreement between day 1 and 2 ranged from 16% (observer 9) to 71% (observer 4; Table 2). The percentage of observations that were within half a score of the previous day's observation ranged from 70 to 98% (Table 2). Similarly (the κ_w values suggest that all but one observer had 'excellent' agreement between days (Table 2). While (observer 9 had a κ_w = 0.61 which indicated 'fair-good' agreement.

Table 1 The percentage (and frequency) of each median body condition score (BCS) showing the number of ewes in each median category, their mean live weight and the distribution of scores that contributed to that score.

Median BCS	n ewes	Live weight (kg)	Distribution of individual BCS for each median value								
			1	1.5	2	2.5	3	3.5	4	4.5	5
1	1	41.5	79.1 (34)	20.9 (9)	-	-	-	-	-	-	-
1.5	4	61.5	18.0 (31)	59.9 (103)	19.8 (34)	2.3 (4)	-	-	-	-	-
1.75	1	58.5	-	50.0 (19)	45.2 (19)	4.8 (2)	-	-	-	-	-
2	3	66.8	-	26.0 (33)	54.3 (69)	19.7 (25)	-	-	-	-	-
2.5	5	69.5	-	1.4 (3)	25.9 (56)	51.9 (112)	19.4 (42)	0.9 (2)	0.5 (1)	-	-
3	6	77.8	-	-	3.1 (8)	19.4 (50)	47.7 (123)	21.7 (56)	6.2 (16)	1.9 (5)	
3.5	6	80.6	-	-	0.4 (1)	2.0 (5)	25.1 (64)	41.2 (105)	22.0 (56)	8.6 (22)	0.8 (2)
4	6	90.9	-	-	-	0.4 (1)	7.0 (18)	24.4 (63)	31.8 (82)	26.4 (68)	10.1 (26)
4.5	8	90.6	-	-	-	-	4.1 (14)	11.9 (41)	23.5 (81)	37.8 (130)	22.7 (78)
5	5	92.2	-	-	-	-	1.4 (3)	2.4 (5)	12.3 (26)	25.0 (53)	59.0 (125)

Figure 1 Frequency of body condition scores of ewes recorded by observers 1 to 22 (observer id is shown in the top left of each panel) on day 1 (open bars) and 2 (closed bars) of observation

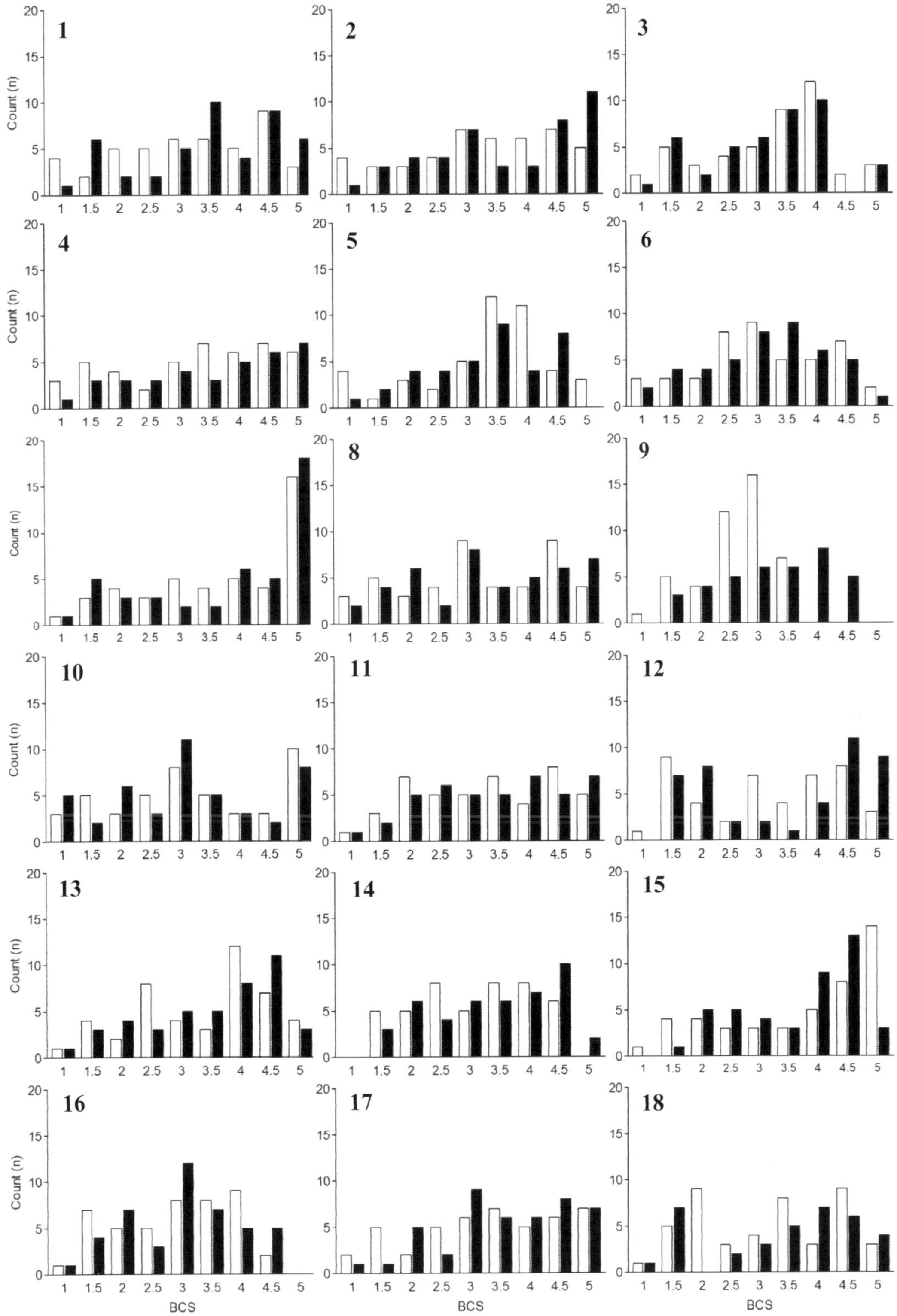

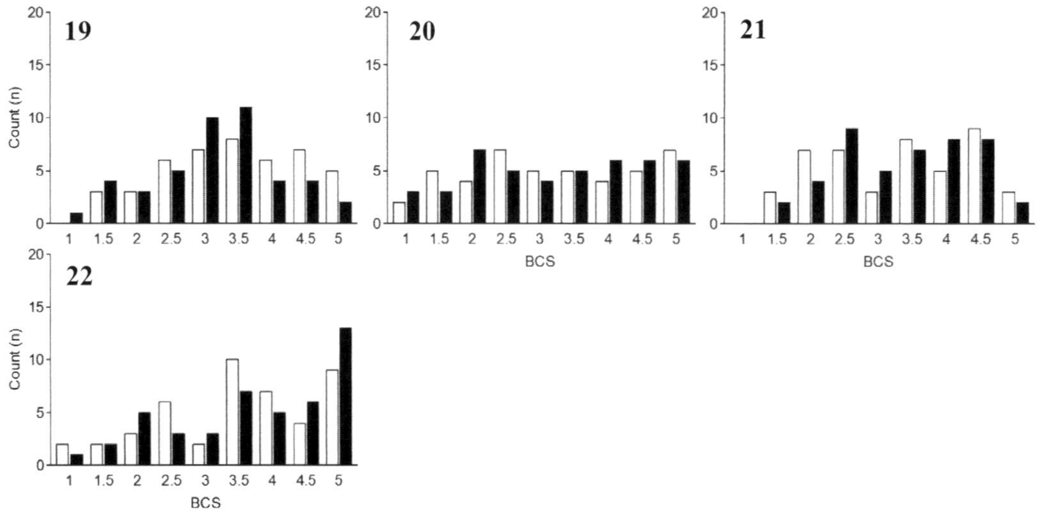

Table 2 Descriptive statistics of body condition scores (BCS) recorded by each observer (Obs) including number of individual ewe BCS observations (n) and the median BCS recorded (the exact agreement and agreement half a score between day 1 and 2 (and the intra-observer weighted kappa (κ_w)

Obs	Observer	BCS		Agreement Day 1 vs 2		Intra-observer
Id		n	Median	Exact (%)	Half score (%)	κw
1	Farmer	90	3.5	42.2	91.1	0.92 (0.87 - 0.97)
2	Farmer	89	3.5	29.5	72.7	0.85 (0.78 - 0.92)
3	Farmer	87	3.5	71.4	97.6	0.96 (0.93 - 0.99)
4	Farmer	80	3.5	51.4	94.3	0.94 (0.91 - 0.98)
5	Farmer	82	3.5	24.3	70.3	0.76 (0.64 - 0.89)
6	Farmer	89	3	50.0	93.2	0.92 (0.88 - 0.96)
7	Farmer	90	4	53.3	95.6	0.96 (0.93 - 0.98)
8	Farmer	89	3	38.6	79.5	0.88 (0.82 - 0.94)
9	Farmer	82	3	16.2	73.0	0.61 (0.45 - 0.76)
10	Farmer	90	3	51.1	86.7	0.90 (0.82 - 0.97)
11	Farmer	88	3.5	41.9	88.4	0.89 (0.82 - 0.96)
12	Farmer	89	3.5	38.6	72.7	0.84 (0.75 - 0.93)
13	Farmer	88	4	38.6	93.0	0.92 (0.88 - 0.97)
14	Farmer	89	3.5	46.5	81.8	0.87 (0.81 - 0.93)
15	Farmer	88	4	45.5	97.7	0.93 (0.91 - 0.96)
16	Farmer	89	3	34.9	88.6	0.89 (0.83 - 0.95)
17	Farmer	90	3.5	56.8	80.0	0.89 (0.83 - 0.94)
18	Farmer	80	3.5	40.0	80.0	0.87 (0.79 - 0.94)
19	Farmer	89	3.5	31.4	86.4	0.83 (0.73 - 0.93)
20	Technician	90	3	40.9	86.4	0.90 (0.85 - 0.96)
21	Technician	90	3.5	46.7	97.8	0.93 (0.90 - 0.96)
22	Technician	90	3.5	53.3	86.7	0.91 (0.86 - 0.97)

Inter-observer variability

The assessment of pairs of observers had κ_w values that ranged between 0.54 (observer 9 vs. 15) and 0.94 (observer 4 vs. 13; Table 3). Among the pairs of observers (the majority were classified as having 'excellent' agreement (>0.75 (n=210) and with the remainder 'Fair-good' (0.4 to 0.75 (n=21). The κ_w between pairs of farmers showed more variability (0.54 to 0.94) than between pairs of technicians (range 0.82 to 0.88; Table 3).

Discussion

BCS in the current study showed both intra- and inter-observer agreement that was 'fair-good' (κ_w=0.4 to 0.75) to 'excellent' (κ_w>0.75). This finding is in agreement with Teixeira et al. (1989) and Shands et al. (2009) who reported that the Pearson's correlation coefficient between experienced observers was between r=0.7 and 0.8. Phythian et al. (2012), however, reported lower agreement between veterinarian assessors with a κ_w of 0.4 and 0.6. It possible that the relatively small range of BCS that study (2 to 3.5) compared with the current study (1 to 5) may have influenced the repeatability.

The prior experience of the farmers in this study was not recorded. Kenyon et al. (2014) reported that

Table 3 Pairwise comparisons of body condition scores (BCS) recorded on days 1 and 2 by each observer (Obs 1 to 22) showing the Pearson's correlation coefficient (above the diagonal) and weighted Kappa (below the diagonal). White areas indicate areas of comparisons between farmer observers (light grey areas are farmer and technician observer comparisons and dark grey areas are technician observers.

	Obs 1	Obs 2	Obs 3	Obs 4	Obs 5	Obs 6	Obs 7	Obs 8	Obs 9	Obs 10	Obs 11	Obs 12	Obs 13	Obs 14	Obs 15	Obs 16	Obs 17	Obs 18	Obs 19	Obs 20	Obs 21	Obs 22
Obs 1	-	0.91	0.91	0.93	0.85	0.90	0.93	0.91	0.82	0.88	0.87	0.87	0.93	0.93	0.91	0.91	0.92	0.93	0.85	0.91	0.93	0.91
Obs 2	0.91	-	0.89	0.91	0.81	0.88	0.92	0.90	0.79	0.87	0.87	0.86	0.89	0.88	0.90	0.90	0.93	0.90	0.81	0.87	0.86	0.90
Obs 3	0.90	0.86	-	0.94	0.89	0.91	0.92	0.89	0.76	0.91	0.88	0.89	0.93	0.89	0.93	0.94	0.92	0.91	0.89	0.91	0.90	0.91
Obs 4	0.92	0.91	0.92	-	0.88	0.91	0.96	0.93	0.79	0.93	0.90	0.89	0.95	0.93	0.94	0.96	0.94	0.93	0.89	0.92	0.91	0.93
Obs 5	0.84	0.80	0.88	0.86	-	0.84	0.87	0.82	0.70	0.82	0.78	0.81	0.88	0.83	0.86	0.86	0.84	0.84	0.81	0.83	0.79	0.85
Obs 6	0.87	0.83	0.90	0.88	0.83	-	0.90	0.88	0.75	0.93	0.86	0.80	0.90	0.89	0.90	0.91	0.92	0.89	0.87	0.89	0.87	0.89
Obs 7	0.87	0.89	0.80	0.91	0.78	0.76	-	0.93	0.82	0.89	0.89	0.87	0.94	0.92	0.94	0.91	0.92	0.94	0.87	0.90	0.90	0.92
Obs 8	0.91	0.89	0.88	0.92	0.81	0.86	0.86	-	0.79	0.89	0.90	0.85	0.90	0.90	0.90	0.88	0.89	0.91	0.85	0.89	0.89	0.88
Obs 9	0.71	0.66	0.71	0.65	0.62	0.71	0.56	0.69	-	0.71	0.75	0.75	0.77	0.82	0.75	0.80	0.80	0.81	0.68	0.75	0.76	0.80
Obs 10	0.87	0.85	0.90	0.92	0.80	0.91	0.80	0.88	0.64	-	0.88	0.83	0.91	0.90	0.90	0.92	0.90	0.90	0.89	0.91	0.89	0.90
Obs 11	0.87	0.86	0.87	0.89	0.77	0.84	0.83	0.89	0.65	0.86	-	0.87	0.90	0.90	0.85	0.90	0.89	0.89	0.84	0.88	0.88	0.86
Obs 12	0.86	0.85	0.87	0.88	0.79	0.77	0.82	0.85	0.66	0.83	0.86	-	0.89	0.87	0.87	0.87	0.85	0.89	0.80	0.88	0.88	0.89
Obs 13	0.92	0.88	0.90	0.94	0.87	0.85	0.89	0.89	0.65	0.87	0.89	0.88	-	0.91	0.92	0.93	0.90	0.94	0.87	0.90	0.91	0.92
Obs 14	0.92	0.85	0.89	0.90	0.82	0.88	0.80	0.89	0.76	0.87	0.89	0.85	0.89	-	0.89	0.93	0.91	0.92	0.84	0.90	0.91	0.90
Obs 15	0.86	0.87	0.83	0.90	0.80	0.78	0.93	0.84	0.54	0.82	0.81	0.82	0.90	0.81	-	0.91	0.91	0.90	0.89	0.91	0.90	0.90
Obs 16	0.84	0.80	0.92	0.86	0.80	0.89	0.69	0.83	0.79	0.87	0.83	0.80	0.83	0.90	0.71	-	0.93	0.93	0.86	0.89	0.91	0.91
Obs 17	0.92	0.92	0.89	0.93	0.83	0.87	0.88	0.87	0.67	0.87	0.88	0.84	0.90	0.88	0.89	0.82	-	0.90	0.83	0.89	0.87	0.90
Obs 18	0.93	0.88	0.91	0.93	0.83	0.88	0.86	0.90	0.69	0.89	0.89	0.89	0.92	0.91	0.83	0.88	0.89	-	0.84	0.91	0.91	0.90
Obs 19	0.84	0.78	0.89	0.86	0.81	0.86	0.77	0.84	0.61	0.87	0.83	0.77	0.85	0.84	0.82	0.81	0.81	0.83	-	0.86	0.85	0.87
Obs 20	0.90	0.85	0.90	0.91	0.81	0.87	0.82	0.89	0.67	0.91	0.87	0.88	0.88	0.88	0.84	0.84	0.87	0.91	0.84	-	0.91	0.92
Obs 21	0.91	0.84	0.89	0.88	0.79	0.85	0.81	0.87	0.68	0.85	0.88	0.86	0.90	0.90	0.84	0.85	0.86	0.90	0.85	0.89	-	0.91
Obs 22	0.89	0.89	0.84	0.91	0.81	0.80	0.91	0.84	0.62	0.84	0.84	0.86	0.90	0.84	0.90	0.75	0.89	0.85	0.82	0.87	0.87	-

BCS repeatability was inconsistent among studies and hypothesised that this was due to difference in the experience of the assessors. For example Yates and Gleeson (1975) reported poor repeatability of inexperienced assessors whereas Evans (1978) and Shands et al. (2009) reported 'good' or 'excellent' agreement. Keinprecht et al. (2016) reported that the experience of six assessors with BCS of sheep and who were trained for one day prior to the evaluation had no effect of on repeatability or reproducibility of scoring. In that study kappa ranged from 0.54 to 0.80 which was lower than in the current study. The lack of difference in this study may have been a result of the small number of assessors, the quality of the training provided and the short interval between training and evaluation. The farmers in the current study may have had some experience with BCS as it is a farm-management tool used by 43% of New Zealand farmers (Corner-Thomas et al. 2015). The agreement between technicians in this study was high, which is perhaps not surprising given that all three technicians regularly conducted BCS as part of their research duties. In addition, the three technicians had received similar training and had worked closely with one another for a number of years.

In the current study, low BCS (1, 1.5 and 2) were comprised of a lesser range of scores than scores of 2.5 or greater. To these authors' knowledge an assessment of the variability of different scores has not been reported. Teixeira et al. (1989) reported that the relationship of BCS with carcass composition measures of fat of sheep showed that ewes with BCS between 1.5 and 2.5 had higher proportions of intermuscular and mesenteric, whereas for ewes with higher BCS had primarily subcutaneous and omental fat. This difference in fat depot location is likely to result in ewes with BCS less than 2.5 being more easily identified due to their lack of sub-cutaneous fat. Further research is required to determine the repeatability of different scores and the influence of subcutaneous fat deposition on BCS.

Conclusion

Body condition scoring is an important 'hands-on' assessment of the condition of sheep that can easily be learnt (Kenyon et al. 2014). The results of this study indicate that both the farmers and technicians that were involved in this study had a high level of agreement between days and each other. This suggests that BCS is a farm-management tool that farmers can use to increase the productivity of their sheep flock. Further work is required, however, to determine the effect of prior experience with the technique, on the intra- and inter-observer variability.

Acknowledgements

This research was funded by Massey University and Partnership for excellence.

References

Beef + Lamb NZ 2013. Ewe body condition scoring (BCS). Wellington, New Zealand, Beef + Lamb New Zealand. 1 p.

Blair HT, Sewell AM, Corner-Thomas RA, Kemp P, Wood BA, Gray DI, Morris ST, Greer AW, Logan CM, Ridler AL, Hickson RE, Kenyon PR 2013. Understanding how farmers learn. Proceedings of the Association for the Advancement of Animal Breeding and Genetics 20: 1-5.

Cohen J 1968. Weighted kappa: Nominal scale agreement provision for scaled disagreement or partial credit. Psychological Bulletin 70: 213.

Corner-Thomas RA, Kenyon PR, Morris ST, Ridler AL, Hickson RE, Greer AW, Logan CM, Blair HT 2015. Influence of demographic factors on the use of farm management tools by New Zealand farmers. New Zealand Journal of Agricultural Research 58: 412-422.

Evans DG 1978. The interpretation and analysis of subjective body condition scores. Animal Science 26: 119-125.

Fleiss JL, Levin B, Paik MC 1981. The measurement of interrater agreement. Statistical methods for rates and proportions 2: 22-23.

Gunn RG, Smith WF, Senior AJ, Bartham E, Sim DA, Hunter EA 1991. Pre-mating herbage intake and the reproductive performance of north country cheviot ewes in different levels of body condition. Animal Production 52: 149-156.

Jefferies BC 1961. Body condition scoring and its use in management. Tasmanian Journal of Agriculture 32: 19-21.

Keinprecht H, Pichler M, Pothmann H, Huber J, Iwersen M, Drillich M 2016. Short term repeatability of body fat thickness measurement and body condition scoring in sheep as assessed by a relatively small number of assessors. Small Ruminant Research 139: 30-38.

Kenyon P, Morel P, Corner-Thomas R, Perez H, Somasiri S, Kemp P, Morris S 2017. Improved per hectare production in a lamb finishing system using mixtures of red and white clover with plantain and chicory compared to ryegrass and white clover. Small Ruminant Research 151: 90-97.

Kenyon PR, Maloney SK, Blache D 2014. Review of sheep body condition in relation to production characteristics. New Zealand Journal of Agricultural Research 57: 38-64.

Phythian C, Hughes D, Michalopoulou E, Cripps P, Duncan J 2012. Reliability of body condition scoring of sheep for cross-farm assessments. Small Ruminant Research 104: 156-162.

Russel AJF 1984. Means of assessing the adequacy of nutrition of pregnant ewes. Livestock Production Science 11: 429-436.

Sezenler T, Özder M, Yildirir M, Ceyhan A, Yüksel M 2011. The relationship between body weight and body condition score in some indigenous sheep breeds in turkey. Journal of Animal and Plant Science 21: 443-447.

Shands CG, Mcleod B, Lollback ML, Duddy G, Hatcher S, O'halloran WJ 2009. Comparison of manual assessments of ewe fat reserves for on-farm use. Animal Production Science 49: 630-636.

Shrout PE, Fleiss JL 1979. Intraclass correlations: Uses in assessing rater reliability. Psychological Bulletin 86: 420-428.

Teixeira A, Delfa R, Colomer-Rocher F 1989. Relationships between fat depots and body condition score or tail fatness in the rasa aragonesa breed. Animal Science 49: 275-280.

Yates W, Gleeson A 1975. Relationships between condition score and carcass composition of pregnant merino sheep. Australian Journal of Experimental Agriculture 15: 467-470.

Predicting internal adipose from selected computed tomography images in sheep

PL Johnson[a*], JL Juengel[a] and WE Bain*[a]

[a]*AgResearch Invermay, Puddle Alley, Mosgiel, New Zealand*

**Corresponding author.* Email: tricia.johnson@agresearch.co.nz

Abstract

Dairy cattle preferentially lay down internal (INT) (e.g., kidney) adipose relative to sub-cutaneous adipose (SCF) tissue, but this pattern is the opposite in beef cattle, which preferentially deposit adipose subcutaneously. It is proposed that these differential patterns of fat distribution evolved to match the different production drivers of these breeds. As the New Zealand sheep industry has become more diverse in terms of breeds and production systems, the role that differential adipose distribution could play in supporting different production systems is of interest. The potential to use commercially obtained Computed Tomography (CT) images (i.e., six images, selected to predict carcass attributes in the live animal), to additionally predict INTF in addition to carcass fatness, was investigated using a full set (i.e., 30-32) of CT images available on 50 maternal ewe lambs. The R^2 between the full- and sub-set of images for absolute amounts ranged from 0.25 for bone to 0.92 for SCF, with INTF 0.77 ($P<0.001$). When adjusted for total weight, correlations were slightly reduced, but still supported the ability of the analysis of the six images to accurately identify animals with differential fat distribution. Future work will include analysis of a further 550 animals from the same data set to determine the genetic correlation between the full and subset of images. If successful, adipose distribution can be predicted from existing and future commercial CT data sets and used to investigate its genetic and phenotypic relationship with production traits.

Keywords: internal adipose; subcutaneous adipose; computed tomography

Introduction

Selection for different production outcomes has been shown to drive differences in body composition in cattle. Specifically, it has been demonstrated that beef-cattle breeds, bred for meat production, lay down more adipose tissue subcutaneously versus internal adipose deposits, the opposite being true for dairy-cattle breeds, bred for milk production (Berg & Butterfield 1976; Wright & Russel 1984). There is evidence that internal deposits are more labile and, therefore, suit the energy demands presented by intensive milk-production systems (Lambe et al. 2005). Overseas, there is similar literature suggesting breed differences in the distribution of body adipose tissue in sheep (McClelland & Russel 1972; Lirette et al. 1984; Chay-Canul et al. 2011).

There is increasing interest in understanding adipose distribution in sheep as it has possible links to many production outcomes. Capturing of such data requires the use of full-body dissection data collected after slaughter or the use of Computed Tomography (CT) scanning. Computed Tomography scanning is used in the New Zealand sheep industry to estimate carcass composition of live animals. Whilst full-body CT images can be generated, the cost of such an approach is prohibitive from a commercial perspective, and research determined that six selected images can accurately predict carcass composition (Kvame et al. 2004) and these are collected routinely as part of commercial scanning systems in New Zealand (Jopson et al. 2009).

The aim of this study was to determine the accuracy with which the commercial sub-set of CT images could be used to describe body adipose distribution compared to a full set of body images, utilising a data set from ewe lambs (approximately one year of age) that had been full- body CT scanned.

Materials and methods

Computed tomography (CT) images were taken on live ewe lambs approximately one year of age as part of a larger study investigating genetic variation in feed efficiency as described by Johnson et al. (2018). In brief the animals were sourced from one of three progeny-test flocks which were based on New Zealand maternal breeds. A sub-set of 50 animals was randomly selected from 400 ewes CT scanned in year two of the study, for further analysis.

The live animals were CT scanned at the end of the feed-efficiency trial period. The animals were scanned with a GE LightSpeed 5.X Pro16 scanner (GE Healthcare, Australia) using the procedures described by Jopson et al. (1997) with a starting position before the 2nd or 3rd cervical vertebrae and an end position at the distal femur/proximal tibia. Images for this study were collected at 30-mm intervals resulting in between 30 and 32 images per animal. Each image was segmented such that the subcutaneous adipose (SCF), adipose associated with muscles (intermuscular adipose), and adipose within the body cavity (internal adipose: INT) were separated. Adipose depot, lean and bone areas were calculated in each image based on the Hounsfield unit (HU) ranges of the three tissues using AUTOCAT (Jopson et al. 1995). HU value ranges were -176 to -26, -25 to 144, 145 to 3017 HU for adipose, lean and bone areas respectively. Tissue area (count of pixels) from each image was numerically integrated and multiplied by the distance between images to estimate the tissue volume for subcutaneous, intermuscular and visceral adipose deposits as well as total lean and total bone calculations (Gundersen et al. 1988). Average pixel density was determined by weighting the average density in the individual images by the pixel area in each image. Pixel density was converted to physical density using the relationship shown between HU value and density by Fullerton (1980), which provided the conversion from volume to weight. All weights within a tissue type were summed for an animal to produce an estimate of subcutaneous-, intermuscular- and visceral-adipose, muscle and bone weight.

A second data set was generated, through selecting six images from all available images that represent the images used in commercial CT scanning of industry animals. Specifically, two scans were obtained from each region: forequarter (5th thoracic vertebrae and 7th cervical vertebrae), the loin (6th lumbar vertebrae), the rack (13th thoracic vertebrae) and the hindleg (2nd caudal vertebrae and 3rd sacral vertebrae). Calculations were made on the resulting data set using the methodology described above to generate data on the same traits of subcutaneous-, intermuscular- and visceral-adipose, muscle and bone weight.

The ratio of SCF to INT (SCF:INT) was calculated using the absolute weights of the two tissues. The correlation between estimates of the different adipose deposits as measured from the full set of CT images and the sub-set of CT images, together with the ratio trait were calculated using the correlation procedure in SAS. The raw weights were used in one analysis, and the residuals from a general linear model fitting TOTAL as a covariate were used in a second analysis.

Results and discussion

Literature from cattle has shown that there are significant differences among breed types in their adipose distribution, e.g., dairy type breeds having higher levels of INT relative to SCF, with more labile adipose type (Berg & Butterfield 1976; Wright & Russel 1984). Breed differences are known to exist in sheep, but the link through to production outcomes has not been shown (McClelland & Russel 1972; Lirette et al. 1984).

The animals from which the images were taken represent New Zealand maternal-breed genetics. A summary of the weights of adipose tissues estimated from both approaches in Table 1. The largest amount of variation was for the weight of subcutaneous adipose, with the weight of lean most consistent between the two groups of images. There was significant tissue-dependent variation in the weight of tissue reported, based on the sub-set compared to all of the images, with the six images underestimating the weight of SCF, INT and non-adipose visceral components and overestimating the weight of intermuscular adipose. These differences occurred because the weight of tissues is calculated including a measure of distance between the different images, and the start and end point for the six images did not include the full length of the carcass that the full scan includes. Additionally, tissues were not uniformly distributed, meaning that the six image approach will predict that some tissue types extend further or less than they actually do.

The correlation between the absolute weights of the tissues estimated from the six images and all images is in Table 2. The set of six images used commercially was selected through analysis to optimise predictions of lean and adipose only within the carcass component of the body, (Kvame et al. 2004; Jopson et al. 2009). Unsurprisingly, the highest correlations existed for subcutaneous adipose and lean tissue weight. The correlation for absolute weights were consistent with the results of Kvame et al. (2004), of R^2 0.87 to 0.98 across carcass cuts for subcutaneous adipose, and R^2 0.80 to 0.99 for lean. They also reported lower correlations for bone of R^2 0.65 to 0.90 for different carcass cuts, although still higher than those reported in the current study. Although internal adipose was not used in determining which images should be used in the commercial scanning, the resulting correlation for absolute weights of internal adipose tissue was high. The correlations between the weight-adjusted estimates (Table 2) were lower for all tissues, although still high for SCF and INT, with bone again the lowest. This indicates that some of the correlations for the absolute weights reflects that heavier animals will

Table 1 Summary statistics for measures of body composition of yearling maternal ewes made using computed tomography scanning using all images taken (n=32), or using a sub-set of six images.

		All images					Sub-set of six images					Difference between six & all images
	N	Mean	Std dev	CV	Min	Max	Mean	Std dev	CV	Min	Max	
Subcutaneous adipose	50	7.8	1.5	19%	4.7	12.2	5.5	1.1	19%	3.4	8.4	71%
Intermusuclar adipose	50	2.9	0.5	18%	1.6	4.2	3.5	0.6	18%	2.2	4.9	119%
Internal adipose	50	6.6	1.0	16%	4.5	9.3	5.4	1.0	18%	3.7	7.7	81%
Carcass lean	50	21.0	1.8	8%	16.4	25.2	20.7	1.6	8%	15.7	24.4	99%
Non-adipose visceral components	50	12.0	1.2	10%	9.6	15.4	9.8	1.2	12%	7.8	12.9	81%
Bone	50	4.7	0.4	8%	3.9	5.4	4.7	0.5	10%	3.8	5.9	100%
Subcut:internal	50	1.18	0.17	14%	0.9	1.7	1.03	0.15	15%	0.75	1.4	87%

Table 2 Correlations (R^2) between estimates of tissue types made using computed tomography scanning using all images or a sub-set of six images. Absolute weights or residuals after adjustment for total weight are shown. All correlations were highly significant (P<0.001), with the exception of residual bone (*) which was significant (P=0.008).

	Correlation (R^2) All Images vs six Images	
	Absolute	Residual (total weight adjusted)
Subcutaneous Adipose	0.92	0.81
Intermuscular Adipose	0.74	0.40
Internal Adipose	0.77	0.62
Lean	0.83	0.68
Non-adipose visceral components	0.59	0.51
Bone	0.25	0.14*
Subcutaneous:Internal	0.61	

have more of all tissue types than do lighter animals, but that there are differences in adipose distribution beyond differences in total weight. The correlation for the SCF:INT ratio was moderate.

The correlations for the total weight-adjusted tissue weights and the ratio trait are graphically represented in Fig. 1. The plots show that individual animals do not appear to significantly re-rank, and animals that have very low, or very high levels of a tissue type do so whether based on all images, or on the subset of images. This further indicates that the differences that are being reported are not strictly due to total weight differences among the animals, but rather that the subset of images is able to identify animals that have differential adipose deposition, i.e., those that are laying down more or less subcutaneous adipose, relative to internal adipose.

These results support further analysis of the remaining data set of 550 animals associated with the feed-efficiency trial to confirm the findings of this study. If successful, it would open up the option of re-analysing existing

Figure 1 Relationship between all computed tomography images and a sub-set of six images for total-body-weight adjusted weights of a) subcutaneous adipose; b) intermuscular adipose; c) internal adipose and d) lean and e) the ratio of subcutaneous adipose to internal adipose based on absolute weights of the respective tissues.

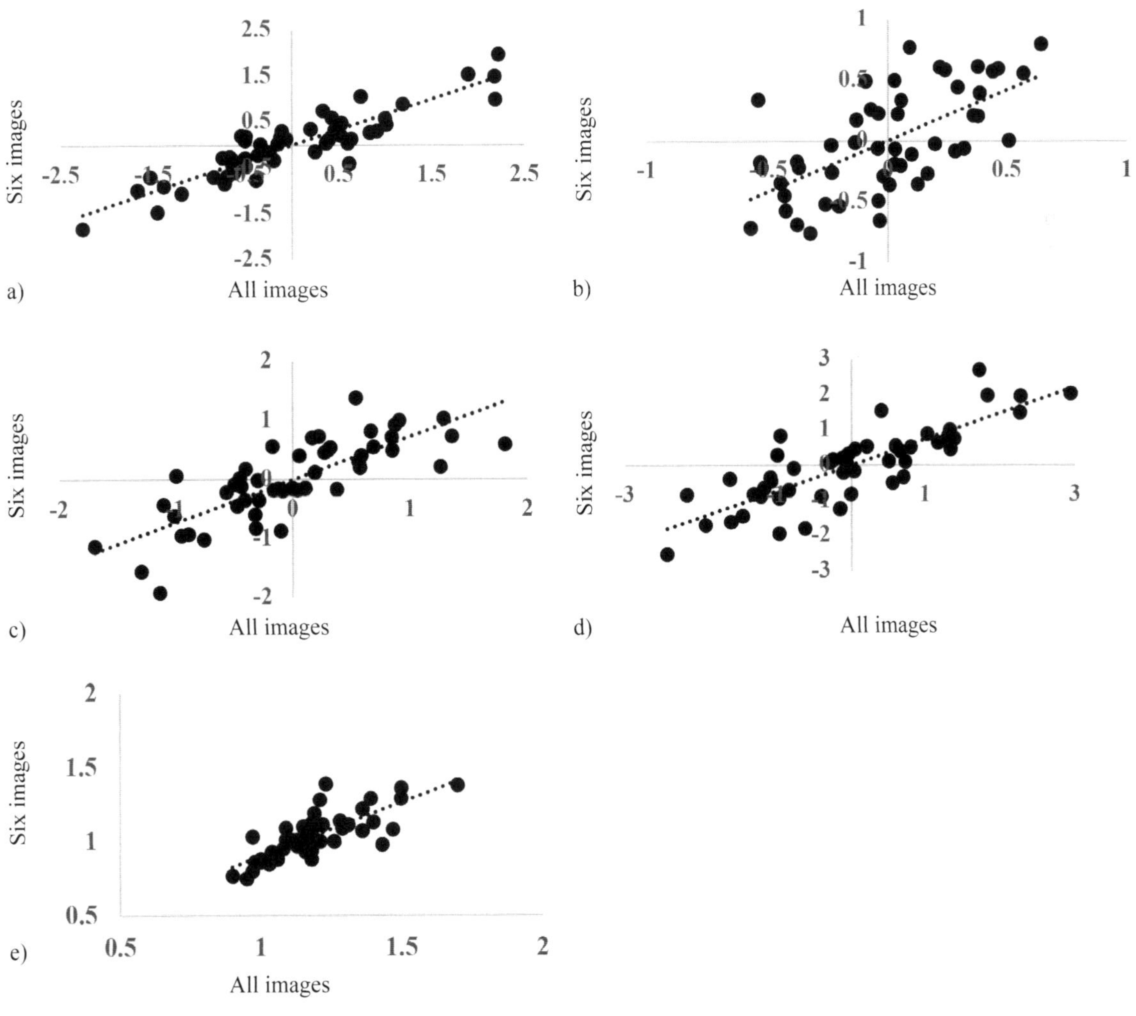

commercial images to determine their internal adipose content. However, the majority of the commercially scanned animals are rams around eight months of age, so further work would be required to determine whether or not they also differentially lay down adipose tissue into different depots. An alternative to using CT scanning to predict internal fat reserves would be to develop predictions based on ultrasound measures of internal adipose depots as has been done recently by Morales-Martinez et al. (2020) in Pelibuey sheep, a breed which reportedly lay down more adipose in internal adipose depots compared with the subcutaneous adipose depot (Chay-Canul et al. 2011). Through measuring kidney adipose thickness using ultrasonography, they were able to predict internal adipose reserves relative to dissected internal adipose reserves with a high level of accuracy ($R^2 = 0.71$).

Ultimately, the aim is to investigate whether or not there is a link between differences in relative body adipose deposition and production traits that can be exploited to improve production outcomes. The results from this study support the use of a lower-input (fewer images) method that will enable generation of more data for further analysis to investigate links between internal fat and production outcomes.

Acknowledgements

Generation and initial processing of the images was part of a Beef + Lamb New Zealand Genetics project funded by the Ministry for Business, Innovation and Employment, Beef + Lamb Zealand, New Zealand Agricultural Greenhouse Gas Research Centre and Pastoral Greenhouse Gas Research Consortia. The animals were sourced from the Woodlands Progeny Test and the Greenhouse Gas Selection lines which were funded by New Zealand Agricultural Greenhouse Gas Research Centre and Pastoral Greenhouse Gas Research Consortia. Internal AgResearch funding was used for analysis of the data. The CT scanning was undertaken by Innervision, and the authors thank Dr Neville Jopson for his assistance with the scanning.

References

Berg RT, Butterfield RM 1976. New Concepts of Cattle Growth. Hemel Hempstead, England, Sydney University Press, Prentice/Hall International, International Book Distributors, Ltd.

Chay-Canul AJ, Ayala-Burgos AJ, Ku-Vera JC, Magana-Monforte JG, Tedeschi LO 2011. The effects of metabolizable energy intake on body fat depots of adult Pelibuey ewes fed roughage diets under tropical conditions. Tropical Animal Health Production 43: 929-936.

Fullerton GD 1980. Tissue imaging and characterisation. Medical Physics Monograph. vol. 6. Fullerton GD and Zagzebski JA, American Institue of Physics.

Gundersen HJG, Bendtsen TF, Korbo L, Marcussen N, Møller A, Nielsen K, Nyenaargd JR, Pakkenberg, B, Sørensen FB, Vesterby A, West MJ 1988. Some new, simple and efficient sterological methods and their use in pathological research and diagnosis. Acta Pathology Microbiology Immunology Scandanavia 96: 379-394.

Johnson PL, Knowler K, Wing J, Hickey SPJ 2018. Preliminary estimates of genetic parameters for residual feed intake in sheep. Proceedings of the World Congress on Genetics Applied to Livestock Production: #608.

Jopson NB, Kolstad K, Sehested E, Vangen O 1995. Computed tomography as an accurate and cost effective alternative to carcass dissection. Proceedings of the Association for the Advancement of Animal Breeding and Genetics 11: 635-638.

Jopson NB, Newman S-AN, McEwan JC 2009. Developments in the sheep meat industry: Genetic evaluation of meat yield. Proceedings of the New Zealand Society of Animal Production 69: 161-164.

Jopson NB, Thompson JM, Fennessy PF 1997. Tissue mobilisation rates in male fallow deer (Dama dama) as determined by computed tomography: the effect of natural and enforced food restriction. Animal Science 65: 311-320.

Kvame T, McEwan JC, Amer PR, Jopson NB 2004. Economic benefits in selection for weight and composition of lamb cuts predicted by computer tomography. Livestock Production Science 90: 123-133.

Lambe NR, Brotherstone S, Young MJ, Conington J, Simm G 2005. Genetic relationships between seasonal tissue levels in Scottish Blackface ewes and lamb growth traits. Animal Science 81: 11-21.

Lirette A, Seoane JR, Minvielle F, Froehlich D 1984. Effects of Breed and Castration on Conformation, Classification, Tissue Distribution, Composition and Quality of Lamb Carcasses. Journal of Animal Science 58: 1343-1357.

McClelland TH, Russel AJF 1972. The distribution of body fat in Scottish Blackface and Finnish Landrace lambs. Animal Production 15: 301-306.

Morales-Martinez MA, Arce-Recinos C, Mendoza-Taco MM, Luna-Palomera C, Ramirez-Bautista MA, Piñeiro-Vazquez ÁT, Vicente-Perez R, Tedeschi LO, Chay-Canul AJ 2020. Developing equations for predicting internal body fat in Pelibuey sheep using ultrasound measurements. Small Ruminant Research 183: 106031.

Wright IA, Russel AJF 1984. Partition of fat, body composition and body condition score in mature cows. Animal Science 38: 23-32.

Changes in live weight and fleece characteristics during the lifetime of three breeds of New Zealand feral sheep that differ in fleece type

RMW Sumner[a]*, DR Scobie[b], D O'Connell[c] and HV Henderson[d]

[a]*Previously at AgResearch Ruakura, Private Bag 3123, Hamilton 3240, New Zealand, now retired;* [b]*AgResearch Lincoln, Private Bag 4749, Christchurch 8140, New Zealand;* [c]*Previously at AgResearch Lincoln, Private Bag 4749, Christchurch 8140, New Zealand, now retired;* [d]*AgResearch Ruakura, Private Bag 3123, Hamilton 3240, New Zealand.*

**Corresponding author:* Email: roland.sumner@xtra.co.nz

Abstract

Live weight after joining and nine fleece characteristics were recorded throughout the lifetime of flocks of Hokonui, Campbell Island and Raglan sheep grazing at Whatawhata and Winchmore Research Centres between 1991 and 2004. The wool characteristics were measured in 585 individual wool samples collected at shearing from 90 breeding ewes sampled between one year of age and up to 12 years of age. Data on live weight, fleece weight, staple length, mean and variability of fibre diameter, fibre curvature, crimping and core bulk were analysed after adjustment for effects of grazing location and reproductive performance during the previous year. The three flocks differed in all measured characteristics, with all except live weight, mean fibre curvature and core bulk exhibiting a significant flock by age interaction. Live weight attained a maximum at six years of age, while greasy fleece weight and staple length decreased after two years of age. Core bulk decreased after three years of age. Fibre curvature decreased and time to form a crimp increased throughout the sheep's life. Fibre diameter variability between and along fibres showed a variable age response between flocks. The three feral flocks exhibited a different age response to continuously farmed breeds.

Keywords: fleece characteristics; age effects; Hokonui; Campbell Island; Raglan

Introduction

Although sheep anecdotally have a life expectancy of 10 to 12 years, this requires healthy incisor teeth to maintain adequate food intake. As a consequence of tooth wear, which can vary between regions, it is common commercial practice in New Zealand to cull all breeding ewes by five or six years of age, at which time their health and associated productivity may have begun to decline (Bruère & West 1993).

While most wool characteristics are known to change with age (Sumner & Bigham 1993), modern instruments are now able to measure more objective wool characteristics than was possible in earlier studies reported for medium-wool Merino ewes in Australia (Brown et al. 1966) and Perendale ewes in New Zealand (Sumner & Dick 1997).

When superfine, fine and medium wool Merino ewes were fleece sampled between two to five years of age, there was a general trend for wool production to increase to a maximum at three years of age and then plateau, while wool quality traits tended to decrease with age, with variation in those trends related to bloodline (Hatcher et al. 2005). Similarly, when British long-wool sheep were culled at five years of age, the time to form a crimp and fibre curvature increased towards an asymptote, although wool bulk did not change with increasing age (Sumner & Dick 1997; Sumner & Upsdell 2001). On the other hand, fleece weight, staple length and fibre diameter attained a maximum at three years of age before decreasing, while fibre curvature and crimp frequency decreased curvilinearly with increasing age (Sumner & Dick 1997; Sumner & Upsdell 2001). The authors are unaware of any published reports of changes in wool characteristics of New Zealand feral or 'continuously farmed' sheep breeds, producing different wool types, living beyond five years of age while grazing in a common environment.

In the study reported here, objective wool measurement data were collected from three flocks of mixed-age New Zealand feral ewes that differed in fleece type and grazed together on the same property between 1990 and 2004. Individual sheep were culled when it was deemed from liveweight records, condition score and tooth condition that it was unlikely they would survive a further year, or when they had ceased to reproduce. The oldest ewe was culled at 12 years of age.

Methods

'Overarching' study

The wool samples measured in this experiment were derived from a larger study in which groups of sheep exposed to a feral existence of between 40 and 75 years, were captured from three different locations around New Zealand (Sumner et al. 2017). After capture, the flocks were managed in a common farming environment. It has become common practice in New Zealand to name flocks of feral sheep by the name of the location in which they lived. The flocks included in this study were the 'Hokonui', captured in the Hokonui Hills in central Southland, 43 km north-east of Invercargill (45°95′S,168°62′E); the 'Campbell Island', captured on Campbell Island situated in the Southern Ocean 590 km south of Bluff (52°33′S,169°09′E) and the 'Raglan', captured on the Paritata Peninsula in Raglan (Whaingaroa) Harbour 30 km west of Hamilton (37°46′S,174°36′E). Each feral flock had a different inherent fleece type and associated wool characteristics sufficient to consider it a distinct breed type (Sumner et al. 2017). Derivation of the Hokonui, is considered to be a Saxon Merino (fine-wool type), Campbell Island a Saxon Merino crossed with a British long-wool breed (known as a New Zealand Halfbred; mid-micron wool type) and Raglan a New Zealand Romney (coarse-wool type).

Details of the history of the three feral flocks in this study, along with their management and overall productivity following capture have been reported previously (Sumner et al. 2017). Briefly the three feral flocks grazed without human intervention for approximately 15 generations before being captured in 1976. Subsequently they were farmed according to normal farm management practices on several Ministry of Agriculture and Fisheries farms until 1990 when they were transferred to Whatawhata Research Centre. In 2000 they were transferred to Winchmore Research Station and finally dispersed in 2004. Some management protocols differed between the two properties.

Flock management in this study

At Whatawhata, the three feral flocks were grazed conjointly with approximately 1,500 experimental ewes of diverse breeds involved in several experiments. While at Winchmore the three feral flocks were combined and run separately from other flocks of experimental sheep. The live weight of all ewes was recorded after joining in April/May at Whatawhata and May/June at Winchmore. Lambs were individually identified at birth and their dam recorded.

Yearling ewes were shorn in September/October at both grazing locations, with the adult ewes being shorn in August (pre-lambing) at Whatawhata using a standard shearing comb (maximum thickness of 3 mm leaving a 2-4 mm stubble (Dabiri et al. 1995)). A 'winter' (or 'cover') shearing comb (maximum thickness of 7 mm leaving a 5 -7 mm stubble (Dabiri et al. 1995)) was used for the ewe shearing in August 2000 after the flocks were transferred to Winchmore. From 2001 onwards, the ewes at Winchmore were shorn in December to alleviate the risk of exposing them to late spring storms using a standard shearing comb. Individual greasy fleece weights were recorded at each shearing.

Sampling protocol

A sample of approximately 15 g of midside fleece was collected with a shearing handpiece using a standard comb, prior to shearing both the yearling and adult ewes. The sample was stored in a labelled plastic bag for later measurement. No wool samples were collected from adult ewes in 1991, 1992 or 1993. To reduce any potential bias due to a greater proportion of samples being measured from more young sheep than older sheep, only wool samples from ewes which supplied four or more wool samples were measured. This generated a total of 585 wool samples across the three feral flocks (Table 1).

The length of five wool staples from each sample were measured with a ruler and the mean calculated. The total number of crimps were counted along each of the five staples measured for staple length and the mean calculated. Mean fibre diameter, fibre diameter standard deviation between fibres, fibre diameter standard deviation along fibres and mean fibre curvature were measured using an OFDA2000 instrument, with a teased staple retained in a polyester slide (Sumner et al. 2009). Mean crimp frequency of each sample was calculated as the mean total number of crimps along each staple divided by the mean staple length. Estimated core bulk was calculated as Log_e core bulk = 1.06 + 0.61 Log_e mean fibre diameter – 0.42 Log_e mean fibre curvature + 0.11 (Log_e mean fibre curvature)^2 (Model 8 reported by Sumner et al. 2009).

To account for changes that occurred when the adult ewes were shorn with a 'winter' comb in 2000, and the different shearing policy at Winchmore when the ewes were shorn in December, greasy fleece weights, staple length and total number of crimps along the staple were adjusted to the amount of fleece grown in 365 days. This was achieved by proportionally adjusting the individual recorded measurement for the interval between the previous and 'current' shearing. Further adjustments were made using assumptions based on the seasonal pattern of wool growth (Bigham et al. 1978; Sumner et al. 1994). The time to form a crimp was calculated as 365 divided by the total number of crimps along the staple adjusted to the amount of fleece grown in 365 days.

Table 1 Number of measured wool samples from each flock by grazing location by age, collected from 24 Hokonui, 36 Campbell Island and 29 Raglan sheep.

Flock	Grazing location	Age (years) 1	2	3	4	5	6	7	8	9	10	11	12	Number of samples
Hokonui	Whatawhata	21	19	18	15	16	12	10	6	0	0	0	0	117
	Winchmore	0	0	2	5	5	12	8	7	6	3	1	0	49
	Total	21	19	20	20	21	24	18	13	6	3	1	0	166
Campbell Island	Whatawhata	31	25	25	21	23	24	15	12	3	0	0	0	179
	Winchmore	0	0	2	6	9	12	12	4	4	2	1	1	53
	Total	31	25	27	27	32	36	27	16	7	2	1	1	232
Raglan	Whatawhata	26	22	23	17	18	18	13	2	1	1	0	0	141
	Winchmore	0	0	1	6	7	11	9	7	4	1	0	0	46
	Total	26	22	24	23	25	29	22	9	5	2	0	0	187
Grand total		78	66	71	70	78	89	67	38	18	7	2	1	585

Table 2 P value of the main effects for flock, age, grazing location and flock by age interaction. An estimate of the maximum and minimum standard error of the difference (SED) for age within flock for live weight and each of the measured wool characteristics is included. Bold text indicates significance at P<0.05.

Effect	Post-join live weight (kg)	Greasy fleece weight adjusted to 365 days (kg)	Staple length adjusted to 365 days (mm)	Mean fibre diameter (µm)	Fibre diameter variability between fibres (µm)	Fibre diameter variability along fibres (µm)	Mean fibre curvature (°/mm)	Crimp frequency (crimps/cm)	Time to form a crimp (days)	Estimated core bulk (cm³/g)
Flock	**<0.001**	**<0.001**	**<0.001**	**<0.001**	**<0.001**	**<0.001**	**<0.001**	**<0.001**	**<0.001**	**<0.001**
Age	**<0.001**	**<0.001**	**<0.001**	**<0.001**	**<0.001**	**0.02**	**<0.001**	0.22	**<0.001**	**<0.001**
Grazing location	0.30	**0.02**	0.17	0.11	**0.02**	**0.02**	**0.01**	**0.01**	**0.02**	0.08
Flock x age	0.56	**0.03**	**<0.001**	**0.02**	**0.003**	**0.002**	0.07	**0.04**	**<0.001**	0.48
SED maximum	4.1	0.4	12	1.7	0.6	0.8	8	0.6	3.3	1.6
SED minimum	0.7	0.1	2	0.3	0.1	0.1	1	0.1	0.6	0.3

Statistical analysis

A linear mixed model was fitted to the data using residual maximum likelihood (REML) in Genstat (VSN International 2019), with ewe and year of record as random effects and flock, grazing location, age, flock by age interaction, and the number of lambs weaned by the ewe, as fixed effects. Relocation of the flocks was not allowed for at the commencement of this study. As a consequence of relocation, the unbalanced number of sheep of each age at each grazing location rendered analysis of interactions involving grazing location meaningless.

Results

Sample number

The number of wool samples collected from each flock by grazing location by age, is shown in Table 1. A total of six Hokonui, 19 Campbell Island and 15 Raglan sheep provided all their samples while grazing at Whatawhata. No sheep provided all their samples while grazing at Winchmore.

Assessed effects

P values of the main effects for flock, age, grazing location and the flock by age interaction, for live weight after joining and each measured wool characteristic are shown in Table 2. The adjusted mean values for the interaction of flock by age for each measured wool characteristic are plotted in Figure 1.

Flock effect

There was a significant flock effect for live weight after joining and all of the measured wool characteristics. In the case of the three measured wool characteristics associated with fibre curvature, namely mean fibre curvature, crimp frequency and estimated core bulk, the between-flock rank was Hokonui highest, followed by Campbell Island and Raglan which was lowest. For all the other measured wool characteristics, except greasy fleece weight adjusted to 365 days wool growth, Raglan was higher than Campbell Island which was higher than Hokonui. In the case of live weight after joining and greasy fleece weight adjusted to 365 days wool growth, Raglan was heaviest, but Campbell Island and Hokonui were not significantly different (Figure 1).

Age effect

There was a significant age effect for all the measured characteristics except crimp frequency. Time to form a crimp, increased at a faster rate with ageing than mean fibre diameter. Live weight after joining increased to six years of age and then decreased, with greasy fleece weight adjusted to 365 days growth falling after two years of age. Mean fibre curvature, estimated core bulk and staple length adjusted to 365 days growth, all decreased linearly with increasing age.

Fibre diameter variability between and along fibres showed a similar trend with age, where the magnitude of the between-fibre variability was associated with the magnitude of mean fibre diameter. On the other hand, the magnitude of the along-fibre variability was less than between-fibre variability, reflecting the reduced rhythm of seasonal wool growth in the Merino compared with other coarse-wool breeds grazed at the same location (Sumner et al. 1994).

Grazing location effect

There was a significant grazing location effect for six of the measured wool characteristics. With relocation of the ewes from Whatawhata to Winchmore greasy fleece weight adjusted to 365 days wool growth, fibre diameter variability between and along fibres, and time to form a crimp increased, while mean fibre curvature and crimp frequency decreased (Table 3).

Flock-by-age effect

There was a significant interaction between flock and age for all the measured characteristics except live weight after joining, mean fibre curvature and estimated core bulk (Figure 1). The pronounced decrease in both greasy fleece weight and staple length adjusted to 365 days growth with increasing age, was more pronounced for the most productive Raglan breed, than for the least productive Hokonui breed, with the Campbell Island being intermediate. Crimp frequency and time to form a crimp,

Figure 1 Mean values for (a) live weight after joining (kg), (b) greasy fleece weight adjusted to 365 days growth (kg), (c) staple length adjusted to 365 days growth (mm), (d) mean fibre diameter (µm), (e) fibre diameter variability between fibres (µm), (f) fibre diameter variability along fibres (µm), (g) mean fibre curvature (°/mm), (h) crimp frequency (crimps/cm), (i) time to form a crimp (days) and (j) estimated core bulk (cm^3/g) within the Hokonui (▲), Campbell Island (■) and Raglan (●) flocks over time. Error bars shown are the minimum (on left) and maximum (on right) standard error of the difference (SED) for ewe age within each flock. Actual SED for a defined comparison is related to the number of measured samples in each age group within each flock (Table 1).

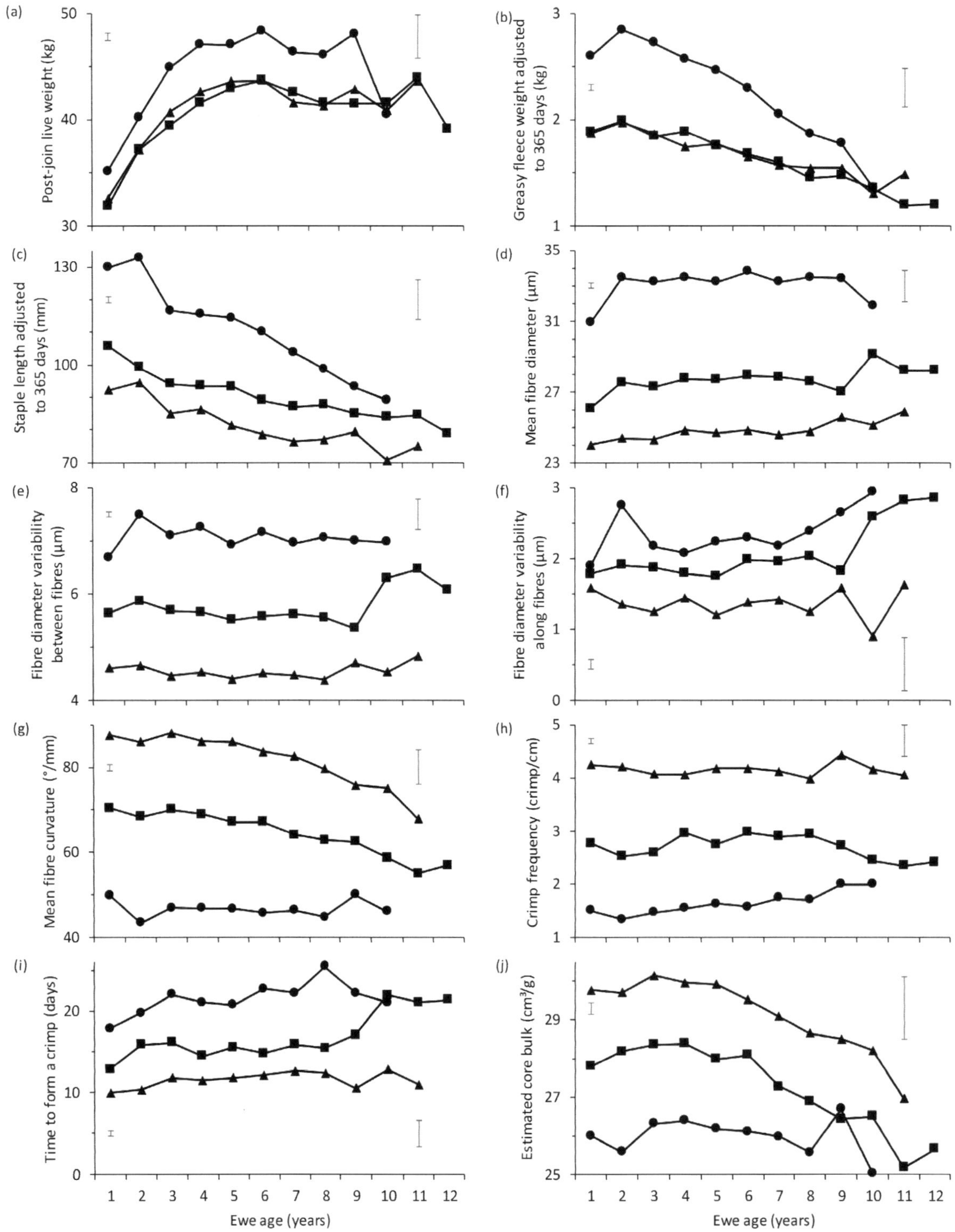

Table 3 Adjusted grazing location means and standard error of difference for live weight and each of the measured wool characteristics.

Effect	Post-join live weight (kg)	Greasy fleece weight adjusted to 365 days (kg)	Staple length adjusted to 365 days (mm)	Mean fibre diameter (μm)	Fibre diameter variability between fibres (μm)	Fibre diameter variability along fibres (μm)	Mean fibre curvature (°/mm)	Crimp frequency (crimps/cm)	Time to form a crimp (days)	Estimated core bulk (cm^3/g)
Whatawhata	40.6	1.7	90	28.2	5.5	1.6	66	3.0	16.2	27.6
Winchmore	43.4	1.9	96	29.0	6.2	2.4	61	2.6	17.8	27.0
Standard error of difference	2.6	0.1	5	0.5	0.3	0.3	2	0.1	0.6	0.3

exhibited a significant interaction between flock and age, where Hokonui sheep with the smallest crimp, exhibited a faster decline in crimp formation with increasing age compared to Raglan sheep with the largest crimp. Campbell Island sheep were intermediate in the rate of crimp development.

Discussion

Although there were statistically significant grazing location effects for six of the measured wool characteristics, the effects are of little practical relevance on account of their small magnitude and the disparity in numbers of ewes at the two grazing locations. These effects will not be further discussed.

In this study the live weight after joining of three flocks of feral sheep with different fleece types, showed a curvilinear relationship that increased to a plateau at five to six years of age before declining. As a comparison the live weight of Australian Merino ewes (Brown et al. 1966) and New Zealand Wiltshire and Perendale ewes (Sumner et al. 2012) began to decline a year earlier with the feral ewes having a lower mean live weight. Possible effects on live weight of sheep living in a feral environment have been discussed by Sumner et al. (2017). Despite the lower live weight of the feral ewes in this study relative to other continuously farmed breeds, the increasing live weight of the feral ewes during much of their lifetime is a clear demonstration that the sampled ewes were fit and healthy with no nutritional impediment to their productivity, particularly wool production.

While there are limited published data reporting age effects on live weight, there are fewer reports of age effects on objectively measured wool characteristics that can be compared with the data reported here, other than a single report for Australian Merino ewes (Brown et al. 1966) and a single report for New Zealand Perendale ewes (Sumner & Dick 1997).

In contrast to the published data the most striking result from this study was that while the ewes were still actively growing, greasy fleece weight declined linearly from two years of age. This is the first shearing after they have attained puberty. These results are in marked contrast to the Merino and Perendale ewes that attained a maximum greasy fleece weight at three to four years of age before declining (Brown et al. 1966; Sumner & Dick 1997).

Staple length in the current study declined linearly in a similar manner to greasy fleece weight from two years of age. In the Australian study, where staple length also declined in a linear fashion from two years of age, maximal greasy fleece weight was not attained until three to four years of age. In the case of the Perendale ewes staple length and greasy fleece weight also followed a similar relationship after achieving a maximal greasy fleece weight at three to four years of age.

Mean fibre diameter was another wool characteristic in this study that exhibited a different response to that observed in Australian Merino and New Zealand Perendale fleeces. In this study mean fibre diameter showed a slight progressive increase from two to eight years of age when the within group variability increased with few ewes remaining at older ages. In the Australian study mean fibre diameter of the Merino ewes increased to a maximum at about six years of age before it began to decline, while in the Perendale mean fibre diameter began declining after three years of age. Fibre diameter variability between fibres within the fleeces of the sheep in this study and the Perendale fleeces increased slowly over time. The authors are unaware of any studies that have reported age effects on fibre diameter variability along fibres within the fleece.

A number of measures of the crimp in staples and fibres have been reported. Crimp frequency in this study did not exhibit a significant age effect while the crimp frequency in Perendale ewes decreased slowly with age. The only characteristics measured in this study that did align well with data from the New Zealand Perendale were fibre curvature and core bulk. Fibre curvature progressively decreased as Hokonui and Campbell Island sheep aged. There was no defined effect for the Raglan sheep. This effect is visually apparent with older sheep having a larger and less clearly defined staple crimp. With the measurement of core bulk being derived by an algorithm involving fibre curvature (Sumner et al. 2009), core bulk of both groups of sheep decreased after two to three years of age as the fleeces exhibited progressively less springiness.

What might be the biological basis of the different age responses exhibited by the ewes in this study compared with those in the published reports?

Wool growth, as described by greasy fleece weight grown over a defined period of time, has previously been considered in Merinos to be derived from the following components (Turner 1956);

$$W = Y \, . \, S \, . \, R \, . \, A \, . \, F \, . \, N \, . \, \rho$$

where W is total clean wool weight per head, Y is percent clean yield, S is smooth body surface area, R is wrinkling factor, A is average fibre cross-sectional area, F is average fibre length, N is number of fibres per unit skin area, and ρ is the specific gravity of wool.

Of the characteristics considered by Turner (1956), approximations of W, S, A and F were measured in the current study with;

$$W' \propto S' \, . \, A' \, . \, F'$$

where W' was greasy fleece weight adjusted to 365 days growth, S' was smooth surface area of the skin estimated from live weight after joining, A' was mean fibre cross-sectional area estimated from mean fibre diameter and F' was mean fibre length estimated from staple length adjusted to 365 days growth.

Of the measured traits, staple length was the dominant characteristic in influencing greasy fleece weight with a correlation of $r = 0.68 \pm 0.02$ ($P<0.001$) explaining 46% of the variation in greasy fleece weight. The other characteristics are clearly of lesser importance as evidenced by the trends shown in Figure 1.

The authors are unaware of any published reports of the biological basis for a decline in wool follicle output as sheep age. It is of note that there was a similar proportional decline exhibited by each of the three flocks. This could be a reflection of a biological response that was present at the time the flocks became feral, before intensive selection for increased fleece weight was applied across the national sheep flock. Alternatively, it could be a survival response that developed during the period that the flocks were not subjected to human intervention to manage their welfare, as suggested by Sumner et al. (2017). The cause cannot be experimentally uncovered as anecdotally all continuously farmed flocks in New Zealand have been 'modified' by their owners during the last 100 years in an attempt to increase their inherent wool productivity. The marked lineal decline in wool growth from two years of age remains in all three feral flocks, which each grow a different wool type, after they have been intensively managed without the application of any selection pressure on wool production for several generations.

It is of note that in an earlier one-year study using a mixed-age sample of the feral flocks evaluated here, the older ewes exhibited a reduction in total wool follicle density and increased fibre seasonality associated with reduced follicle activity during winter compared to younger ewes relative to modern breed counterparts (Pearson et al. 1999).

The varied responses in terms of age effects recorded for the measured wool characteristics shown by these flocks, relative to Australian Merinos and New Zealand Perendales, highlight the complexity of the biological processes associated with wool growth and the expression of fibre crimp (Harland et al. 2018). In these feral flocks the time to form a crimp in the Raglan ewes is proportionately longer than in the Campbell Island and Hokonui flocks resulting in a significant flock by age effect ($P<0.001$). This aligns closely with the decline in staple length which also exhibited a significant flock by age effect ($P<0.001$). Clearly a different follicle regulation mechanism operates within these three feral flocks compared with the Australian Merino and New Zealand Perendale, which themselves differ slightly for some characteristics.

With the feral sheep demonstrating a different response while ageing to those reported for Australian Merino and New Zealand Perendale sheep, the trends reported here cannot be extrapolated to modern breeds beyond the normal age of culling. Further studies are required to understand the biological factors regulating cell division within the follicle that result in the different pattern of wool growth expressed by sheep that have lived in a feral environment for several generations, relative to ancestrally related sheep that have been farmed continuously.

Acknowledgements

Objective fibre measurements were undertaken with investment from the Rare Breeds Conservation Society of New Zealand. The late Drs Murray Bigham and Francis Cockrem had the foresight to preserve these sheep flocks for scientific study. The field and technical staff at Whatawhata Research Centre and Winchmore Research Station for assistance in management of the sheep and collection of field data.

References

Bigham ML, Sumner RMW, Elliott KH 1978. Seasonal wool production of Romney, Coopworth, Perendale, Cheviot and Corriedale wethers. New Zealand Journal of Agricultural Research 21: 377-382.

Brown GH, Turner HN, Young SSY, Dolling CHS 1966. Vital statistics for an experimental flock of Merino sheep. III. Factors affecting wool and body characteristics including the effect of age and its possible interaction with method of selection. Australian Journal of Agricultural Research 17: 557-581.

Bruère AN, West DM 1993. Dental abnormalities. In: The sheep. Foundation for Continuing Education of the New Zealand Veterinary Association, Massey University, Palmerston North, New Zealand. Pp 197-220.

Dabiri N, Holmes CW, McCutcheon SN, Parker WJ, Morris ST 1995. Resistance to cold stress in sheep shorn by cover comb or standard comb. Animal Science 60: 451-456.

Harland DP, Vernon JA, Woods JL, Nagase S, Itou T, Koike K, Scobie DR, Grosvenor AJ, Dyer JM, Clerens S 2018. Intrinsic curvature in wool fibres is determined by the relative length of orthocortical and paracortical cells. Journal of Experimental Biology 221, jeb 172312. Doi 10.1242/jeb.172312.

Hatcher S, Atkins KD, Thornberry KJ 2005. Age changes in wool traits of Merino sheep in Western NSW. Proceedings of the Sixteenth Conference of the Association for the Advancement of Animal Breeding and Genetics 16: 314-317.

Pearson AJ, Ashby MG, Nixon AJ, Sumner RMW 1999. Seasonal wool growth patterns and the follicle and fibre characteristics of New Zealand feral sheep. Proceedings of the New Zealand Society of Animal Production 59: 34-38.

Sumner RMW, PB Baxter, MP Upsdell 2009. Prediction of core bulk using OFDA instruments. International Journal of Sheep and Wool Science 57: 10-24.

Sumner RMW, Bigham ML 1993. Biology of fibre growth and possible genetic and non-genetic means of influencing fibre growth in sheep and goats – a review. Livestock Production Science 33: 1-29.

Sumner RMW, Clarke JN, Pearson AJ, Speedy PM 1994. Repeatability of seasonal wool growth in Merino sheep. Proceedings of the New Zealand Society of Animal Production 54: 163-165.

Sumner RMW, Dick JL 1997. Changes in fibre and follicle characteristics related to wool bulk during the lifetime of Perendale ewes. Proceedings of the New Zealand Society of Animal Production 57: 65-69.

Sumner RMW, Scobie DR, O'Connell D, Henderson HV 2012. Relative performance of Wiltshire and Perendale sheep. Proceedings of the New Zealand Society of Animal Production 72: 28-34.

Sumner RMW, Scobie DR, O'Connell D, Henderson HV 2017. Relative live weight, fleece weight and reproductive rate of farmed feral sheep (*Ovis aries* L.). New Zealand Journal of Zoology 44: 319-341.

Sumner RMW, Upsdell MP 2001. Age effects and interrelationships between wool characteristics of genotypes used to develop GrowBulk sheep. Proceedings of the New Zealand Society of Animal Production 61: 100-103.

Turner HN 1956. Measurement as an aid to selection in breeding sheep for wool production. Animal Breeding Abstracts 24(2): 87-118.

VSN International 2019. Genstat for Windows 20th Edition. VSN International, Hemel Hempstead, UK. Web page: Genstat.co.uk

BRIEF COMMUNICATION: The behaviour of sheep around a natural waterway

AS Bunyaga*, RA Corner-Thomas, LL Burkitt, I Draganova and PR Kenyon

School of Agriculture and Environment, Massey University, Private Bag 11222, Palmerston North, 4442, New Zealand.

**Corresponding author:* Email: A.Bunyaga@massey.ac.nz

Abstract

Access of cattle to waterways has been shown to be a potential cause of poor-water quality, due to nutrients and pathogens deposited via urination and defecation. In addition, cattle can pug the banks of waterways and, thus, cause sediment loss. Although government-imposed regulations to fence waterways currently only applies to dairy cattle in New Zealand, it is likely that some exclusion restrictions will apply to sheep and beef in the future. This is a concern, as there is very little research examining the behaviour of sheep around natural waterways in NZ. Video recordings were made to observe the interaction of mixed-age Romney ewes (n=40) with a natural waterway at Massey University's hill-country farm Tuapaka. Ewe behaviour and movements were monitored continuously for two weeks using GPS devices and motion-activated trail cameras. Ewes were offered reticulated water (week 2) or were restricted from accessing the water trough (week 1). Riparian zones were accessed by some ewes (n=20) whose behaviours observed appeared to be influenced by time of day and environmental temperature. When in the riparian areas, ewes spent 68% of their time grazing, 15.9% stationary and 2.2% drinking. Access to the water trough had no effect (P>0.05) on the drinking behaviour of ewes. It was concluded that, during winter, although only a small number of sheep drank from waterways, ewes accessed riparian zones to graze.

Keywords: behaviour; ewes; waterways; riparian areas

Introduction

Access of cattle to waterways, such as streams can be a cause of poor water quality, due to urination, defecation and pugging (O'Callaghan et al. 2019; Cournane et al. 2011). Little information is available, however, on the behaviour of sheep in and around natural waterways. It has previously been shown that the water contained in pasture consumed has the potential to meet daily water requirements of sheep during some periods of the year (i.e., cooler periods) without negatively impacting performance (Macfarlane et al. 1958). In environments where the moisture content of the pasture is low or feed intake is inadequate, however, sheep may need to drink water to meet their requirements (Daneshi et al. 2012; McGregor 1986). In New Zealand, on sheep farms, water is often provided through reticulated water troughs, or natural waterways such as streams or dams, which on large farms may be the main source of water. Thus, it is important to understand sheep behaviour while near waterways and how they interact with them. The objective of this study was to examine the behaviour of sheep around natural waterways during the winter period. We also investigated whether water restriction influenced behaviour of sheep.

Materials and methods

All the procedures in this study were carried out with the approval of the Massey University Animal Ethics Committee (MUEC 19/62). The study was conducted at Massey University's hill country farm Tuapaka, located approximately 15 km north-east of Palmerston North (40.3346° S, 175.7316° E). Mixed-age, single-bearing (n=40) ewes were managed in a 1.56 ha paddock that contained a discrete natural stream. Ewes were continuously stocked on a perennial ryegrass pasture in which masses were maintained above 1000 kg DM/ha. The stream was classified as a fifth-order stream (based on high resolution 1 m LiDAR digital elevation data). The stream was 233 m long, 1 m wide and less than 30 cm deep. Ewe behaviour was observed for two weeks during winter from 16 to 30 August 2019. Twenty-four-hour video surveillance cameras (n=6, Moultrie® model MCG-13297, n=4, TechView® model QC8027 and n=4, Bushnell © model 119736) were positioned along the waterway to monitor the movement and behaviour of ewes around the banks of the creek. Cameras were placed at intervals of 14 to 18 m and recorded footage clearly up to a distance of 15 m (riparian zone) (stream S, see Fig. 1). Once triggered, cameras were set to record for 30 seconds, followed by a non-recording period of 10 seconds. If the animal was still within the range of the camera after the non-recording period another 30s of footage was recorded. The cameras contained an infrared LED flash to allow footage to be captured during hours of darkness without visible light being emitted. The cameras also had a built-in temperature sensor to allow recording of ambient temperature data. All ewes were fitted with a GPS unit (Custom build units, DataCarter, weighing 100 g) attached to a collar. Ewes also had a uniquely numbered plastic collar to allow identification from video footage.

The study used a crossover design whereby ewes were offered reticulated water from a trough (week 2) or restricted from accessing the trough by covering it (week 1). Moisture content of pasture was determined once a week. At approximately 1 pm, six pasture samples of approximately 50 g and a height of 5-15 cm were collected from randomly selected positions within the paddock by hand plucking. Samples were oven dried at 80°C for 48 h to determine dry matter yields and moisture content. It rained for a short while on the 17 August 2019 and drizzled on the 26 of August 2019 for about 2 hours, but no puddles were formed.

Global positioning system (GPS) data from sheep in the paddock were analysed using ArcGIS mapping tools (ArcGIS Pro 2.2.4). An ethogram was developed that included the following behaviours; grazing, walking, stationary, drink (further categorised by whether ewe stood on the bank or in the water), sniff, walk in the stream, and out of view. Sheep behaviour in video footage was coded using BORIS software [version 7.8.2; Friard and Gamba (2016)]. Soon after coding, a time-budget of single or grouped observations was extracted and generated a summary of the main behaviours. Statistical analyses were performed using R 3.6.0. To determine if water-trough restriction influenced the behaviours of ewes (e.g., % grazing, drinking) a two-factor analysis of variance (ANOVA) was utilised. Linear regression was used to determine if behaviours of ewes were associated with time of day or environmental temperature.

Results and discussion

The aim of this study was to observe the behaviour of single-bearing mature ewes around a natural waterway. Grazing was the predominant behaviour observed when ewes were in the riparian zone during the study (Table 1).

The average time of the day and environmental temperature when sheep accessed the riparian zone was 14.7±0.5 h and 13.3±0.4°C respectively. Ewes in the riparian areas spent 68% of their time grazing, 15.9% stationary and 2.2% drinking from the stream. Ewes were also observed to sniff the water (0.5% of total visit time), and on one occasion a ewe walked in the stream (0.1%, see Table 1). Ewes spent less time in the riparian zone (0.2%) than to the rest of the paddock. During the study the moisture content of the pasture was 77.0 ± 0.48%.

Table 1 A time budget showing the number of occurrences, duration and proportion of time that ewes spent showing each behaviour during the two weeks of the study.

Behaviour	Total number of occurrences (n)	Total duration (s)	Mean duration (s)	% of the total time
Stationary	52	433	8	15.9
Grazing	96	1853	19	68.0
Walking	53	306	6	11.2
Drink	5	60	12	2.2
Sniff	5	12	2	0.5
Out of view	4	57	14	2.1
Walk in the stream	1	3	3	0.1
Total	216	2724	9	100

During the study, half of the ewes (n=20) did not approach within 15 m of the waterway (riparian zone) at any time during the study. Of those ewes that were observed within 15 m of the waterway the period of most frequent activity was between 15:30 and 18:00 h. Most of the ewes that were observed within 15 m of the waterway, grazed within 3 m of the water (i.e., within the riparian zone). On several occasions (n=7) a single ewe was observed to jump over the stream rather than walking through the water. All ewe drinking behaviours were observed during the warmer hours of the day when the ambient temperatures recorded by the cameras were above 20°C between 11:00

Figure 1 Map of a paddock displaying the movement of one ewe based on GPS collar readings over a period of two weeks in August 2020. GPS points are represented by white dots, and the stream represented by the solid line (S).

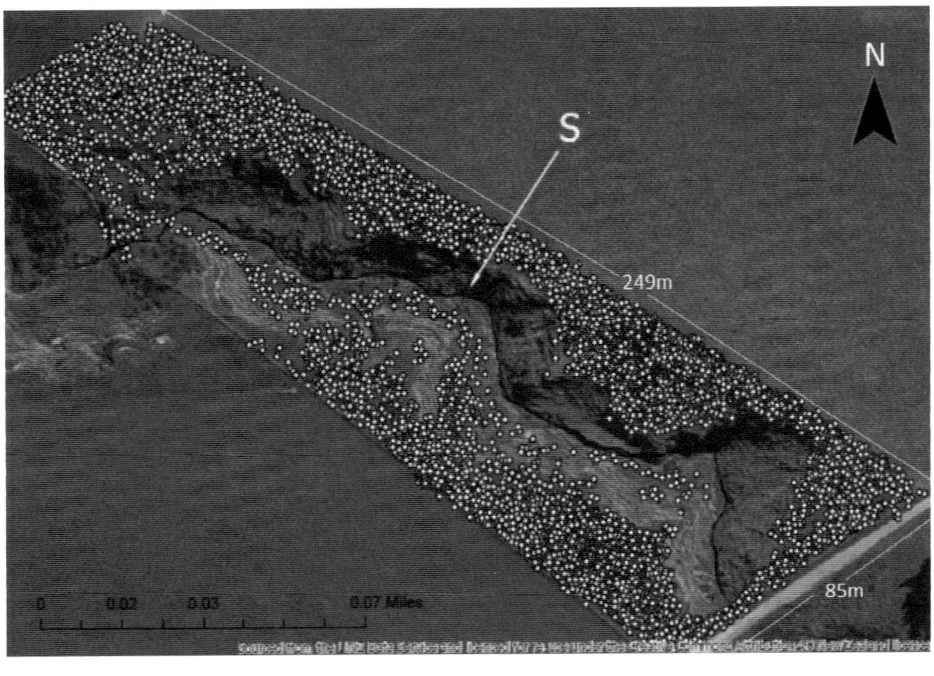

h and 16:00 h. Al-Ramamneh et al. (2012) also observed a higher drinking frequency between 10:00 h and 16:00 h among German black-head mutton sheep housed indoors under temperate conditions. Similarly, bighorn sheep were reported to visit water sources in summer in the United States of America between 11:14 h and 17:30 h (Whiting et al. 2009). The period of peak grazing observed in the current study almost completely overlapped with that reported by Whiting et al. (2009). It is possible that, in the current study the high grazing activity may have provided ewes with sufficient water from the ingestion of pasture. Our results were contrary to those of Al-Ramamneh et al. (2012) who reported that drinking times later in the day were associated with active grazing periods of straw. In their study, however, Al-Ramamneh offered straw which is likely to require greater water intake as the moisture content of feeds is associated with water intake requirements (Forbes 1968).

Over the two-week period, there was only one occasion on which a ewe was observed to walk in the stream. Observations of ewes drinking showed that they attempted to keep their feet out of the water by kneeling on the bank to drink on two of the five occasions. In the remaining three occasions, ewes stood on the bank while drinking water from the stream. One ewe was observed to drink water twice on two different days; all other ewes were only observed to drink once. Some ewes (n=20) were not observed to go near the waterway, even when the trough was covered (Fig. 1). In the current study, the low frequency of ewes that drank from the stream when the trough was covered suggests that the water contained in the pasture may have been sufficient to meet the requirements of these ewes. This is in agreement with previous studies that showed that sheep could fulfil their water requirements from pasture in cooler months (Macfarlane et al. 1958; Turner & Boyd 1970). In the current study it appeared that during winter, sheep approached the waterway primarily to graze. The riparian zone had green pasture which appeared to be preferred, as the study sheep spent 68% of their time in this area grazing. Neuronal studies have reported that sheep were attracted by the sight of food but not by the sight of water unless motivated by other factors (Mungarndee et al. 2002).

In the current study, restricted access to the water trough had no effect on ewe drinking behaviour. Similarly Cain et al. (2008), reported in desert bighorn sheep that no changes in behaviour were observed when water was restricted. During warmer months (15-40°), sheep have biological mechanisms that can allow them to withstand scarcity of water including reducing faecal water loss, urine volume and loss of moisture by evaporation (Ahmed & Abdelatif 1994; Jaber et al. 2004; Maloiy & Taylor 1971).

In conclusion, this study showed that during winter, under the conditions of this study, the ewes rarely drank from natural waterways but many ewes showed a daily pattern of accessing the riparian areas around natural waterways, although some did not. Additional studies are required to determine if the same pattern is seen during spring, summer and autumn.

Acknowledgements

We gratefully acknowledge the financial support for this project from C. Alma Baker Trust and Massey University. Many thanks to all staff at Tuapaka farm for technical assistance.

References

Ahmed MM, Abdelatif A 1994. Effects of restriction of water and food intake on thermoregulation, food utilization and water economy in desert sheep. Journal of Arid Environments 28: 147-153.

Al-Ramamneh D, Riek A, Gerken M 2012. Effect of water restriction on drinking behaviour and water intake in German black-head mutton sheep and Boer goats. Animal 6: 173-178.

Cain III JW, Krausman PR, Morgart JR, Jansen BD, Pepper MP 2008. Responses of desert bighorn sheep to removal of water sources. Wildlife Monographs 171: 1-32.

Cournane, FC, McDowell R, Littlejohn R and Condron L 2011. Effects of cattle, sheep and deer grazing on soil physical quality and losses of phosphorus and suspended sediment losses in surface runoff. Agriculture, ecosystems and environment 140 (1-2), 264-272.

Daneshi M, Barani H, Rezaei H, Bahremand A 2012. Determination of linear regression model to estimate the water requirements of sheep (case study: Pastures of northern golestan province). Journal of Livestock Science 3: 72-78.

Forbes J 1968. The water intake of ewes. The British Journal of Nutrition 22: 33-43.

Friard O and Gamba M. (2016) BORIS: a free, versatile open-source event-logging software for video/audio coding and live observations. Methods in Ecology and Evolution 7(11), 1325-1330.

Jaber L, Habre A, Rawda N, Said MA, Barbour E, Hamadeh S 2004. The effect of water restriction on certain physiological parameters in Awassi sheep. Small Ruminant Research 54: 115-120.

Macfarlane W, Morris R, Howard B 1958. Heat and water in tropical merino sheep. Australian Journal of Agricultural Research 9: 217-228.

Maloiy GMO, Taylor CR 1971. Water requirements of african goats and haired-sheep. The Journal of Agricultural Science 77: 203-208.

McGregor BA 1986. Water intake of grazing angora wether goats and merino wether sheep. Australian Journal of Experimental Agriculture 26: 639-642.

Mungarndee SS, Baldwin BA, Chindadoungratana C, Kotchabhakdi N 2002. Hypothalamic and zona incerta neurons in sheep, initially only responding to the sight of food, also respond to the sight of water after intracerebroventricular injection of hypertonic saline or angiotensin ii. Brain Research 925: 204-212

O'Callaghan P, Kelly-Quinn M, Jennings E, Antunes P, O'Sullivan M, Fenton O, Huallachain DO 2019. The environmental impact of cattle access to watercourses: A review. Journal of Environmental Quality 48: 340-351.

Turner J, Boyd P 1970. Water consumption by desert bighorn sheep. Desert Bighorn Council Transactions 14: 189-197.

Whiting JC, Bowyer RT, Flinders JT 2009. Diel use of water by reintroduced bighorn sheep. Western North American Naturalist 69: 407-412.

BRIEF COMMUNICATION: Meta-analysis of beef cow live weights in the mid-2000s

BC Thomson*, NB Smith and PD Muir

On-Farm Research, PO Box 1142, Hastings

**Corresponding author:* Email: bev@on-farm.co.nz

Abstract

As traditional beef cows are rarely weighed, there are few quality data available on beef cow live weights. Data were collected on 12 farms between 2008/09 and 2009/10 as part of a project validating the data used in the New Zealand Agricultural Greenhouse Gas Inventory Model. Beef cow live weights were collected on both herd cows (mean 541.3 kg) and on cull cows (mean 552.6 kg). Carcass data were collected at slaughter to obtain better values for dressing-out (42.6%). Carcass data provided by Landcorp Farming Ltd indicated that their average beef cow live weights were 568 kg in 2008/09. Carcass data collected by the B+LNZ Economic Service from 8511 beef cows in 2007/08 indicated that cow live weights averaged 537 kg. An unpublished MAF Sustainable Farming Fund study reported weights for 1120 cows across 15 farms and found an average beef cow live weight of 576 kg in 2006/07. An average across all these studies suggested that beef cow weaning weights between 2006 and 2010 were around 553 kg.

Keywords: beef cow; liveweight; dressing-out %

Introduction

New Zealand's Agricultural Greenhouse Gas Inventory Model calculates methane emissions from animal live weights and estimated energy and feed intakes (Clark 2008). Accurate live weight values are important as they can have a significant impact on methane values when scaled up over the national herd. Live weights are calculated from carcass weight but in the case of beef cows, this calculation is difficult because the carcass weights of dairy and beef cows are not separated in national slaughter statistics. The Agricultural Greenhouse Gas Inventory Model, therefore, uses a number of assumptions to estimate the beef carcass weight and uses a dressing-out percentage of 45% to estimate beef cow live weight (433 kg in the 2007/08 season). This project set out to collect data on beef cow live weight because of the paucity of current data available on beef cow live weight or dressing-out percentage (Muir et al. 2008).

Materials and methods

Data on breeding cow live weights were collected from 12 North Island farms in 2008/09 and 2009/10 (Table 1). Live weights were collected at weaning/pregnancy testing cows to be retained in the herd (1065 cows were weighed in 2008/09 and 735 cows were weighed in 2009/10). Where herds were very large, a sub-sample of at least 20% of the herd was weighed. All cull cows were weighed (188 in 2008/09 and 371 in 2009/10). Live weight was recorded soon after yarding. Carcass weight (as per killing sheets) was collected from the cull cows on a mob basis and this was used to calculate dressing-out percentage. Breed data was as supplied by the farmers. No data analysis was undertaken as in some cases the data was provided by the farmers as group means.

Additional data were collected from three sources (Table 2). Unpublished South Island data was supplied by Craig Thomas of Mid-Canterbury Vet Services from a Ministry of Agriculture and Fisheries Sustainable Farming Study (MAF SFF) involving 2100 breeding cows across 15 South Island farms in 2006/07. Geoff Nicol of Landcorp Farming Ltd provided carcass data from 96,176 cull beef cows slaughtered between 1997/98 and 2008/09. The B+LNZ Economic Service, which undertakes an annual survey of 560 sheep and beef farms, collected carcass weights from 8511 beef cows in 2007/08.

Results and discussion

On average, the North Island beef cows being retained in the herd were 541 kg and the cows being culled were 546 kg (Table 1). There was a large difference in cow weights between years (510 kg in 2008/09 and 573 kg in 2009/10). Data were collected in late summer/autumn when cows are likely to be at their heaviest and, thus, this may overestimate beef cow live weight over the year. For example, over three years (2001-2003) beef cow live weights averaged 511 kg at weaning and 505 kg in winter (Morris et al. 2006). However, the same study showed that the largest variation was between years, with weaning weights ranging from 475 kg to 552 kg. Since beef cows are used to harvest and manage surplus grass it is not surprising that within-year and between-year fluctuations in feed supply impact beef cow live weights. During the 2008/09 farm survey, cull cows were heavier than herd cows (527 kg *vs* 510 kg) but in 2009/10 the cull cows were lighter than their herd mates (566 kg *vs* 573 kg). These differences probably reflect the feed conditions and culling decisions being made at the time. The cull cows had an average dressing-out of 42.6% – compared with a figure of 45% used in the Inventory model.

The majority of the 2100 breeding cows across the 15 South Island farms in 2006/07 were Angus or Hereford x Angus crosses with an average weight of 568 kg.

Table 1 North Island beef-cow live weights and carcass weights (kg) recorded in 2008/09 and 2009/10.

Farm	Breed	Herd cow weight (kg)	Cull cow weight (kg)	Carcass weight (kg)	Dressing-out %
2008/09					
1	A	505.7	547.7*	224.0	40.8
2	A	474.0	489.7	205.6	42.0
3	A × F	539.1	539.2	229.3	42.5
4	A	459.9	479.8	200.4	41.7
5	A × S	543.6	587.4	262.0	44.6
6	A	534.8	554.9	203.3	36.6
Mean		509.6	533.1	220.8	41.4
SD		35.8	40.96	23.38	2.66
2009/2010					
1	A × F	515.2	515.0*	202.8	39.4
2	H × F	543.0	626.3	274.9	43.9
3	A	632.8	570.7	265.7	46.6
4	A	635.7	586.0	265.6	45.3
5	A	524.4	533.9	231.2	43.3
6	H × F	586.7	600.1*	269.7	44.9
Mean		573.0	572.4	251.7	43.9
SD		53.7	71.7	33.9	2.36
Overall Mean		541.3	552.6	236.2	42.6

*Weight prior to slaughter. Cull cows were farmed on before slaughter.
A = Angus, A × F = Angus x Friesian, A × S = Angus × Simmental, H × F = Hereford × Friesian

Table 2 Summary of beef cow data collected from four sources (North Island farms, South Island farms, Landcorp Farming Ltd and Beef & Lamb NZ Economic Service.

	Live weight (kg)	Carcass weight (kg)	DO%
Current study (2008/09 and 2009/10)	541	236.2	42.6
Thomas (Unpublished data 2006/07)	568 (2100 cows)		
Landcorp Farming Ltd (2007/08)	568* (8995 cows)	242	
B+LNZ Econ Service (2007/08)	537* (8511 cows)	229	
Average liveweight	553.5	235.7	42.6

* Live weight calculated from carcass weight using dressing-out of 42.6%

Figure 1 Changes in carcass weight (kg) of cull Angus beef cows between 1997/98 and 2008/09 (Landcorp Farming Ltd) (P< 0.001 for fitted line)

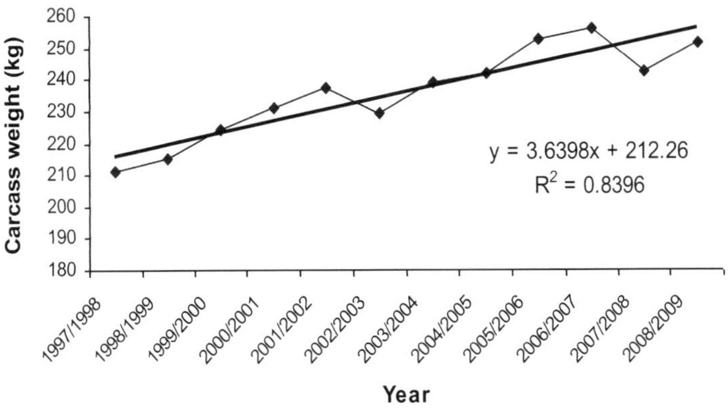

In 2007/08 the average carcass weight of the 8995 cows slaughtered across Landcorp Farming Ltd. was 242 kg. Using the dressing-out of 42.6% collected in the present study, the live weight of cows on Landcorp farms would have averaged 568 kg in 2007/08. There is also evidence of a linear trend with carcass weights increasing by 3.64 kg a year between 1997/98 and 2008/09 (Figure 1). Using a dressing-out of 42.6%, this suggests that Landcorp beef cow live weights have been increasing by 8.5 kg/year.

The average carcass weight from 8511 beef cows collected by the B+LNZ Economic Service was 229 kg and using a dressing-out of 42.6% from the present study, the average live weight of these cull cows would have been 537 kg.

The data on beef cow live weights have been summarized in Table 2. Average beef cow live weights appear to be around 553 kg for the period in which data were collected (2007-2010). This is significantly higher than the 433 kg predicted by the inventory model for 2007/08. The data from Landcorp Farming Ltd also indicates that beef cow live weights have been increasing at 8.5 kg/year. Current beef cow live weights of 553 kg can be contrasted with the beef cow live weights of 422 kg reported by Smeaton et al. (1986) for Angus and Hereford x Friesian cows. These heavier weights are likely to be a result of on-going selection for larger animals as well as a move away from high stocking rates associated with farming subsidies in the 1980s to high-performance sheep systems of the 1990s. Whilst beef cow live weight will vary with breed, feed supply and time of the year, beef cow live weights are clearly heavier than many believe. This may mean that the stock-unit relativity between cows and ewes needs to be re-examined, as previously suggested by Nicol and Brookes (2007).

Acknowledgements

To the farmers who willingly co-operated in supplying data for this report and to the late Geoff Nicoll of Landcorp Farming Ltd for beef cow carcass weights. Craig Thomas of Mid-Canterbury Vet Services provided South Island data on beef cow live weights from the MAF SFF project on beef-cow efficiency (Grant 06/11). Data on beef-cow carcass weight was kindly provided by Rob Davison of B+LNZ.

References

Clark H 2008. Guidelines to accompany computerized inventory. June 2008. Report produced for the Ministry of Agriculture and Forestry.

Morris ST, Morel PCH, Kenyon PR 2006. The effect of individual liveweight and condition of beef cows on their reproductive performance and birth and weaning weights of calves. New Zealand Veterinary Journal 54(2): 96-100.

Muir PD, Thomson BC, Hegarty RS 2008. A Review of New Zealand's National Methane Inventory Model. Report prepared for the Ministry of Agriculture and Forestry.

Nicol AM, Brookes IM 2007. Pasture and Supplements for Grazing Animals. NZSAP Occasional Publication No 14. Chapter 10, pp. 151-172.

Smeaton DC, McCall DG, Clayton JB 1986. Calving date effects on beef cow productivity Proceedings of the New Zealand Society of Animal Production 46: 149-152.

Persistency and lactation curves modelled using nonlinear random regression in dairy cows milked once a day

H Jiang[a], RE Hickson[a], OT Woods[a], M Morandeau[b], JL Burke[a], M Correa-Luna[a], DJ Donaghy[a] and N Lopez-Villalobos[a*]

[a]*School of Agriculture and Environment, Massey University, Palmerston North, New Zealand;* [b]*Université Clermont-Auvergne, INRAE, VetAgro Sup, UMR Herbivores, F 63122 Saint-Genès Champanelle, France*

**Corresponding author.* Email: N.Lopez-Villalobos@massey.ac.nz

Abstract

Modelling lactation curves of dairy cows is important for improved feed management and breeding decisions. The objectives of this study were to compare measures of lactation persistency obtained from the modelling of lactation curves for daily yields of milk, fat and protein using a nonlinear random regression model in dairy cows milked once a day under grazing conditions. A total of 1,955 monthly herd-test records of milk, fat and protein from 55 Holstein-Friesian (F), 64 Jersey (J), and 123 F×J crossbreds of different lactations were used to obtain lactation curves for each cow using a random regression model with the Wood function. Three measures of persistency were calculated based on ratios of yields and compared with persistency calculated based on parameters of the Wood function. Jersey cows in lactation 3 had the greatest persistency for all persistency measures. In first-lactation cows, there were no significant breed differences in persistency. Persistency measures were strongly correlated with each other ($r \geq 0.97$; $P<0.001$). The conclusion from this study is that parameters of the lactation curve (peak yield, day of peak and persistency) can be precisely estimated using the random regression model with the Wood function.

Keywords: modelling; lactation curve; persistency; once-a-day milking

Introduction

A lactation curve illustrates the pattern of daily milk production during lactation in dairy cows (Wood 1967). A typical lactation curve of milk production can be divided into three phases: an increasing phase between calving and peak yield, a maintaining phase of peak yield and a decreasing phase after the peak (Gengler 1996). Lactation persistency is usually defined as the ability of the cow to maintain a consistent level of milk production after peak yield (Gengler 1996; Wood 1967). A cow is more persistent if her lactation curve is flatter after peak yield, than a cow with the same total yield but with a lactation curve that rapidly decreases after peak yield (Gengler 1996; Macciotta et al. 2011; Wood 1967). Knowledge of the shape of the lactation curve is useful to define feeding and breeding strategies.

A once-a-day milking system (OAD) has been adopted by about 8% of New Zealand dairy farmers for a range of reasons, including reduced farm costs, lifestyle improvement for the farmers and health and welfare improvement for cows (Clark et al. 2006; Edwards 2018). However, production losses of milk volume were reported in OAD compared to twice-a-day (TAD) milking systems (Clark et al. 2006; Hickson et al. 2006; Lembeye et al. 2016), ranging from 21 to 31% in whole lactation studies in New Zealand. Furthermore, cows milked OAD had lower peak yield and fewer days in milk than did cows milked TAD (Clark et al. 2006; Hickson et al. 2006), indicating that improving persistency is the main option to reduce production losses in OAD milking systems. Therefore, selection based on persistency in cows milked OAD would be important to ensure a good transition from TAD to OAD milking.

Many studies have reported the modelling of lactation curves using nonlinear models (Wood 1967; Dijkstra et al. 2010; Piccardi et al. 2017). These studies focused on the modelling of the lactation curve for predicting daily milk yield of individual cows based on about 8 to 10 test-day records. Since 1980, the attention of modelling lactation curves has gradually transferred from modelling the lactation curve for better feed management to modelling the lactation curve for genetic evaluation using random linear regression (Jakobsen et al. 2002; Jamrozik & Schaeffer 1997). A random regression model (RRM) describes the lactation curve of the population of cows (fixed regression coefficients) and the deviations (random regression coefficients) from the fixed regression for each cow. The RRM is more flexible when fitting lactation curves and allows variation among individuals' lactation curves, along with the prediction of daily yields of cows with a limited number of herd-test records, provided that a covariance matrix between the estimates of regression coefficients for any linear mathematical function is available.

However, few studies have explored the use of RRM with nonlinear mathematical functions to model lactation curves and predict total milk yields when cows have a lower (two or three) number of herd-tests. Piccardi et al. (2017) fitted phenotypic lactation curves for milk yield using RRM with three nonlinear functions (Wood, Milkbot and diphasic) and suggested that the Wood function had the best performance to predict lactation traits in the RRM. The objectives of the present study were: a) to model the lactation curves at the phenotypic level for daily yields of milk, fat and protein using RRM with the Wood function in dairy cows milked OAD; b) to compare lactation curves and persistency in Holstein-Friesian (F), Jersey (J) and crossbred (FJ) cows of different parities and investigate the correlations between different persistency measures.

Materials and methods

Data

The data set included 1,955 monthly herd-test records for milk yield (MY), fat yield (FY) and protein yield (PY) obtained from 242 cows milked OAD at Massey University Dairy 1 during the 2018-19 season. There were 55 Holstein Friesian (F), 64 Jersey (J), and 123 F×J crossbred cows with 201 herd-test records from first parity lactations and 420 records from second parity lactations. All the rest were records from third lactation or later lactations which were considered together.

Feeding system and cow management

All cows had access to fresh perennial ryegrass (*Lolium perenne*) and white clover (*Trifolium repens*) pasture but the diet composition differed during the production season. In September and December, cows had 100% fresh perennial ryegrass and white clover pasture. Mixtures of plantain (*Plantago lanceolata*) and chicory (*Cichorium intybus*) were offered in October, November and February, accounting for 13%, 33% and 23% of the dry matter intake, respectively. Turnips (*Brassica campestris ssp. rapifera*) were offered in January at 63% of the dry matter intake. From February to April, due to severe pasture shortage, pasture silage was fed directly on the paddock at a percentage of 34%, 67% and 14%, of the daily feed allowance, respectively. Similarly, in August and April, maize (*Zea mays*) silage was offered at 25% and 32% of the dry matter intake, respectively.

Cows were milked OAD at 6:30 AM. Milk yield, and percentages of fat and protein were determined on samples using a Fossomatic FT120 (Foss Electric, Hillerød, Denmark) during routine herd-testing occurred monthly from August to April. Daily yields of fat (FY) and protein (PY) were obtained by multiplying MY by the respective percentages of fat and protein. Calving was from 8 July to 2 October 2018 and all cows were dried off before May 2019.

Lactation curves

Lactation curves for the population and each cow were modelled with RRM based on the Wood function (Wood 1967) using the NLMIXED procedure of SAS version 9.4 (SAS Institute Inc.), which was represented as,

$$y_{it} = (At^{B}e^{Ct}) + (a_i t^{b_i} e^{c_i t}) + e_{it}$$

where y_{it} is the milk yield of cow (i) at day (t), parameter A, B and C are the fixed regression coefficients for the population, parameter a_i, b_i and c_i, are the random regression coefficients expressed as deviations from the population for each cow, and e_{it} is the random residual error. The estimation of ai, bi and ci depends on the estimation of the (co)variance matrix **W** of random regression coefficients

$$\mathbf{W}=\begin{bmatrix}\sigma_a^2 & \sigma_{ab} & \sigma_{ac}\\ \sigma_{ab} & \sigma_b^2 & \sigma_{bc}\\ \sigma_{ac} & \sigma_{bc} & \sigma_c^2\end{bmatrix}$$

Lactation parameters and persistency

Total yield, peak yield and day at peak were obtained using the predicted daily yields for each cow using the predicted daily yields. Three different measures of persistency (P1, P2, and P3) were calculated for each cow based on the ratio of predicted yields:

$$P1 = \frac{\text{Lactation yield from day 181 to 270}}{\text{Lactation yield from day 1 to 90}} \times 100$$

$$P2 = \frac{\text{Lactation yield from day 121 to 180}}{\text{Lactation yield from day 1 to 60}} \times 100$$

$$P3 = \frac{\text{Total laction yield}}{\text{Peak yield} \times 270} \times 100$$

Persistency (P_W) was measured based on the parameters of the Wood function (Wood 1967) as follows:

$$P_W = -(b+1)\ \ln(-c)$$

where ln is the natural logarithm, and a, b and c are the estimates of the Wood function for each cow.

Statistical analysis

Estimates of random regression coefficients for each cow obtained from the Wood function, and measures of persistency, peak yield, day at peak and total yields for MY, FY and PY were analysed with a linear model with the MIXED procedure of SAS version 9.4 (SAS Institute Inc.). The linear model was the following:

$$y_{jki} = \mu + G_j + L_k + GL_{jk} + \beta_1 k_{jki} + e_{jki}$$

where y_{jki} is the dependent variable measured in cow i, μ is the population mean; G_j is the fixed effect of breed j; L_k is the fixed effect of lactation number k; $GL_{jk}$is the fixed effect of interaction between breed j and lactation number k; β_1 is the regression coefficient of the dependent variable on deviation from median herd calving date of cow i; e_{jki} is the residual random error associated to the observation y_{jki}. Least-squares means and standard error of the means for the fixed effects were obtained and used for multiple mean comparisons using the Fisher's Least Significant Difference as implemented in the LSMEANS option of the MIXED procedure. Significant differences between means were declared at $P<0.05$.

Pearson's correlations between the parameters of the lactation curves, persistency measures and each of its components were calculated using the CORR procedure of SAS version 9.4 (SAS Institute Inc.).

Results

The least-squares means and standard error of the means for the total yield, peak yield and day at peak for MY, FY and PY modelled using RRM with the Wood function for the different breed groups and lactation numbers are presented in Table 1. Lactation curves fitted to the different breed groups by lactation number for milk, fat and protein

Table 1 Least-squares means and standard error of the means of total yield (kg/cow), peak yield (kg/cow) and day at peak for milk, fat and protein yield modelled using the random regression model with the Wood function fitted to Holstein-Friesian (F), Jersey (J) and crossbred F×J cows of different lactation number milked once a day at Massey University Dairy 1 farm in 2018.

		Milk yield			Fat yield			Protein yield		
Breed	Lactation	Total yield	Peak yield	Day of peak	Total yield	Peak yield	Day of peak	Total yield	Peak yield	Day of peak
F	1	$3,273^{fg}\pm281$	$14.8^{fghi}\pm1.6$	$51^{ab}\pm4$	$158^{gh}\pm13$	$0.73^{fgh}\pm0.07$	$43^{a}\pm4$	$122^{efgh}\pm10$	$0.51^{fghi}\pm0.06$	$53^{ab}\pm5$
	2	$4,213^{cd}\pm162$	$21.0^{cd}\pm0.9$	$36^{cdef}\pm2$	$205^{c}\pm8$	$1.00^{c}\pm0.04$	$29^{cde}\pm2$	$163^{c}\pm6$	$0.77^{d}\pm0.04$	$28^{cde}\pm3$
	3	$5,279^{a}\pm106$	$26.9^{a}\pm0.6$	$32^{f}\pm1$	$241^{ab}\pm5$	$1.20^{a}\pm0.03$	$24^{e}\pm2$	$203^{a}\pm4$	$1.01^{a}\pm0.02$	$20^{f}\pm2$
F×J	1	$3,060^{gh}\pm180$	$13.9^{ghi}\pm1.0$	$49^{ab}\pm2$	$167^{efgh}\pm8$	$0.77^{efgh}\pm0.05$	$40^{a}\pm3$	$121^{fgh}\pm7$	$0.51^{ghi}\pm0.04$	$50^{ab}\pm3$
	2	$3,510^{ef}\pm140$	$16.4^{efg}\pm0.8$	$45^{b}\pm2$	$182^{def}\pm7$	$0.84^{def}\pm0.04$	$40^{a}\pm2$	$141^{de}\pm5$	$0.62^{ef}\pm0.03$	$42^{b}\pm3$
	3	$4,831^{b}\pm66$	$24.3^{b}\pm0.4$	$33^{ef}\pm1$	$251^{a}\pm3$	$1.23^{a}\pm0.02$	$26^{de}\pm1$	$195^{a}\pm2$	$0.92^{b}\pm0.01$	$23^{ef}\pm1$
J	1	$2,442^{i}\pm258$	$10.9^{i}\pm1.5$	$53^{a}\pm3$	$142^{h}\pm12$	$0.65^{h}\pm0.07$	$48^{a}\pm4$	$102^{h}\pm9$	$0.42^{i}\pm0.06$	$58^{a}\pm5$
	2	$2,593^{hi}\pm156.86$	$11.7^{hi}\pm0.91$	$50^{a}\pm2$	$152^{gh}\pm7$	$0.69^{gh}\pm0.04$	$47^{a}\pm2$	$112^{gh}\pm6$	$0.46^{hi}\pm0.04$	$54^{a}\pm3$
	3	$3,985^{d}\pm97.16$	$19.6^{d}\pm0.56$	$35^{def}\pm1$	$234^{b}\pm5$	$1.12^{b}\pm0.03$	$31^{de}\pm1$	$170^{bc}\pm4$	$0.79^{cd}\pm0.02$	$26^{def}\pm2$

[a,b,c,d,e,f,g,h,i]Least-squares means with different superscripts in each column are significantly different among combination of breeds and lactation number (P<0.05).

Table 2 Least-squares means and standard error of the means of persistency[1] for milk, fat and protein yield modelled using the random regression model with the Wood function fitted to Holstein-Friesian (F), Jersey (J) and crossbred F×J cows of different lactation number milked once a day in Massey University Dairy 1 farm in 2018.

		Milk yield				Fat yield				Protein yield			
Breed	Lactation	P1 (%)	P2 (%)	P3 (%)	P_W	P1 (%)	P2 (%)	P3 (%)	P_W	P1 (%)	P2 (%)	P3 (%)	P_W
F	1	$70^{a}\pm3$	$89^{a}\pm3$	$82^{a}\pm2$	$6.63^{a}\pm0.10$	$68^{a}\pm2$	$85^{a}\pm2$	$81^{a}\pm2$	$6.48^{a}\pm0.09$	$83^{ab}\pm3$	$95^{ab}3\pm$	$89^{a}\pm2$	$6.81^{ab}\pm0.12$
	2	$59^{bcd}\pm2$	$77^{bcde}\pm2$	$76^{cd}\pm1$	$6.25^{bcde}\pm0.06$	$61^{cd}\pm1$	$77^{cd}\pm1$	$76^{cde}\pm1$	$6.16^{cde}\pm0.05$	$69^{cd}\pm2$	$82^{cde}\pm2$	$81^{cd}1\pm$	$6.30^{cde}\pm0.07$
	3	$54^{e}\pm1$	$73^{e}\pm1$	$73^{e}\pm1$	$6.12^{e}\pm0.04$	$58^{e}\pm1$	$74^{e}\pm1$	$75^{e}\pm1$	$6.04^{e}\pm0.03$	$62^{f}\pm1$	$76^{f}\pm1$	$75^{e}\pm1$	$6.06^{f}\pm0.04$
F×J	1	$70^{a}\pm2$	$88^{a}\pm2$	$82^{a}\pm1$	$6.59^{a}\pm0.06$	$66^{a}\pm1$	$84^{a}\pm1$	$80^{a}\pm1$	$6.41^{a}\pm0.06$	$82^{a}\pm2$	$94^{ab}\pm2$	$89^{a}\pm2$	$6.77^{ab}\pm0.08$
	2	$66^{a}\pm1$	$85^{a}\pm2$	$80^{a}\pm1$	$6.48^{a}\pm0.05$	$66^{a}\pm1$	$84^{a}\pm1$	$80^{a}\pm1$	$6.42^{a}\pm0.05$	$77^{b}\pm2$	$89^{b}\pm2$	$86^{a}\pm1$	$6.60^{b}\pm0.06$
	3	$55^{de}\pm1$	$74^{de}\pm1$	$74^{de}\pm0$	$6.17^{de}\pm0.02$	$59^{de}\pm0$	$75^{de}\pm1$	$76^{de}\pm0$	$6.09^{de}\pm0.02$	$65^{e}\pm1$	$78^{ef}\pm1$	$79^{d}\pm1$	$6.16^{e}\pm0.03$
J	1	$72^{a}\pm3$	$91^{a}\pm3$	$83^{a}\pm2$	$6.67^{a}\pm0.09$	$70^{a}\pm2$	$88^{a}\pm2$	$82^{a}\pm1$	$6.57^{a}\pm0.08$	$85^{a}\pm3$	$97^{a}\pm3$	$91^{a}\pm2$	$6.90^{a}\pm0.11$
	2	$71^{a}\pm2$	$89^{a}\pm2$	$83^{a}\pm1$	$6.62^{a}\pm0.06$	$69^{a}\pm1$	$88^{a}\pm1$	$82^{a}\pm1$	$6.56^{a}\pm0.05$	$83^{a}\pm2$	$95^{a}\pm2$	$89^{a}\pm1$	$6.81^{a}\pm0.07$
	3	$59^{c}\pm1$	$77^{c}\pm1$	$76^{bc}\pm1$	$6.23^{cd}\pm0.03$	$62^{bc}\pm1$	$78^{bc}\pm1$	$78^{bc}\pm1$	$6.21^{bc}\pm0.03$	$68^{d}\pm1$	$81^{d}\pm1$	$81^{bc}\pm1$	$6.27^{d}\pm0.04$

[1]Measures of lactation persistency were P1= persistency calculated as lactation yield from day 181 to 270 divided by the lactation yield from day 1 to 90, expressed as a percentage; P2= persistency calculated as lactation yield from day 121 to 180 divided by the lactation yield from day 1 to 60, expressed as a percentage; P3= persistency calculated as the total 270-day lactation yield divided by the production of the peak lactation yield multiplied by 270, expressed as a percentage; $P_W = -(b+1)\ln(-c)$, calculated based on the parameters of the Wood function.

[a,b,c,d,e,f]Least-squares means with different superscripts in each column are significantly different among combinations of breeds and lactation number (P<0.05).

yield are presented in Figure 1. For F and F×J cows, total yields and peak yields for all milk traits significantly increased as the lactation number increased, while day of peak decreased as the lactation number increased. The same trends were also observed in J cows, however, there were no significant differences for these traits between first- and second-lactation cows. In second- and third-lactation cows, F cows produced the highest (P<0.05) total milk yield with the highest peak yield, followed (P<0.05) by F×J and then by J cows (P<0.05). In first-lactation cows, F and F×J had similar total milk yield, but higher (P<0.05) than J cows.

The differences among breeds and lactation numbers for the lactation curve of milk yield were also observed for the lactation curves for fat and protein yields, with some exceptions. In second-lactation cows, no significant differences were detected for day of peak fat yield between J and F×J. In third-lactation cows, no significant differences were detected for total fat yield, peak fat yield and total protein yield between F cows and F×J cows. No significant differences for day of peak for all milk traits were found among three breeds in third-lactation cows.

Least-squares means and standard error of the means for different measures of persistency for MY, FY and PY for different breed groups by lactation number are presented in Table 2. Persistency decreased as the lactation number increased in all three breeds. In first-lactation cows, there were no significant breed differences for persistency. In second-lactation cows, J cows had the highest protein persistency and had no significant difference to F×J cows in the persistency for milk and fat yield. In the third lactation, J cows had the highest persistency while F cows had the lowest persistency for all milk traits. Pearson correlations among the four persistency measures were strongly correlated with each other for all milk traits (r≥0.97, P<0.001).

Figure 1 Lactation curves for (a) milk, (b) fat and (c) protein yields modelled using the random regression model with the Wood function fitted to Holstein-Friesian (F), Jersey (J) and crossbred F×J cows of different lactation number milked once a day at Massey University Dairy 1 farm in 2018. The panels at the right are estimates of parameters of the Wood function (a, b and c).

a)

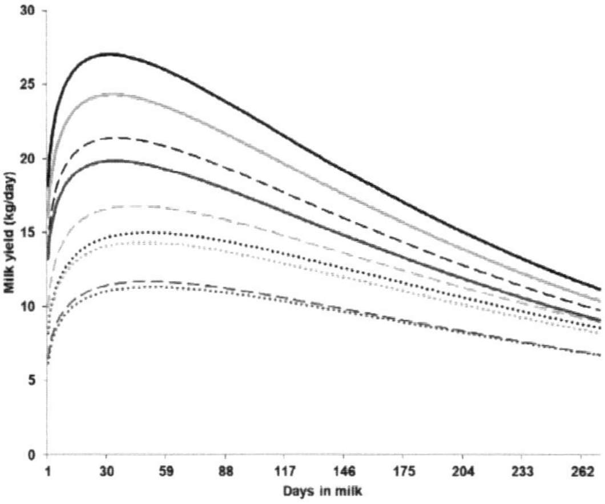

	a	b	c
F3	18.26	0.161	-0.0051
F2	14.03	0.166	-0.0048
F1	8.27	0.205	-0.0041
F×J3	16.15	0.165	-0.0050
F×J2	10.00	0.187	-0.0043
F×J1	8.29	0.190	-0.0040
J3	13.27	0.159	-0.0047
J2	6.53	0.201	-0.0040
J1	6.23	0.203	-0.0039

b)

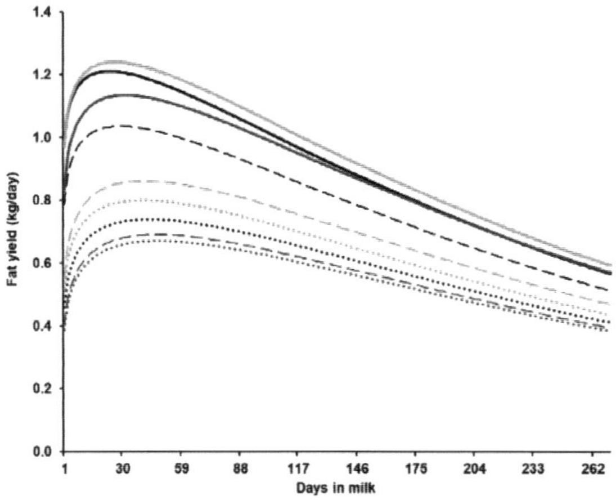

	a	b	c
F3	0.985	0.0951	-0.00402
F2	0.789	0.1152	-0.00398
F1	0.461	0.1709	-0.00396
F×J3	0.976	0.1055	-0.00403
F×J2	0.557	0.1614	-0.00398
F×J1	0.521	0.1590	-0.00396
J3	0.833	0.1263	-0.00402
J2	0.406	0.1862	-0.00397
J1	0.390	0.1885	-0.00397

c)

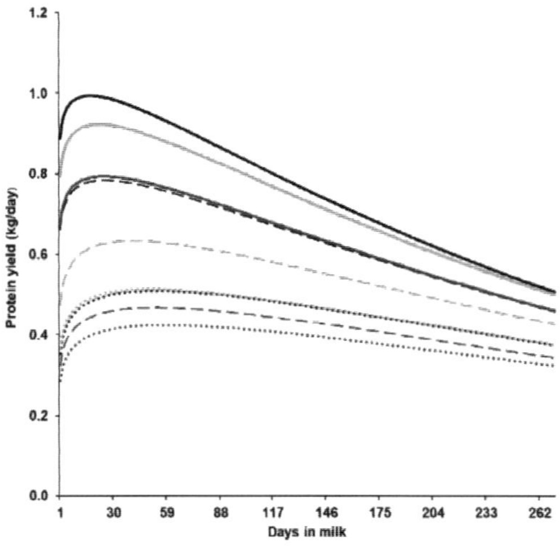

	a	b	c
F3	0.891	0.0582	-0.00329
F2	0.665	0.0732	-0.00289
F1	0.354	0.1227	-0.00233
F×J1	0.796	0.0705	-0.00318
F×J2	0.477	0.1046	-0.00258
F×J3	0.369	0.1138	-0.00229
J3	0.675	0.0727	-0.00292
J2	0.324	0.1240	-0.00236
J1	0.287	0.1277	-0.00220

Table 3 Estimates of variance (on the diagonal), covariance (below diagonal) and correlation (above diagonal) matrix of the parameters (a, b and c) for daily milk, fat and protein yields modelled using the random regression model with the Wood function in cows milked once a day at Massey University Dairy 1 farm in 2018.

	a	b	c
Milk yield			
a	2.38E+01	–0.70	–0.88
b	–1.10E-01	1.03E–03	0.57
c	–2.70E-03	1.14E–05	3.90E–07
Fat yield			
a	8.22E-02	–0.90	–0.58
b	–1.26E-02	2.40E–03	0.16
c	–7.60E-06	3.68E–07	2.10E–09
Protein yield			
a	6.10E-02	–0.85	–0.92
b	–7.71E-03	1.35E–03	0.69
c	–1.10E-04	1.23E–05	2.34E–07

Estimates of (co)variance matrix **W** and correlation among of the parameters (a, b, and c) for MY, FY and PY modelled using RRM with the Wood function are presented in Table 3. The variance for parameter a was larger than the variance for the parameters b and c for all milk traits. The estimates of the correlations among the parameters of the Wood function for milk yield were negative and moderate. For protein yield, the correlation between parameter a and b and between a and c were moderate and negative, but the correlation between b and c was low and negative. For fat yield the correlation between a and b was moderate and negative, but the other correlations were close to zero.

Discussion

Significant differences were observed in the shape of the lactation curves for the different breed groups and lactation numbers (Figure 1). Within first-lactation cows, the F×J cows had the greatest initial production of milk, fat and protein. In the other lactation numbers, however, the initial production of F×J cows was intermediate between F cows and J cows. The individual variations in the slope of the increasing and the decreasing phases for lactation curves of daily PY were smaller than that of daily MY or FY, which is consistent with previous research in OAD milking systems (Hickson et al. 2006), as well as in a system with higher milking frequency (Schutz et al. 1990).

Many studies showed that total yield and peak yield increased as the lactation number increased, while day at peak decreased as the lactation number increased (Wood 1969; Stanton et al. 1992; Tekerli et al. 2000; Horan et al. 2005); these trends were also found in the current study. Previous studies showed that F cows had the highest total MY (Hickson et al. 2006) while F×J cows had the highest total FY and PY, compared to J cows (Lembeye et al. 2016). In the current study, however, F cows of all lactation numbers had the highest total yields and peak yields for all milk traits and no significant differences were found between F and F×J cows for FY and PY in the first and third lactation. Hickson et al. (2006) reported no significant differences between the day of peak for Jersey and Holstein-Friesian in a OAD milking system. In the current study, breed effects were only found in the second lactation cows for all milk traits.

It has been reported that first-lactation cows have higher persistency for MY than do multiparous cows (Wood 1980; Stanton et al. 1992; Gengler 1996; Tekerli et al. 2000), a result also found in the present study. Miller et al. (2006) reported that primiparous cows were more persistent than multiparous cows because they were able to maintain the population of secretory cells at a higher level.

Lembeye et al. (2016) reported that J cows had the highest persistency for FY and that F×J cows had the highest persistency for MY and PY, while F cows had the lowest persistency in an OAD milking system. In the current study, no breed differences for persistency in any milk traits were found in the first-lactation cows. In third-lactation cows, J cows had the highest persistency compared to other breeds for all milk traits. Results of the current study suggested that J cows were more suitable for an OAD milking system than F cows. Jersey cows are reported to be able to accumulate milk in the udder for longer periods than F cows (Davis et al. 1999).

Although the persistency estimates varied using different measures, correlations among four persistency measures in the current study were all strongly and positively correlated ($r \geq 0.97$) and were significantly different from zero ($P<0.001$) for each of the milk traits, indicating that these measures express the lactation curve in the same way. However, correlations between different persistency measures have been reported to vary from 0.24 to 0.91 (Madsen 1975; Tekerli et al. 2000; Lopez-Villalobos 2005) depending on the definition. Few studies have investigated the correlations among persistency measures based on the parameters of the Wood function and other measures. Madsen (1975) reported significant correlations among five measures of persistency ranging from 0.42 to 0.91. Those differences in results may not only be due to different persistency measures used, but also to the inaccurate prediction of the lactation yield.

Estimates of (co)variances provided in Table 3 can be used for estimation of parameters of the Wood function and predicted yields on new cows or cows with few herd-test records using the properties of RRM as illustrated by Schaeffer and Dekkers (1994). Parameter a of the Wood function is associated with the level of milk production at the start of the lactation; the higher the a value, the higher the level of production at the start of the lactation. The parameter b is associated with the peak yield; the higher the b value, the higher the peak yield. The parameter c is associated with the level of production at the end of the lactation; the lower the estimate (more negative), the lower the yield after the peak yield. The strong negative correlations between parameters a and b and between a and c, with a medium positive correlation between b and c, indicated that cows with a higher initial yield would have slower increasing rate before the peak, and a low level of production after the peak yield. The trend of these correlations was similar for the MY, FY and PY, but the correlation between a and b was more negative for FY than for MY and PY, and the correlation between b and c was weaker for FY than MY and PY. The strong positive correlations between parameters b and c for daily MY and PY, indicated that cows with a greater increasing rate before the peak had a greater decreasing rate after the peak, leading to a lower persistency. Similar results were obtained in previous studies (Tekerli et al. 2000; Macciotta et al. 2011). For daily FY, greater rate of increase before the peak may not result in lower persistency due to the lower correlation between parameters b and c (r=0.16).

Conclusions

Holstein-Friesian cows in their third lactation had the greatest total yield, peak yield and earliest day at peak for all milk traits, but they had the lowest persistency compared with all other lactations and breeds. Jersey cows of third lactation had the greatest persistency for all persistency measures. In first-lactation cows, there were no significant breed differences for persistency. Persistency measures were strongly correlated with each other. The conclusion from this study is that the parameters of the lactation curve (peak yield, day of peak and persistency) can be precisely estimated using RRM with the Wood function.

Acknowledgement

The authors are grateful to the staff at the Massey University Dairy 1 farm for support and collecting data.

References

Clark DA, Phyn CVC, Tong MJ, Collis SJ, Dalley DE 2006. A systems comparison of once- versus twice-daily milking of pastured dairy cows. Journal of Dairy Science 89: 1854-1862.

Davis SR, Farr VC, Stelwagen K 1999. Regulation of yield loss and milk composition during once-daily milking: a review. Livestock Production Science 59: 77-94.

Dijkstra J, Lopez S, Bannink A, Dhanoa MS, Kebreab E, Odongo NE, Fathi Nasri MH, Behera UK, Hernandez-Ferrer D, France J 2010. Evaluation of a mechanistic lactation model using cow, goat and sheep data. Journal of Agricultural Science 148: 249-262.

Edwards JP 2018. A comparison of profitability between farms that milk once or twice a day. Animal Production Science 60: 102-106.

Gengler N 1996. Persistency of lactation yields: a review. Interbull Bulletin 12: 87-96.

Hickson RE, Lopez-Villalobos N, Dalley DE, Clark DA, Holmes CW 2006. Yields and persistency of lactation in Friesian and Jersey cows milked once daily. Journal of Dairy Science 89: 2017-2024.

Horan B, Dillon P, Berry D, O'Connor P, Rath M 2005. The effect of strain of Holstein–Friesian, feeding system and parity on lactation curves characteristics of spring-calving dairy cows. Livestock Production Science 95: 231-241.

Jakobsen JH, Madsen P, Jensen J, Pedersen J, Christensen L, Sorensen D 2002. Genetic parameters for milk production and persistency for Danish Holsteins estimated in random regression models using REML. Journal of Dairy Science 85: 1607-1616.

Jamrozik J, Schaeffer LR 1997. Estimates of genetic parameters for a test day model with random regressions for yield traits of first lactation Holsteins. Journal of Dairy Science 80: 762-770.

Lembeye F, Lopez-Villalobos N, Burke JL, Davis SR 2016. Milk production of Holstein-Friesian, Jersey and crossbred cows milked once-a-day or twice-a-day in New Zealand. New Zealand Journal of Agricultural Research 59: 50-64.

Lopez-Villalobos N 2005. Estimation of lactation persistency in crossbred grazing dairy cattle. Proceedings of the New Zealand Society of Animal Production 65: 300-305.

Macciotta NP, Dimauro C, Rassu SP, Steri R, Pulina G 2011. The mathematical description of lactation curves in dairy cattle. Italian Journal of Animal Science 10: e51.

Madsen O 1975. A comparison of some suggested measures of persistency of milk yield in dairy cows. Animal Science 20: 191-197.

Miller N, Delbecchi L, Petitclerc D, Wagner GF, Talbot BG, Lacasse P 2006. Effect of stage of lactation and parity on mammary gland cell renewal. Journal of Dairy Science 89: 4669-4677.

Piccardi M, Macchiavelli R, Funes AC, Bó GA, Balzarini M 2017. Fitting milk production curves through nonlinear mixed models. Journal of Dairy Research 84: 146-153.

Schaeffer LR, Dekkers JCM 1994. Random regressions in animal models for test-day production in dairy cattle. World Congress of Genetics Applied Livestock Production. 18: 443-446.

Schutz MM, Hansen LB, Steuernagel G, Kuck A 1990. Variation of milk, fat, protein, and somatic cells for dairy cattle. Journal of Dairy Science 73: 484-493.

Stanton T, Jones L, Everett R, Kachman SD 1992. Estimating milk, fat, and protein lactation curves with a test day model. Journal of Dairy Science 75: 1691-1700.

Tekerli M, Akinci Z, Dogan I, Akcan A 2000. Factors affecting the shape of lactation curves of Holstein cows from the Balikesir province of Turkey. Journal of Dairy Science 83: 1381-1386.

Wood P 1967. Algebraic model of the lactation curve in cattle. Nature 216: 164.

Wood P 1969. Factors affecting the shape of the lactation curve in cattle. Animal Science 11: 307-316.

Milk composition and productive and reproductive performance of cows from A1 and A2 β-casein variants, milked once or twice a day

Y Lu[a], RE Hickson[a], K Gedye[b], M Correa-Luna[a], DJ Donaghy[a] and N López-Villalobos[a*]

[a]*School of Agriculture and Environment, Massey University, Private Bag 11-222, Palmerston North 4410, New Zealand;*
[b]*School of Veterinary Sciences, Massey University, Palmerston North, New Zealand.*

**Corresponding author.* Email: N.Lopez-Villalobos@massey.ac.nz

Abstract

Protein is an important component of milk and it plays an essential role in all living organisms. β-casomorphins-7 (BCM-7) is derived from A1 β-casein and has been implicated in some human health issues. This A1 β-casein is produced by cows with the A1A1 or A1A2 genotype, whilst cows with the A2A2 genotype produce A2 β-casein, which has not been implicated in the same human health issues. Given the potential importance of A2 milk for public health and its apparent commercial potential, selection based on the A2 genotype and its impact on production and reproduction traits should be investigated. The objective of the current study was to compare the productive and reproductive performance of dairy cows based on A2 genotype in two different dairy farms. From July 2017 to May 2018, 206 cows (including 122 A2A2 genotype; "A2 cows") were milked once a day at Dairy 1 and 451 cows (including 217 A2 cows) were milked twice a day at Dairy 4. Records of lactation yields of milk, fat and protein, fat percentage, protein percentage, days from start of mating to conception, pregnancy rate to first service, the submission rate at 21 days and the pregnancy rate at 21 and 42 days (PR42) after the start of mating from 642 cows in two herds were analysed. The effects of A2 genotype on production and reproduction traits were not significant. The interaction between farm and β-casein genotype was significant for PR42 ($P<0.05$) but not for any other traits. The interactions between parity number and genotype were not significant for any of the traits. The results indicated that cows of different β-casein genotypes have similar production and reproductive performance.

Keywords: β-casein genotype; A2 milk; protein percentage; pregnancy rate at 42 days

Introduction

Proteins play an essential role in the formation, maintenance and repair of the body tissue in all living organisms. In addition to providing a source of energy, proteins are important because they also provide essential amino acids for the human body. Milk is an important food and source of protein for both infants and adults. Caseins and whey proteins are two major groups of milk protein. The four major caseins in cow's milk are α_{s1}-, α_{s2}-, β- and κ-casein (Eigel et al. 1984) with β-casein comprising about 30% of total protein (Walstra et al. 1984). A1 and A2 types are two major genetic variants of β-casein proteins in bovine milk (Ng-Kwai-Hang et al. 1990; Caroli et al. 2009; Massella et al. 2017). Cows with homozygous genes (A1A1 or A2A2) produce milk exclusively with A1 or A2 β-casein, whereas heterozygous cows (A1A2) produce milk with both types of β-casein.

Food-derived peptides are cut away and released from protein molecules under the influence of enzymatic hydrolysis in the process of digestion (Kamiński et al. 2007). One of the bioactive peptides derived from β-casein digestion is known as β-casomorphins-7 (BCM-7). There is a histidine at position 67 of the milk protein sequence in A1 β-casein and a BCM-7 can be cut off from it, whereas the proline residue in A2 β-casein protects the bond between Ile^{66} and Pro^{67} from hydrolysis by digestive enzymes (Jinsmaa et al. 1999). A1 β-casein and BCM-7 have been implicated in some human health issues, as it has been suggested that bioactive BCM-7 may have detrimental impacts throughout the body, such as on the gastrointestinal tract, and the central nervous, cardiovascular and immune systems, by acting as an mu-opioid receptor agonist (Korhonen et al. 2006; Kamiński et al. 2007).

The A2 Milk Company was founded in New Zealand in 2000 and markets milk and dairy products only with the A2 β-casein variant to New Zealand, Australian and US markets. With the commercial success of the A2 Milk Company, a large number of dairy farms within New Zealand contain herds with a higher percentage of the A2 allele (Woodford 2007). According to the Livestock Improvement Corporation (LIC 2020), in the year 2019 about 30% of dairy cows in New Zealand produced milk containing only A2 β-casein.

Given the potential importance of A2 milk for public health and its apparent commercial potential, the influences of the A2 β-casein variant on production and composition of milk should be investigated before using A2 genotype as an additional criterion in bull selection. In addition, reproduction traits are also economically important. Poor fertility is the biggest cause of culling of dairy cows in New Zealand (Xu & Burton 2000; Martinez Rocha 2017), resulting in substantial economic losses to dairy farmers. Therefore, the effects of selection for certain milk casein genotypes on cow fertility warrants investigation. The association of β-casein polymorphism with milk production (Ng-Kwai-Hang et al. 1986; Çardak 2005; Heck et al. 2009), milk composition (Aleandri et al. 1990; Winkelman et al. 1997; Ikonen et al. 1999) and fertility (Lin et al. 1987; Ruottinen et al. 2004; Demeter et al. 2010) in dairy cows has been investigated. However, the literature in relation to the productive performance and fertility of the cows with A2 β-casein genotype in New Zealand is scarce. The objective of the current study was to compare the productive and reproductive performance of dairy cows with A1 and A2 β-casein genotypes in two different dairy farms.

Materials and methods

The data were collected from Dairy 1 and Dairy 4 farms at Massey University, Palmerston North. Dairy 1 farm is managed as a low-input farm and has a spring-calving, once-a-day (OAD) milking system. It is pasture based with paddocks containing ryegrass with white and red clover mix (100 ha), plantain and chicory with white and red clover mix (10 ha) and a lucerne crop (10 ha). Dairy 4 farm is managed as a high-input farm with a spring-calving and twice-a-day (TAD) milking system. Dairy 4 farm is pasture based and the pastures are predominantly perennial ryegrass and white clover.

Cows in Dairy 1 farm were milked once daily at 6:30 am, whereas those in Dairy 4 were milked twice a day at 5:30 am and 2:30 pm throughout lactation. Calving began in mid-July on both farms in 2017 and cows were milked until May the following year. The breeding season began on October 18th and ended on December 23rd.

Animal information consisted of breed composition, lactation length and genotype. A radio frequency electronic identification system (Allflex New Zealand Ltd., Palmerston North, New Zealand) was used to identify each cow. Lactation length was calculated as the number of days in milk between calving and drying off. The genetic test for the β-casein genotype of a cow has been developed by LIC, and can be either a test of the milk sample via herd testing, or a test of some hairs along with the skin follicle cells collected from the animal (tissue test). In the current study, the A1/A2 status of cows was determined based on a tissue test.

The production traits comprised milk yield (MY), fat yield (FY), protein yield (PY), fat percentage (FP) and protein percentage (PP). The yield of milk solids (MSY) was calculated as the sum of FY and PY. The records of MY, FY, PY and somatic cell count (SCC) were obtained from monthly herd testing conducted by LIC. The SCC from herd-test records was log-transformed to somatic cell score (SCS). The average SCS was calculated as the mean of SCS obtained in all herd tests over the lactation year. The reproduction traits measured on each cow included days from start of mating to conception (SMCO), pregnancy rate at first service (PRFS), the submission rate at 21 days (SR21) and the pregnancy rate at 21 (PR21) and 42 days (PR42) after the start of mating.

Genotypic information of all the first lactation cows in Dairy 4 was unavailable in the original data set. In order to keep an identical data structure for the comparison between two farms, the first lactation cows of Dairy 1 were also excluded from this study. Complete records were available for 642 cows of parity ≥2 and these were used in this analysis.

The cows were Holstein Friesian (F), Jersey (J) and crossbred (F×J). In general, a cow was considered purebred when she had ≥87.5% of F or J, otherwise she was considered FxJ. There were 206 cows from Dairy 1 farm in the analysis. The breed structure was 49 F, 50 J and 107 F×J. By comparison, there were 451 dairy cows from Dairy 4 including 139 F, 4J and 308 F×J. It is worth noting that the proportion of F (pF) was used as a variable rather than cattle breeds in the current study when analysing the fixed effect of breed on milk production, milk composition and fertility.

The lactation number of the cows included in the current study ranged from two to six. For statistical analysis, the cows were divided into two groups: (1) second parity and (2) third or greater than third parity. Due to the fact that both A1A1 and A1A2 cows produce A1 protein, cows were grouped by A1 cows (cows with either A1A1 or A1A2 genotypes) and A2 cows (cows with only A2A2 genotypes) to minimise the inaccuracy of statistical analysis caused by small sample size, as there were only six cows with homozygous A1A1 genotypes in Dairy 1. There were 84 A1 and 122 A2 cows in Dairy 1, and 234 A1 and 217 A2 cows in Dairy 4.

The dataset was analysed using SAS version 9.4 software (SAS Institute Inc., Cary, NC, USA). Descriptive statistics were generated with the MEANS procedure. Analysis of variance for MY, FY, PY, FP, PP, SMCO, PRFS, SR21, PR21 and PR42 were performed using the MIXED procedure with the following mixed linear model:

$$y_{ijkm} = \mu + F_i + L_j + G_k + FG_{ik} + LG_{jk} + \beta_1 p^F + \beta_2 h_{F\times J} + \beta_3 d + e_{ijkm}$$

where y_{ijkm} is the dependent trait measured in a cow m^{th}; μ is a general mean; F_i is the fixed effect of farm; L_j is the fixed effect of the parity; G_k is the fixed effect of the genotype; FG_{ik} is the interaction between farm i and genotype k; LG_{jk} is the interaction between lactation number j and genotype k; β_1 is the regression coefficient of the dependent variable on pF; β_2 is the regression coefficient of the dependent variable on F×J heterosis ($h_{F\times J}$); β_3 is the regression coefficient of the dependent variable on deviation from median calving date (d); e_{ijkm} is the random residual error associated with the observation of y_{ijkm}. Binominal variables (PRFS, SR21, PR21 and PR42) were analysed using the GLIMMIX procedure with the same mixed linear model described above after a logit transformation. Least-squares means and standard errors were obtained and used for multiple mean comparisons using Fisher's least-significant difference as implemented in the LSMEAN option. Significant differences among means were declared at P<0.05.

Results

The milk yield ranged from 1,491 kg to 7,371 kg per lactation with a mean value of 4,696 kg (Table 1). The range for FP was from 2.91 to 7.22% and was less than PP which ranged from 3.13 to 4.94%. The mean value of SMCO was 16 days with a range from 0 to 69 days. Pregnancy rate at first service averaged 50%, and SR21 was high (>90%). The pregnancy rates at 21 and 42 days were 54% and 77%, respectively.

The MY and PY were both significantly greater (P<0.05) in Dairy 4 than in Dairy 1 (Table 2), whereas FY was not significantly different between two farms. The FP and PP were both significantly greater (P<0.05) in Dairy 1 than in Dairy 4. The milk composition was not affected by parity number, whereas the MY, FY and PY were all significantly greater (P<0.05) in parity ≥3. The effect of interaction between farm and β-casein genotype was not significant on any of the production traits. The interaction between parity and β-casein genotype was not significant for any of the production traits. The effect of pF was significant (P<0.05) for all the traits except for FY. Heterosis had no significant effect on any of the production traits, whereas deviation from median calving date had a significant effect (P<0.05) on all production traits.

The PRFS, PR21 and PR42 were all significantly higher (P<0.05) in Dairy 1 than in Dairy 4, whereas SR21 was significantly lower (P<0.05) in Dairy 1 than in Dairy 4 (Table 3). The SMCO was significantly greater (P<0.05) in second parity than in ≥3 parity cows, whereas the other reproduction traits were not significantly different between parity. The β-casein genotype had no significant effect on any reproduction trait. The effect of interaction between farm and β-casein genotype was significant (P<0.05) on PR42 but not on any other reproduction traits. The interaction between parity and β-casein genotype was not significant for any of the reproduction traits. The SR21 was significantly affected (P<0.05) by pF, but the effect of pF was not significant for any other reproduction traits. Heterosis was not significant for any of the reproduction

Table 1 Mean, standard deviation (SD), minimum and maximum values of lactation yields of milk, fat and protein, fat percentage, protein percentage, days from start of mating to conception (SMCO), pregnancy rate at first service (PRFS), submission rate at 21 days (SR21) and pregnancy rate at 21 (PR21) and 42 days (PR42) after the start of mating in Massey University Dairy 1 and 4 farms in 2017.

Traits	Mean	SD	Minimum	Maximum
Milk yield, kg	4,696.3	1,063.60	1,491	7,371
Fat yield, kg	222.5	46.7	59	353
Protein yield, kg	179.4	38.2	56	278
Fat percentage	4.81	0.69	2.91	7.22
Protein percentage	3.85	0.32	3.13	4.94
SMCO, days	16.8	14.1	0	67
PRFS, %	50	50		
SR21, %	90	31		
PR21, %	54	50		
PR42, %	77	42		

Table 2 Least squares means, standard errors (SE) and P values of factors affecting productive performance of cows in Massey University Dairy 1 and Dairy 4 farms in 2017.

	Trait[1]									
	MY		FY		PY		FP		PP	
Effect	Mean	SE	Mean	SE	Mean	SE	Mean	SE	Mean	SE
Farm										
Dairy 1	4,188[b]	71	210.3	3.4	165.4[b]	2.7	5.10[a]	0.04	3.97[a]	0.02
Dairy 4	4,639[a]	59	213.1	2.8	173.9[a]	2.2	4.67[b]	0.03	3.78[b]	0.02
Parity										
2	4,110[b]	91	196.3[b]	4.4	157.3[b]	3.5	4.9	0.05	3.87	0.02
≥3	4,717[a]	43	227.1[a]	2.1	182.0[a]	1.6	4.88	0.02	3.88	0.01
β-casein genotype[2]										
A1	4,444	76	212.4	3.6	169.7	2.9	4.87	0.04	3.85	0.02
A2	4,383	65	211.0	3.1	169.6	2.5	4.91	0.04	3.90	0.02
Interaction Farm×β-casein genotype										
P-value	0.127		0.564		0.321		0.146		0.106	
Interaction Parity×β-casein genotype										
P-value	0.438		0.709		0.386		0.421		0.688	
pF[3]										
Effect	1,107.20	125.8	3.62	6.04	22.22	4.78	-1.21	0.07	-0.5	0.03
P-value	<0.0001		0.549		<0.0001		<0.0001		<0.0001	
Heterosis										
Effect	-82.7	121.1	6.21	5.82	2.51	4.6	0.09	0.07	0.05	0.03
P-value	0.495		0.286		0.585		0.178		0.124	
dmcd[4]										
Effect	-15.5	2.23	-0.97	0.11	-0.76	0.08	-0.005	0.001	-0.004	0.001
P-value	<0.0001		<0.0001		<0.0001		<0.0001		<0.0001	

[1]MY = milk yield, FY = fat yield, PY = protein yield, FP = fat percentage and PP = protein percentage. [2]β-casein genotype A1 = cows with either A1A1 or A1A2 genotypes, and A2 = cows with only A2A2 genotype. [3]pF = proportion of Holstein-Friesian. [4]dmcd = deviation from median calving date. [a, b] Least-squares means with different superscripts within column are significantly different (P<0.05).

Table 3 Least-squares means, standard errors and P values of factors affecting fertility traits of cows in Massey University Dairy 1 and Dairy 4 farms in 2017.

	Trait[1]									
	SMCO		PRFS		SR21		PR21		PR42	
Effect	Mean	SE	Mean	SE	Mean	SE	Mean	SE	Mean	SE
Farm										
Dairy 1	16.8	1.2	58.2[a]	4.0	79.8[b]	3.4	67.7[a]	3.8	82.7[a]	3.2
Dairy 4	18.3	1.0	41.7[b]	3.3	93.4[a]	1.5	44.4[b]	3.4	73.8[b]	3.1
Parity										
2	19.9[a]	1.5	45.7	5.1	86.4	33.6	52.9	5.3	76.8	4.5
≥3	15.3[b]	0.7	54.3	2.5	89.8	1.5	59.9	2.6	80.3	2.1
β-casein genotype[2]										
A1	17.4	1.3	50.6	4.3	87.9	2.6	60.0	4.4	81.3	3.6
A2	17.9	1.1	49.3	3.7	88.6	2.4	52.8	3.7	75.6	3.2
Interaction Farm×β-casein genotype										
P value	0.884		0.925		0.470		0.232		0.036	
Interaction Parity×β-casein genotype										
P value	0.1322		0.2424		0.1259		0.2336		0.9286	
pF[3]										
Effect	0.57	2.17	0.13	0.07	-0.09	0.04	0.05	0.07	-0.07	0.06
P value	0.793		0.053		0.045		0.435		0.281	
Heterosis										
Effect	-0.40	2.12	0.04	0.07	-0.02	0.04	-0.01	0.07	-0.02	0.06
P value	0.851		0.568		0.780		0.876		0.699	
dmcd4										
Effect	0.17	0.04	-0.003	0.001	-0.002	0.001	-0.004	0.001	-0.003	0.001
P value	<0.0001		0.023		0.034		0.002		0.004	

[1]SMCO = start of mating to conception, PRFS = pregnancy rate at first service, SR21 = submission rate at 21 days after the start of mating, PR21 = pregnancy rate at 21 days after the start of mating and PR42 = pregnancy rate at 42 days after the start of mating. [2]β-casein genotype A1 = cows with either A1A1 or A1A2 genotypes, and A2 = cows with only A2A2 genotype. [3]pF = proportion of Holstein-Friesian. [4]dmcd = deviation from median calving date. [a, b] Least-squares means with different superscripts within column are significantly different (P<0.05).

traits, whereas the effect of deviation from median calving date was significant (P<0.05) for all binomial reproduction traits.

Discussion

Analysis of variance in the current study showed that the β-casein genotype had no significant effect on total MY, FY or PY. The effects of β-casein polymorphism on milk production traits have been investigated, but the results from previous research conflict in relation to the significance and the size of genetic effects. For example, some studies reported that β-casein variants A1 and A2 did not significantly affect MY, FY or PY in F cows (Ng-Kwai-Hang et al. 1986; Çardak 2005), which was in agreement with the current study. In herds with a mixed population of J and F cattle, McLean et al. (1984) also reported that β-casein A1 and A2 genotypes had no significant effect on total MY and FY over a complete lactation. The first study to examine the influence of protein phenotypes on productive performance in New Zealand dairy cows was carried out by Winkelman et al. (1997), and similar to the present study, no relationship between β-casein variants and production traits was reported.

Conversely, Bech et al. (1990) and Ng-Kwai-Hang et al. (1990) investigated the relationship between A1 and A2 β-casein genotypes and MY during the first three lactations in Holstein herds, and A2A2 cows produced more milk than did A1A1 cows. The increase in PY resulting from greater milk production by cows with the A1 allele has also been reported (Heck et al. 2009). Although Lin et al. (1986) suggested that the loci of A1 and A2 β-caseins had no significant effect on the 308-day MY of first-lactation cows, they found that the effect was significant on PY (P<0.05). Their results suggested that the A2 genotype was superior to the A1 genotype, and increasing A2 allele frequency over A1 would improve first-lactation MSY. In New Zealand dairy cows, Morris et al. (2005) found that carriers of the A2A2 variant had significant higher FY (P<0.05) and PY (P<0.10) than did those of the A1A1 variant. The productive advantage of the A2 allele over the A1 allele has been also reported by others (Ng-Kwai-Hang et al. 1984; Bech et al. 1990; Ikonen et al. 1999). However, the results from those studies in relation to the influence of genetic variants of β-casein on MY and MSY were inconsistent. The reason for contradictory results might be gene linkage. Casein genes on bovine chromosome 6 are closely linked in the sequence of α_{s1}-, β-, α_{s2}-, and κ-casein (Threadgill et al. 1990; Rijnkels et al. 1997). Therefore, sometimes it is difficult to distinguish whether the influence of the β-casein genotype is due to the effect of its linked gene or the loci of β-casein themselves. Some of the aforementioned studies were conducted in F cows and others were in herds with a mixed-breed population. The difference between MY, FY and PY were significant for A1 and A2 β-casein genotypes in Simmentaler cows, but not in F cows (Çardak 2005), which likely indicated the differential effect of a linked gene in different breeds.

The current study found no significant difference in FP between β-casein variants, which was supported by early studies (Ng-Kwai-Hang et al. 1986; Gonyon et al. 1987). A significant relationship between the β-casein A2A2 genotype and milk fat content has been previously reported, but the results were less consistent. Several studies highlighted the association of β-casein A2A2 genotype with reduced FP in Holstein cows (Aleandri et al. 1990; Ng-Kwai-Hang et al. 1990) and Finnish Ayrshire cows (Ikonen et al. 1999), whereas one study reported the opposite results for a mixed population of J and F cows (McLean et al. 1984).

The difference in PP for β-casein A1 and A2 genotypes was not significant, which was supported by early studies with Holstein cows (Ng-Kwai-Hang et al. 1986; Ng-Kwai-Hang et al. 1990), Guernsey (Haenlein et al. 1987) and a mixed herd (McLean et al. 1984). Çardak (2005) examined the effects of the β-casein genotype and reported a significant increase in the protein concentration for A2A2 over the A1A2 genotype in Simmentaler cows. However, the differences in PP between the A1A1 and A2A2 genotypes were not significant in the Holstein cattle in the same study. In addition, some studies reported that the A2 genotype had a detrimental effect on whey protein concentration (McLean et al. 1984) and casein (Ng-Kwai-Hang et al. 1986), but not on the concentration of PP. The conflicting observations in milk composition may be partially explained by gene linkage in different breeds of the herds as discussed previously.

The effects of interactions between farm and β-casein genotype and between parity and β-casein genotype on production traits were no significant. To the best of our knowledge, few previous studies have investigated the interaction of the β-casein genotype A1 and A2 with other effects. Only one study reported the presence of a significant interaction between β-casein genotype and breed (Winkelman et al. 1997). Their results showed that about 2% more milk, fat and protein was produced by A2A2 F than A1A1 F cows, whereas A2A2 J cows produced 3-4% less milk than did A1A1 J cows.

The influence of the β-casein genotype was not significant for all fertility traits in the current study. The effect of milk protein polymorphism on reproductive performance of the cows has been reported in limited literature (Hargrove et al. 1980; Lin et al. 1987; Demeter et al. 2010), but supported the current study with respect to β-casein genotype A1 and A2.

Pregnancy rate at 42 days after the start of mating of A1 and A2 cows in Dairy 1 were 87.1±5.1 % and 75.3±4.1 % and corresponding values of the genotypes in Dairy 4 were 72.0±4.0 % and 75.2±3.9 %, which explains the significant interaction between farm and β-casein genotype. The A1 cows had higher PR42 in Dairy 1 whereas the A2 cows had higher PR42 in Dairy 4. However, the association between β-casein genotype and fertility was examined by analysing a relatively small dataset, which could impair the consistency of the results from the present study. The major issue in determining the effect of the β-casein variant on fertility traits is that the majority of the variation in fertility traits is due to environmental factors (Hodel et al. 1995). Consequently, most of the fertility traits have very low heritability (Weigel et al. 2000). Therefore, for future studies on the effect of the A2 β-casein genotype on fertility traits, analyses of large and accurate data sets are necessary.

Conclusions

The results indicated that cows of different β-casein genotypes have similar production and reproductive performance. Selection of animals based on the A2 genotype should have no negative impact on their production and fertility.

References

Aleandri R, Buttazzoni LG, Schneider JC, Caroli A, Davoli R 1990. The effects of milk protein polymorphisms on milk components and cheese-producing ability. Journal of Dairy Science 73: 241-255.

Bech A-M, Kristiansen KR 1990. Milk protein polymorphism in Danish dairy cattle and the influence of genetic variants on milk yield. Journal of Dairy Research 57: 53-62.

Çardak AD 2005. Effects of genetic variants in milk protein on yield and composition of milk from Holstein-Friesian and Simmentaler cows. South African Journal of Animal Science 35: 41-47.

Caroli AM, Chessa S, Erhardt GJ 2009. Invited review: Milk protein polymorphisms in cattle: Effect on animal breeding and human nutrition. Journal of Dairy Science 92: 5335-5352.

Correa-Luna M, Lopez-Villalobos N, Almeida JGA, Donaghy DJ, Kemp PD 2018. Phenotypic correlations of milk urea and the efficiency of crude protein utilization with milk yield traits and cow performance in two contrasting dairy systems in New Zealand. New Zealand Journal of Animal Science and Production 78: 76-81.

Demeter RM, Markiewicz K, Van Arendonk JAM, Bovenhuis H 2010. Relationships between milk protein composition, milk protein variants, and cow fertility traits in Dutch Holstein-Friesian cattle. Journal of Dairy Science 93: 5495-5502.

Eigel WN, Butler JE, Ernstrom CA, Farrell HM, Harwalkar VR, Jenness R, Whitney RM 1984. Nomenclature of proteins of cow's milk: Fifth revision. Journal of Dairy Science 67: 1599-1631.

Gonyon DS, Mather RE, Hines HC, Haenlein GFW, Arave CW, Gaunt SN 1987. Associations of bovine blood and milk polymorphisms with lactation traits: Holsteins. Journal of Dairy Science 70: 2585-2598.

Haenlein GFW, Gonyon DS, Mather RE, Hines HC 1987. Associations of bovine blood and milk polymorphisms with lactation traits: Guernseys. Journal of Dairy Science 70: 2599-2609.

Hargrove GL, Kiddy CA, Young CW, Hunter AG, Trimberger GW, Mather RE 1980. Genetic polymorphisms of blood and milk and reproduction in Holstein cattle. Journal of Dairy Science 63: 1154-1166.

Heck JML, Schennink A, van Valenberg HJF, Bovenhuis H, Visker MHPW, van Arendonk JAM, van Hooijdonk ACM 2009. Effects of milk protein variants on the protein composition of bovine milk. Journal of Dairy Science 92: 1192-1202.

Hodel F, Moll J, Kuenzi N 1995. Analysis of fertility in Swiss Simmental cattle-Genetic and environmental effects on female fertility. Livestock Production Science 41: 95-103.

Ikonen T, Ojala M, Ruottinen O 1999. Associations between milk protein polymorphism and first lactation milk production traits in Finnish Ayrshire cows. Journal of Dairy Science 82: 1026-1033.

Jinsmaa Y, Yoshikawa M 1999. Enzymatic release of neocasomorphin and β-casomorphin from bovine β-casein. Peptides 20: 957-962.

Kamiński S, Cieślińska A, Kostyra E 2007. Polymorphism of bovine beta-casein and its potential effect on human health. Journal of Applied Genetics 48: 189-198.

Korhonen H, Pihlanto A 2006. Bioactive peptides: production and functionality. International Dairy Journal 16: 945-960.

LIC. 2020. A2 bulls. Livestock Improvement Corporation. [https://www.lic.co.nz/products-and-services/artificial-breeding/a2-bulls/] Accessed 02-Mar-20.

Lin CY, McAllister AJ, Ng-Kwai-Hang KF, Hayes JF 1986. Effects of milk protein loci on first lactation production in dairy cattle. Journal of Dairy Science 69: 704-712.

Lin CY, McAllister AJ, Ng-Kwai-Hang KF, Hayes JF, Batra TR, Lee AJ, Roy GL, Vesely JA, Wauthy JM, Winter KA 1987. Association of milk protein types with growth and reproductive performance of dairy heifers. Journal of Dairy Science 70: 29-39.

Martinez Rocha JF 2017. An evaluation of traits other than production and its association with the survival of dairy cows milked once a day in New Zealand. Master of AgriScience thesis, Massey University, Palmerston North, New Zealand.

Massella E, Piva S, Giacometti F, Liuzzo G, Zambrini AV, Serraino A 2017 Evaluation of bovine beta casein polymorphism in two dairy farms located in northern Italy. Italian Journal of Food Safety 6: 6904-6904.

McLean DM, Graham EB, Ponzoni RW, McKenzie HA 1984. Effects of milk protein genetic variants on milk yield and composition. Journal of Dairy Research 51: 531-546.

Morris CA, Hickey SM, Cullen NG, Prosser CG, Anderson RM, Tate ML 2005. Associations between β-casein genotype and milk yield and composition in grazing dairy cows. New Zealand Journal of Agricultural Research 48: 441-450.

Ng-Kwai-Hang KF, Monardes HG, Hayes JF 1990. Association between genetic polymorphism of milk proteins and production traits during three lactations. Journal of Dairy Science 73: 3414-3420.

Ng-Kwai-Hang KF, Hayes JF, Moxley JE, Monardes HG 1984. Association of genetic variants of casein and milk serum proteins with milk, fat, and protein production by dairy cattle. Journal of Dairy Science 67: 835-840.

Ng-Kwai-Hang KF, Hayes JF, Moxley JE, Monardes HG 1986. Relationships between milk protein polymorphisms and major milk constituents in Holstein-Friesian cows. Journal of Dairy Science 69: 22-26.

Rijnkels M, Kooiman PM, De Boer HA, Pieper FR. 1997. Organization of the bovine casein gene locus. Mammalian Genome 8: 148-152.

Ruottinen O, Ikonen T, Ojala M 2004. Associations between milk protein genotypes and fertility traits in Finnish Ayrshire heifers and first lactation cows. Livestock Production science 85: 27-34.

Threadgill DW, Womack JE 1990. Genomic analysis of the major bovine milk protein genes. Nucleic Acids Research 18: 6935-6942.

Walstra P, Jenness R 1984. Dairy Chemistry & Physics. John Wiley & Sons.

Weigel K, Rekaya R 2000. Genetic parameters for reproductive traits of Holstein cattle in California and Minnesota. Journal of Dairy Science 83: 1072-1080.

Winkelman AM, Wickham BW 1997. Associations between milk protein genetic variants and production traits in New Zealand dairy cattle. Milk protein polymorphism, Palmerston North, New Zealand.

Woodford KB 2007. A2 milk, farmer decisions, and risk management. Proceedings of the 16th International Farm Management Congress. pp. 641-648.

Xu Z, Burton L 2000. Reproductive performance of dairy cows in New Zealand. Proceedings of the Australian & New Zealand combined Dairy Veterinarians Conference incorporating the 17th Annual Seminar of the Society of Dairy Cattle Veterinarians of the NZVA. Pp 23-40.

Implications of using an extended lactation to change from a spring-calving to an autumn-calving farm system in South Taranaki

JWM Jarman[a]*, JK Kay[b], M Neal[b], D Donaghy[a] and P Tozer[a]

[a]*School of Agriculture and Environment, Massey University, Private Bag 11222, Palmerston North 4442, New Zealand.*
[b]*DairyNZ Ltd., Private Bag 3221, Hamilton, 3240, New Zealand*

**Corresponding author:* Email: jake.jarman@dairynz.co.nz

Abstract

Recent changes to pasture-supply curves in South Taranaki, and the availability of winter milk premiums have increased farmer interest in changing from a spring-calving to an autumn-calving farm system. One approach to changing the season of calving from spring to autumn is to extend the calving interval (CI) by delaying the mating period by ~8 months, so that they next calve in autumn and undertake an extended lactation [>305 days in milk (DIM)]. A large-scale farmlet experiment was established in South Taranaki to investigate the production and reproduction responses of cows using this approach. In June 2017, 602 spring-calving cows were allocated to two farmlets. In one farmlet (SPR) 301 cows were mated in October to maintain a 12-month CI spring-calving pattern. In the other farmlet (AUT, n=301 cows), mating was delayed for eight months, and cows underwent an extended lactation (mean DIM, 488; max DIM, 577) to calve next in autumn 2019. The experiment analysed two lactations for the AUT farmlet and two and a half lactations for the SPR farmlet. Across the total experimental period, milksolids (MS) production was similar between farmlets (1,194 *vs.* 1,174 kg MS/cow), however, cows in the AUT farmlet were fed more supplementary feed [2,371 *vs.* 1,951 kg dry matter (DM)/cow]. The extended lactation changed the relationship between feed supply and herd demand, which led to excessive BCS gain and ryegrass staggers for AUT farmlet cows. Further research is required to examine grazing management during extended lactations and to assess the economic implications of this approach.

Keywords: autumn calving; spring calving; extended lactation

Introduction

In South Taranaki, there is increasing farmer-led interest in changing season of calving from spring to autumn in response to climatic constraints and milk-price incentives. There is evidence that the minimum daily temperature during winter, and thus, the number of growing degree days for pasture, has increased in South Taranaki in the past 39 years (J. Jarman, Unpublished data). Combined with more sporadic rainfall (Baldi & Salinger 2008) and low soil moisture causing variable summer pasture growth (Roberts & Thomson 1984), this has resulted in increased pasture-growth rates (PGR) in winter relative to summer (J. Clough, unpublished data). Autumn calving is expected to mitigate the impact of low summer PGR and exploit greater winter PGR (relative to summer) by shifting the herd feed-demand profile to better match the pasture-growth profile. Furthermore, international market demand for short-shelf-life products (e.g., ultra-heat-treated milk and cream) has led to milk-processing companies requiring greater milk supply during winter (Chikazhe et al. 2017), and consequently, to offer a 'winter milk premium', in addition to the farmgate milk price, for milk produced between May 15th-July 15th (Spaans et al. 2019). As a result, autumn-calving systems may receive greater revenue from milk sales compared with that from spring-calving systems, assuming the production of MS is similar.

Autumn-calving system performance has been compared with spring-calving systems in farm-system experiments (Fulkerson et al. 1987; Garcia et al. 2000; Pacheco-Navarro 2000; Ryan et al. 1998; Spaans et al. 2019). However, these previous results, as well as two modelling studies (Chikazhe et al. 2017; Figueredo 2003), assume both calving systems are operating in a steady state, and they do not account for the management decisions and implications to the farm system when changing the season of calving.

Many different approaches exist to change from spring to autumn calving, including selling the spring-calving herd, or first adopting split calving. Another common approach is to change the whole herd in one and a half years by extending the CI from 12 months (e.g., calving every July) to ~20 months, so that the herd next calves in autumn, and returning to a 12-month CI thereafter (calving every March). Consequently, the herd undergoes an extended lactation (>305 DIM) between their last calving in spring and their first calving in autumn.

Grainger et al. (2009, p 1419) reported that "no studies have been conducted on subsequent lactations with cows that have initially had an extended lactation and been managed under pasture-based systems". Therefore, it is important to understand the implications of the extended lactation required to change season of calving on the subsequent lactation and farm-system performance. It is hypothesised that extending the CI for one lactation, to change season of calving from spring to autumn, will have farm-system implications that carry over when the herd returns to a 12-month CI. This paper reports the production and reproduction responses of cows that change from spring to autumn calving using an extended lactation.

Materials and methods

Animal and paddock allocation

In June 2017, 602 spring-calving cows were managed

as one herd according to best-management practice of NZ pasture-based systems (Macdonald & Penno 1998) at Kavanagh Farm, Hawera, Taranaki (39°36'34" S, 174°17'21" E). On October 1st 2017, all cows were randomly allocated, balanced for age, breeding worth, DIM, live weight (LWT), body condition score (BCS) and current MS production, into one of two farmlets (autumn calving, AUT; spring calving, SPR) to form two equal herds of 301 cows. On the same day heifers and yearlings, currently grazing off the milking platform, were randomly allocated to each farmlet, balanced for LWT. Subsequent mating dates were altered so heifers in the AUT farmlet returned to the milking platform to calve in February 2019 (~30 months old), while in the SPR farmlet they returned to calve in June 2018 and June 2019 for lactation two and lactation three (~23 months old), respectively. Paddocks were randomly allocated to the farmlets, balanced for area, distance from the milking parlour, pasture species and age, previous cropping history and effluent application. Thirty paddocks (total area = 104.8 ha) were assigned to the AUT farmlet and 29 paddocks (total area = 104.0 ha) to the SPR farmlet. Stocking rate (SR; cows/ha) at the commencement of the experiment was approximately 2.9 cows/ha for both farmlets.

Initiation of the change of calving season

AUT farmlet cows were withheld from mating over October -December 2017, and instead, were mated at 311 ± 30 DIM, beginning June 2018 to achieve a planned start of calving (PSC) of March 15th 2019. SPR farmlet cows were mated beginning October 1st 2017, and every year thereafter.

Farmlet management

Each farmlet was managed as a closed system and daily operational decisions were made for each farmlet independently based on the same pre-written set of decision rules, similar to those described by Macdonald and Penno (1998). Briefly, cows in both farmlets were milked through the same milking parlour twice a day for the majority of each lactation. During the first, second and third lactations (L1, L2 and L3, respectively) for the SPR farmlet, and L2 for the AUT farmlet, drying off and mating protocols were the same. During L1 (extended lactation) for the AUT farmlet, cows producing <10 L milk/day at monthly herd testing were dried off. Both farmlets targeted 1,500-1,600 kg DM/ha post-grazing residuals for lactating cows and 2,200-2,400 kg DM/ha average pasture cover (APC) at PSC.

Unwell or lame cows from both farmlets were grazed together in a 'sick' cow mob that rotated between paddocks allocated to each farmlet to reduce any bias. In-line water dispensing of zinc sulphate, and paddock spraying of Sporeguard® (Ravensdown, active ingredient carbendazim) between February and April was used to control facial eczema. Prior to calving, dry cows received magnesium oxide dusted onto pasture and magnesium chloride dissolved into their water trough. After calving, lactating cows received magnesium oxide and limeflour in their in-shed supplementary feed. Colostrum cows (1 - 4 days post calving) also received limeflour dusted onto their pasture.

Maintenance fertiliser was applied to farmlets based on two-yearly soil nutrient tests. Nitrogen was applied independently to each farmlet as required based on feed-budget forecasts and soil-moisture conditions. During June – August 2018 and 2019, gibberellins (Progibb®, Nufarm) were applied to the AUT farmlet paddocks following a grazing event.

Both farmlets grew ~6 ha of maize *(Zea mays)* for maize silage on the milking platform each year. Approximately 4 ha of turnips *(Brassica rapa)* were grown on both farmlets in 2017/18, and then just on the SPR farmlet in 2018/19 and 2019/20. Pasture silage and hay were harvested from conserved pasture independently on each farmlet, based on the farmlet feed budget. Meal and palm kernel expeller (PKE), stored in one silo, were offered to both farmlets, via in-shed feeding, as determined by the feed budget.

Measurements

Bulk-milk supply data could not be used for MS production analysis because milk from both farmlets was collected into one vat during the 2017/18 season. Instead, monthly herd testing of individual cows, commenced August 2017 and was provided by Livestock Improvement Corporation (LIC) qualified technicians, recording individual cow milk yield, and fat, protein and MS percentage. Herd test data were used before and after the herd test date, either from the date halfway between the current test date and the previous test date, or between the current test date and the subsequent test date. Exceptions were for the first and last herd test data, which were used from the start of lactation and end of lactation, respectively. Rectangles were formed based on the height of the herd test record and the width of the base between the two dates, such that individual cow performance was calculated as the sum of the rectangles, as per the rectangular sum approach (Johnson 1996). Individual cow production was accumulated within lactation to calculate farmlet-level production. Individual cow LWT and BCS [1-10 scale, 0.5 increments; Roche et al. (2009)] were recorded monthly by electronic walk-over scales and visually by the same trained assessor, respectively. Reproductive performance was extracted from LIC InCalf Fertility Focus reports as defined by Hemming et al. (2018).

Pasture herbage mass (kg DM/ha) was measured fortnightly in both farmlets during 2017/18 and then weekly during 2018/19 and 2019/20, using a combination of a tow-behind C-Dax Pasture Meter©, rising-plate meter, or visual assessment for each paddock. Pasture growth rate (kg DM/ha/day) was calculated by dividing the increase in pasture mass by the days between observations, excluding grazing events. Seasonal (winter, June to August inclusive; spring, September to November inclusive; summer, December to February inclusive; autumn, March to May inclusive) PGR were calculated as the average growth rate for each paddock during each season multiplied by the number of days within that season. Yearly pasture growth was calculated as the mean of the seasonal sum for each paddock for the dairy season [i.e., June 1st – May 31st. Year one (Y1), 2017/18; year two (Y2), 2018/19]. Due to the timeline of the experiment, year three (Y3) cannot be calculated. Except for turnips, farm staff recorded daily supplementary feed offered (kg DM/cow/day) by recording the wet weight on electronic scales and multiplying by a DM% calculated from either oven drying of a sample or density calculation of the feed bunker (DairyNZ 2016). Turnips fed was estimated as 90% of the visually assessed turnip yield, assuming 10% wastage (Harris et al. 1998). Supplementary feed offered between June 2017 – January 2018 in L1 was not recorded, so L1 results are less than those of other lactations. However relative differences between farmlets are valid as both farmlets were managed equally during this period.

Statistical analysis

During the experimental period, the cows in the AUT farmlet completed two lactations (one extended, 20-month CI; and one normal, 12-month CI), whereas, cows in the SPR farmlet completed two and a half lactations (all 12-month CI). Milk production, LWT, BCS and supplementary feed data were divided into respective lactations, and farmlet means are presented accordingly. Pasture growth data were divided into respective dairy season (i.e., 1st June-31st May), and least-squares means presented accordingly. Data manipulation and analysis was completed using R software (R Core Team 2019; Wickham et al. 2019). Due to the nature of the experiment, replication by herd or by year was not possible. Either individual cow or individual paddock was the experimental unit and was compared within lactations. A Student's t-test was used to determine difference of means. Significance was declared at $P \leq 0.05$.

Results

Cows in the AUT farmlet produced 299 kg MS (67%; P<0.001) and 105 kg MS (25%; P<0.001) more MS compared with cows in the SPR farmlet during L1 and L2, respectively (Table 1). However, as cows in the SPR farmlet underwent an additional lactation (i.e., L3; Figure 1), total MS production per cow was similar between farmlets across the total experimental period (AUT, 1,194 *vs.* SPR, 1,174 kg MS). Cows in the AUT farmlet were offered 147%, 32% and 22% (625, 320, 420 kg DM/cow) more supplementary feed during L1, L2 and the total experimental period than were cows in the SPR farmlet, respectively. The additional supplementary feed was mainly offered during the winter months to these cows. Pasture growth was similar between farmlets in both Y1 and Y2 (P>0.05 for both; Table 1).

During L1, AUT farmlet cows had greater DIM (488 *vs.* 261; P<0.001), and produced milk containing greater fat and protein percentages (P<0.05) compared with that of SPR farmlet cows (Table 1). During L1, 92%, 86%, 67% and 52% of the AUT farmlet cows were still lactating at 300, 400, 500 DIM and final dry off (January 31st 2019), respectively. Average DIM was 488, while maximum DIM was 577. Cows in the AUT farmlet gained greater LWT and BCS (P<0.001), and at drying off (January 2019 for AUT, May 2018 for SPR) were heavier and had a greater BCS than cows in the SPR farmlet (P<0.001; Table 2).

During L2, AUT farmlet cows had greater DIM (293

Figure 1 Daily milksolids (MS) production per cow (kg MS/cow/day) in autumn-calving (AUT; solid line) and spring-calving (SPR; dotted line) farmlets during the experimental period (June 1st, 2017-January 31st, 2020). Grey shade indicates 95% confidence interval.

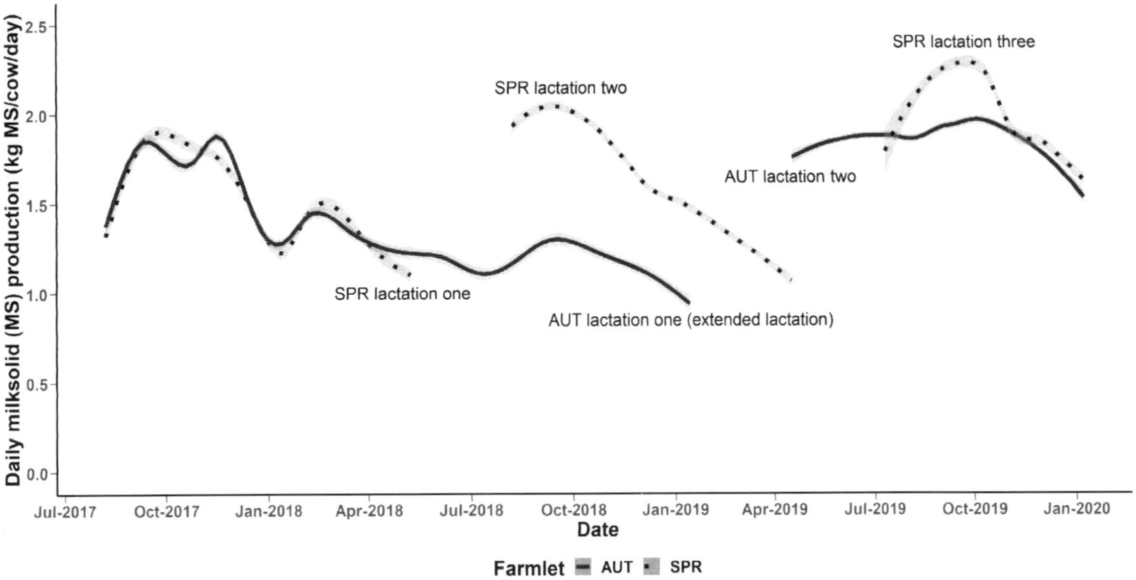

Table 1 Peak numbers of cows milked and least-squares means, standard error of the difference (SED) and significance of the difference between means of days in milk (DIM), total milksolids (MS), MS per day, concentration of fat and protein in milk per cow and supplementary feed offered [kg of dry matter (DM)/cow] during each lactation of the experimental period (June 2017-January 2020), and yearly (June 1st-May 31st) pasture growth in autumn-calving (AUT) and spring-calving (SPR) farmlet herds. Lactation one for the AUT farmlet is an extended lactation. Lactation three for the SPR farmlet is a part lactation, ending January 31st 2020.

	Item	AUT	SPR	SED	P value
Lactation 1	Peak cows milked	301	301		
Production, per cow	DIM	488	261	6.5	<0.001
	MS (kg)	661	395	10.8	<0.001
	MS (kg)/day	1.36	1.51	0.02	<0.001
	Fat (%)	5.21%	5.08%	0.06	0.03
	Protein (%)	4.32%	4.06%	0.03	<0.001
	Supplementary feed (kg DM/cow)[1]	1,049	424		
Lactation 2	Peak cows milked	306	305		
Production, per cow	DIM	293	268	3.0	<0.001
	MS (kg)	533	428	7.4	<0.001
	MS (kg)/day	1.82	1.61	0.02	<0.001
	Fat (%)	5.14%	5.04%	0.05	0.04
	Protein (%)	4.09%	4.15%	0.02	0.02
	Supplementary feed (kg DM/cow)	1,322	1,002		
Lactation 3	Peak cows milked		310		
Production, per cow	DIM		178		
	MS (kg)		351		
	MS (kg)/day		1.98		
	Fat (%)		4.77%		
	Protein (%)		4.05%		
	Supplementary feed (kg DM/cow)		525		
Experimental period[2]					
Production, farmlet total	MS(kg)	362,028	358,869		
Production, per cow	MS (kg)	1,194	1,174		
	DIM	781	707		
	MS (kg)/day	1.53	1.66		
	Supplementary feed (kg DM/cow)	2,371	1,951		
Pasture growth[3]					
Year 1	Pasture growth (kg DM/ha)	11,512	10,878	508	0.22
Year 2	Pasture growth (kg DM/ha)	12,707	13,349	516	0.49

[1] Supplementary feed offered in lactation 1 (L1) between June 2017-January 2018 was not recorded so L1 results are less than other lactations. However relative differences between farmlets are valid as both farmlets were managed equally during this period.
[2] Combined production from all lactations.
[3] Due to the timeline of the experiment, year 3 cannot be presented.

vs. 268; P<0.001), produced milk containing greater fat percentage (P<0.001), and lactated for an additional 25 days (P<0.001), compared with SPR farmlet cows. Cows in the AUT farmlet also displayed greater lactation persistency (Figure 1). AUT farmlet cows begun L2 heavier and with greater BCS, gained greater LWT and BCS, and were heavier and with greater condition at drying-off compared with SPR farmlet cows (all P<0.001).

Compared with the SPR farmlet herd, the AUT farmlet herd had numerically better reproductive performance during L1, while both performed similarly during L2 (Table 3).

There was no difference in the recorded incidence of hypocalcaemia or facial eczema between farmlets. During the dry period between L1 and L2, incidences of ryegrass staggers were recorded for the AUT farmlet cows but not SPR farmlet cows.

Discussion

During L1, MS production from cows in the AUT farmlet followed a similar profile to that in other farm-systems experiments in which cows have undergone an extended lactation (Kolver et al. 2007). Persistency of MS production continued to decline after 305 DIM (typically when cows with 12-month CI are dried off), but there was then an additional MS peak that corresponded to the second spring period. This peak is most probably due to the greater quantity and quality of spring pasture in the diet (Kolver et al. 2007).

During L2 (12-month CI for both herds), cows in the AUT farmlet did not produce as much milk at peak lactation (88 days since PSC), compared with those in the SPR farmlet (106 days since PSC), but MS production did not decline as rapidly following peak (Figure 1). Cows in the AUT farmlet also had greater DIM compared with cows

Table 2 Least-squares means, standard error of the difference (SED) and significance of the difference between means of live weight and body condition score [BCS; 1-10 scale (Roche et al. 2009)] at the start of lactation[1], dry off[2] and change[3] between, of autumn-calving (AUT) and spring-calving (SPR) farmlet herds during each lactation of the experimental period. Lactation one for AUT is an extended lactation. Lactation three for SPR is a part lactation, and end of experiment is presented instead of dry off.

Live weight (kg)		AUT	SPR	SED	P value
Lactation 1	Start of lactation	469	461	4.6	0.09
	Dry off	578	497	4.9	<0.001
	Change	109	36	3.4	<0.001
Lactation 2	Start of lactation	518	476	5.1	<0.001
	Dry off	573	503	5.1	<0.001
	Change	54	27	2.8	<0.001
Lactation 3	Start of lactation		485		
	End of experiment		495		
	Change		9		
Body condition score					
Lactation 1	Start of lactation	4.2	4.1	0.0	0.35
	Dry off	5.4	4.2	0.1	<0.001
	Change	1.3	0.0	0.1	<0.001
Lactation 2	Start of lactation	4.7	4.2	0.1	<0.001
	Dry off	4.6	4.3	0.0	<0.001
	Change	-0.1	0.1	0.1	<0.001
Lactation 3	Start of lactation		4.3		
	End of experiment		4.3		
	Change		0.0		

[1] First recorded observation after calving

[2] Last recorded observation before drying off.

[3] Change in live weight/BCS divided by the number of days between the first and last recorded observation.

Table 3 Three-week submission rate (3wk SbR), six-week in-calf rate (6wk InC) conception rate (CR), not-in-calf rate (NinC) and differences between autumn-calving (AUT) and spring-calving (SPR) farmlet herds for mating periods during each lactation. Lactation one for the AUT farmlet is an extended lactation. Lactation three for the SPR farmlet is a part lactation, ending January 31st, 2020.

		AUT	SPR	Difference
3wk SbR	Lactation one	88%	72%	16%
	Lactation two	80%	81%	-1%
	Lactation three	-	86%	
6wk InC	Lactation one	80%	64%	16%
	Lactation two	65%	66%	-1%
	Lactation three	-	74%	
CR	Lactation one	73%	51%	22%
	Lactation two	54%	57%	-3%
	Lactation three	-	58%	
NinC	Lactation one	8%	16%	-8%
	Lactation two	14%	12%	2%
	Lactation three	-	11%	

in the SPR farmlet, which is consistent with other literature (Garcia & Holmes 2001; Garcia et al. 2000). However, as to whether the increased production is due to different calving season or due to other farm-system changes during this lactation is unknown. Spaans et al. (2019) concluded that there was no difference in DIM or MS production between autumn- and spring-calving herds that were managed the same, stating that differences reported by the former authors were due to farm-system changes such as SR or supplementary feed, and not calving season *per se*. Therefore, as the quantity of supplementary feed offered varied in this current experiment, MS production was also confounded by this factor.

Cows in the AUT farmlet gained excessive LWT and BCS during the extended lactation. This is primarily due to the feed-supply and feed-demand relationship changing in the latter stages of the extended lactation (Auldist et al. 2007; Grainger et al. 2009; Kolver et al. 2007). To maximise DIM and achieve grazing-management targets outlined in the farmlet decision rules, lactating cows were offered pasture diets in which feed supply (i.e., energy input) exceeded herd feed demand (i.e., energy output) during the second spring of the extended lactation. Cows selectively bred for 12-month CI preferentially convert this excess energy to adipose tissue rather than milk production, thus, increasing BCS (Kolver et al. 2007). In response to the increased risk of periparturient metabolic disease with excessive BCS (e.g., hypocalcaemia; Roche et al. 2013a), non-lactating cows in the AUT farmlet were offered a restricted diet by slowing the rotation length. Consistent with reports in the literature, this management strategy improved the metabolic status of cows after calving and there was no difference in incidence of hypocalcaemia between farmlets. However, the restricted pasture allocation was a factor in increasing the incidence of ryegrass staggers during March and April, because cows in the AUT farmlet grazed lower into the sward (Cosgrove

& Edwards 2007), increasing their intake of mycotoxins (di Menna et al. 2012). Therefore, restricting pasture intake in non-lactating cows reduced the BCS gain and the risk of metabolic disease, but exacerbated pasture management issues. This highlights the challenge of achieving greater DIM and revenue from milk production during an extended lactation, while achieving pasture management and BCS targets at calving in NZ dairy cows bred for 12-month CI (Kolver et al. 2007).

Cows in the AUT farmlet had a greater milk-fat percentage compared with that of cows in the SPR farmlet. We postulate that this was due to the greater body tissue mobilisation during L2 because of greater BCS at calving. There is a positive association between calving BCS and milk-fat percentage, potentially due to greater lipolysis providing long chain fatty acids for milk-fat production (Roche et al. 2009; Roche et al. 2013b). Furthermore, recent increases in the farmgate value of fat relative to protein (Edwards et al. 2019) mean that the value of milk produced in L2 by the AUT farmlet may be greater than that of the milk produced by the SPR farmlet.

The improved reproductive performance of AUT farmlet cows during L1 (extended lactation) tends to align with other farm-systems' literature (Butler et al. 2010; Kolver et al. 2007), however, accurate comparisons are confounded by the methods used by the former authors to create an extended lactation (e.g., mating and abortions), and low cow numbers in those experiments. Regardless, a possible explanation may be that increasing the CI allows the cow greater time to regain positive energy balance and clear any uterine infections. A negative energy balance during early lactation, that coincides with the mating period in a 12-month CI system, is an accepted factor involved in poor reproductive performance (Berry et al. 2016). Cows are more likely to have cycled multiple times and be in a positive energy balance later in lactation, which is when mating occurred for the AUT cows in the current experiment. Uterine infections typically occur 1 - 21 days postpartum, but can persist for longer than 70 days, suppressing reproductive performance in the typical mating period for 12-month CI (Sheldon et al. 2009). An implication of greater reproductive performance during the extended lactation is a more-condensed calving pattern at the beginning of L2, which requires greater feed availability and higher peak workload for staff.

Conclusion

As MS production did not differ between farmlets, there was no MS production penalty incurred in this approach to changing calving season within the timeframe considered in this paper. However, there was greater use of supplementary feed in the AUT farmlet and a higher milk price received from the higher fat percentage and winter milk premium, thus, the cost/benefit of this approach to changing to an autumn-calving system still needs to be determined. There are potential farm-system implications if an extended lactation is used to change the season of calving. The implementation of grazing decisions, considered best management practice in spring-calving systems (Macdonald & Penno 1998), in addition to maximising DIM in the latter stages of the extended lactation, led to excessive BCS gain as well as animal-health implications. Future research is required to investigate optimal strategies to alleviate the implications reported in this current experiment. Furthermore, as the increase in BCS and reproductive performance during the extended lactation have carry-over effects on the subsequent lactation, we propose that the first calving in autumn (12-month CI; L2 in the present experiment) is not representative of a steady-state system, and should be considered as part of the system change.

Acknowledgements

Dairy Trust Taranaki (DTT); Debbie McCallum, DTT operations manager; Matt Butler, farm manager; Linda Cruickshank, DTT technician; Barbara Kuhn-Sherlock for statistical guidance.

References

Auldist MJ, O'Brien G, Cole D, Macmillan KL, Grainger C 2007. Effects of varying lactation length on milk production capacity of cows in pasture-based dairying systems. Journal of Dairy Science 90(7):3234-3241. doi: 10.3168/jds.2006-683.

Baldi M, Salinger J 2008. Climate trends, hazards and extremes - Taranaki. Synthesis Report. New Plymouth: NIWA.

Berry DP, Friggens NC, Lucy M, Roche JR 2016. Milk production and fertility in cattle. Annual Review of Animal Biosciences 4: 269-290.

Butler ST, Shalloo L, Murphy JJ 2010. Extended lactations in a seasonal-calving pastoral system of production to modulate the effects of reproductive failure. Journal of Dairy Science 93(3): 1283-1295.

Chikazhe T, Mashlan K, Beukes PC, Glassey CB, Haultain J, Neal M 2017. The implications of winter milk premiums for sustainable profitability of dairy systems. Journal of New Zealand Grasslands 79:49-54.

Cosgrove GP, Edwards GR 2007. Control of grazing intake. In: Rattray PV, Brookes IM & Nicol, AM (eds.) Pasture and Supplements for Grazing Animals. Hamilton, New Zealand Society of Animal Production.

DairyNZ. 2016. How much silage is in my stack? [Online]. DairyNZ. Available: www.dairynz.co.nz/media/3476270/1-49-how-much-silage-is-in-my-stack.pdf [Accessed 30 January 2020].

di Menna ME, Finch SC, Popay AJ, Smith BL 2012. A review of the Neotyphodium lolii / Lolium perenne symbiosis and its associated effects on animal and plant health, with particular emphasis on ryegrass staggers. New Zealand Veterinary Journal 60(6): 315-328. doi: 10.1080/00480169.2012.697429.

Edwards JP, Spaans OK, Neal M, Macdonald KA 2019. Short communication: Milk fat payment affects the relative profitability of Jersey and Holstein-Friesian cows at optimal comparative stocking rate. Journal of Dairy Science 102(10): 9463-9467. doi: 10.3168/jds.2018-16152.

Figueredo F. 2003. Economic Aspects of Changing the Seasonality of Milk Production in New Zealand. Master of Agricultural Science thesis, Lincoln University.

Fulkerson WJ, Franks DR, Michell P 1987. Comparison of autumn and spring calving management strategies. Interim Report. Elliott Research Station, Tasmania, Australia.

Garcia SC, Holmes CW 2001. Lactation curves of autumn- and spring-calved cows in pasture-based dairy systems. Livestock Production Science 68(2-3): 189-203.

Garcia SC, Holmes CW, MacDonald A, Lundman M, Lundman J, Pacheco-Navarro R 2000. Comparative efficiency of autumn and spring calving for pasture-based dairy systems. Asian Australiasian Journal of Animal Sciences 13: 533-537.

Grainger C, Auldist MJ, O'Brien G, Macmillan KL, Culley C 2009. Effect of type of diet and energy intake on milk production of Holstein-Friesian cows with extended lactations. Journal of Dairy Science 92(4): 1479-1492.

Harris SL, Clark DA, Waugh CD, Copeman PJA, Napper AR 1998. Use of 'Barkant' turnips and 'Superchow' sorghum crops to increase summer-autumn milk production. Proceedings of the New Zealand Society of Animal Production 58 :121-124.

Hemming NV, McNaughton LR, Couldrey C 2018. Brief communication: Reproductive performance of herds milked once a day all season compared with herds milked twice a day all season. New Zealand Journal of Animal Science and Production 78: 170-172.

Johnson DL 1996. Estimation of lactation yield from repeated measures of test day yields. Proceedings of the New Zealand Society of Animal Production 56: 16-18.

Kolver ES, Roche JR, Burke CR, Kay JK, Aspin PW 2007. Extending lactation in pasture-based dairy cows: I. Genotype and diet effect on milk and reproduction. Journal of Dairy Science 90(12):5518-5530. doi: 10.3168/jds.2007-0324.

Macdonald KA, Penno JW 1998. Management decision rules to optimise milksolids production on dairy farms. Proceedings of the New Zealand Society of Animal Production 58: 132-135.

Pacheco-Navarro RA. 2000. Reproductive efficiency in dairy cattle calving during autumn or spring. Master of Applied Science in Animal Science thesis, Massey University.

R Core Team. 2019. R: A langauge and environment for statistical computing. [Online]. Vienna, Austria: R Foundation for Statistical Computing. [Accessed 12 December 2019. v.3.6.2].

Roberts AHC, Thomson NA 1984. Seasonal distribution of pasture production in New Zealand XVIII. South Taranaki. New Zealand Journal of Experimental Agriculture 12(2): 83-92. doi: 10.1080/03015521.1984.10421416.

Roche JR, Friggens NC, Kay JK, Fisher MW, Stafford KJ, Berry DP 2009. Invited review: Body condition score and its association with dairy cow productivity, health, and welfare. Journal of Dairy Science 92(12): 5769-5801. doi: 10.3168/jds.2009-2431.

Roche JR, Kay JK, Friggens NC, Loor JJ, Berry DP 2013a. Assessing and managing body condition score for the prevention of metabolic disease in dairy cows. Veterinary Clinics: Food Animal Practice 29(2): 323-336.

Roche JR, Macdonald KA, Schütz KE, Matthews LR, Verkerk GA, Meier S, Loor JJ, Rogers AR, McGowan J, Morgan SR, Taukiri S, Webster JR 2013b. Calving body condition score affects indicators of health in grazing dairy cows. Journal of Dairy Science 96(9): 5811-5825. doi: 10.3168/jds.2013-6600.

Ryan G, Crosse S, Fitzgerald S 1998. The development of feeding and management strategies for milk production systems with very contrasting milk supply patterns. Moorepark, Fermoy, Co. Cork, Ireland: Teagasc.

Sheldon IM, Cronin J, Goetze L, Donofrio G, Schuberth H 2009. Defining postpartum uterine disease and the mechanisms of infection and immunity in the female reproductive tract in cattle. Biology of Reproduction 81(6): 1025-1032.

Spaans OK, Macdonald KA, Neal M, Auldist MJ, Lancaster JAS, Bryant AM, Doole GJ, Roche JR 2019. A quantitative case study assessment of biophysical and economic effects from altering season of calving in temperate pasture-based dairy systems. Journal of Dairy Science 102(12). doi: 10.3168/jds.2018-15911.

Wickham H, Averick M, Bryan J, Chang W, McGowan L, François R, Grolemund G, Hayes A, Henry L, Hester J 2019. Welcome to the Tidyverse. Journal of Open Source Software 4(43): 1686.

Seasonal effects of two forage-based nutrition regimens on intake and average daily gain of three genotypes of young red deer (*Cervus elaphus*)

DR Stevens* and ID Corson

AgResearch Invermay, Private Bag 50034, Mosgiel

**Corresponding author:* Email: david.stevens@agresearch.co.nz

Abstract

The red deer genotypes currently being farmed in New Zealand have different forage-use habits and exhibit different growth profiles in different seasons. Three genotypes (NZ red, eastern European and elk-cross) were subjected to low and high nutritional regimens during autumn, winter and spring. Few differences among genotypes were found in autumn, but in winter the elk-cross genotype grew faster than did the NZ red and eastern European genotypes. NZ red deer consumed approximately 9% of their diet as hay in both autumn and winter, while eastern European and elk-cross deer had much higher intakes of hay (up to 44%). Divergence in response to the high- or low-nutrition regimens imposed developed in winter. Liveweight gain averaged 84 g/d on the low nutrition regimen and ranged from 132 to 199 g/d for NZ red and elk-cross genotypes respectively on the high-nutrition regimen. Eastern European deer were immediate. In spring as the NZ red genotype did not respond to increasing feed availability, while the eastern European and elk-cross deer increased growth rate by approximately 50 g/d and 100 g/d, respectively, in response to increased feed availability. This was matched by increases in forage and metabolisable energy intake. Understanding these interactions provides information that will enable feeding systems to be tailored to deer genotype to improve on-farm resource-use efficiency.

Keywords: diet selection; energy; forage intake; genotype; liveweight gain; red deer; seasonality.

Introduction

Recent developments in the New Zealand deer industry have seen the inclusion of a range of genotypes from different regions of the world (Rowe et al. 2015). Main red deer types include the original imported Scottish red deer (*Cervus elaphus* ssp. *scoticus*), North American elk (*C. e.* ssp. *nelsoni*), and Eastern European genotypes (*C. e.* ssp. *hippelaphus*). There is potential for each of these genotypes to respond differently to seasonal signals of day-length and temperature, and to nutrition regimen, based on their evolutionary circumstance (Rhind et al. 2002).

Previous research has indicated that red and elk × red deer may grow at different rates throughout the year (Judson & Nicol 1997; Nicol & Barry 2003), though variation among herds can be great, as reported by Stevens et al. (2003). The different dry matter intakes (DMI) of NZ red deer (*C.E. scoticus*) and red x elk (*C.E. nelsoni*) were explained by live weight differences rather than genotype as DMI were similar when expressed in terms of metabolic body weight.

This experiment aimed to define the autumn, winter and spring dry matter intakes of the three major red deer sub-species in New Zealand and investigate how the genotypes responded to different amounts of feed offered, to aid farmers in using this variation to develop profitable farming systems.

Materials and methods

One hundred and twenty-six five-month-old red deer were assigned to one of two nutrition regimens in early autumn 2003 at the Winchmore Research Station (43 80S; 171 78E). High- and low-nutrition regimens, represented by a single mob for each, were imposed using a leader (High) - follower (Low) rotational-grazing system, with the High treatment being allocated 1 kg barley/head/d plus approximately 0.4 kg DM as lucerne hay during autumn and winter, while the Low treatment was allocated 0.5 kg barley/head/d plus *ad libitum* meadow hay during autumn and winter. During spring, the leader-follower grazing system was used without supplement. Within each mob were 21 deer of three genotypes – NZ red (*Cervus elaphus scoticus*), eastern European (*C. e. hippelaphus*) and elk-cross (2/3 NZ red x 1/3 elk *C. e. nelsoni*).

In each season seven animals of each genotype were used to determine the forage intake and digestibility for each nutrition regimen using the alkane dilution technique as described by Dove and Mayes (1991) using controlled-release alkane capsules as described by Stevens and Corson (2006). Animals were dosed with a controlled-release capsule, delivering an assumed constant supply of C_{32} and C_{34} on April 24, June 19 and October 17. Faecal collections were taken on days 14 and 15 following dosing to assess fecal concentrations of both dosed and natural alkanes. Endpoint samples to determine release rate of dosed alkanes were taken between days 18 and 22. Digestibility estimates were then used to calculate the metabolisable energy concentration of individual intakes using the following equation (AFRC 1990)

$$\text{ME (MJ/kg DM)} = 0.81*(18.4*\text{Digestibility}(\%)/100).$$

Samples of diet were determined from plucked pasture samples representative of the diet selected, and grab samples of supplements. Both diet and faecal samples were snap frozen and freeze dried before analysis. Live weights were measured every two weeks and average daily gain assigned to each season based on the calendar months

March to May (autumn), June to August (winter) and September to November (spring). Herbage mass before and after grazing was determined by taking 40 readings within the grazing area using a rising-plate meter and published equations (L'Huillier & Thomson 1988). Pre- and post-grazing pasture composition was determined by dissection of approximately 40-g samples into grass leaf, grass stem, legume, weed and dead material from 20 random grab samples taken to ground level.

Diet composition (hay and pasture) were determined using the procedure of Mayes et al. (1995), adjusted for recovery by the method of Dillon (1993). Diet alkane proportions were then allocated on this basis and forage intake calculated using the C_{31}:C_{32} ratios. Analysis of the data recognised a potential bias due to high dead-material intakes of deer on the Low-nutrition regimen in autumn. This was not apparent in winter or spring. Plucked samples represent the diet as predominantly green leaf. Much of the dead material was seedhead left from summer. Based on the much higher alkane concentrations measured in the inflorescence of grasses (Dove et al. 1996), secondary calculations were done on the autumn Low samples. This assumed that the hay samples were representative of the dead material in the pastures and diet alkane proportions were adjusted to reflect the 30% of the intake from dead material. These were re-analysed and are presented in the results.

Animal data for each season were analysed separately by ANOVA (GenStat 2015) as a 2 x 3 factorial randomised-plot design with individual animals being used as replicates. The ability to determine both intake and the energy concentration of the diet of individuals provided the means to define the diet of those individuals. Thus the comparison of the relative treatments can be refined and described by those differences, enabling the use of the individual as replication of the nutritional treatments. Pasture samples were taken three times within each season. These samplings were used as replication of the pre- and post-grazing herbage. Different paddocks were used in each season and, therefore, the paddocks become independent of the nutritional treatments. The experiment was approved by the AgResearch Invermay Animal Ethics Committee in accordance with New Zealand animal-welfare regulations.

Results

The amount of pasture on offer (kg DM/ha) differed significantly between the nutrition treatments and between seasons (Table 1; $P<0.05$). However, when expressed as the amount offered per head, the difference only occurred between nutrition regimens (Table 1). Botanical composition of the offered and residual pasture, when measured as the proportion as grass leaf, clover and dead material, did not differ significantly between nutrition regimes or among seasons (Table 1). The residual pasture cover was 2060 and 1290 kg DM/ha after the High and Low treatments had grazed the pastures (Table 1; $P<0.01$).

During autumn, data were analysed as recorded, and then recalculated to reflect the high dead-material intake of the Low regimen. No significant differences were found in deer growth rate (Table 2; mean=142 g/d), though estimated dry matter intake was significantly lower (Table 2; $P<0.001$) for the High treatment compared with the Low treatment. The digestibility of the Low diet was also higher than that of the High diet (Table 2; $P<0.001$). The proportion of hay in the diet was greater in the Low regimen compared with the High regimen. The addition of barley to the diet substituted for the forage, leading to similar metabolisable energy intakes on both treatments. No differences were found between the liveweight gains of the genotypes in autumn. The NZ red and eastern European deer were similar weights (60.6 and 57.2 kg respectively) while the elk-cross were heavier at 72.5 kg (Table 2). Intake of hay was low for the NZ red, intermediate for the elk-cross and greatest for the eastern European deer.

Recalculation of the intakes to reflect high dead-material intakes (approximately 30% of the forage diet, Table 2) reduced the estimated forage intake of the Low regimen by approximately 0.3 kg DM/d (Table 2) compared

Table 1 Herbage mass and botanical composition of the offered and residual pasture fed in two differing nutrition regimens to three red deer genotypes over three seasons.

		Nutrition			Season			
		Low	High	LSD (0.05)	Autumn	Winter	Spring	LSD (0.05)
Pasture on offer	kg DM/ha	1760	2850	545	2300 ab[1]	1840 b	3020 a	950
	kg DM/head	5.1	8.0	2.8	7.2	5.3	7.8	3.7
Pasture residual	kg DM/ha	1290	2060	540	1530 b	1370 b	2310 a	665
Botanical composition (on offer)								
Grass	%	74.4	81.1	11.6	72.8	79.6	81.2	14.3
Clover	%	6.2	10.2	7.8	9.8	3.6	12.8	9.6
Dead	%	19.4	8.7	12.1	17.4	16.8	5.6	14.9
Botanical composition (residual)								
Grass	%	64.5	77.2	14.9	74.8	65.1	75.0	18.4
Clover	%	5.8	4.8	5.1	7.7	3.6	4.6	6.3
Dead	%	29.7	18.0	16.7	17.5	31.3	20.5	20.6

[1]Values within rows with different letters are significantly different

Table 2 Forage intake, digestibility, and energy intake of three strains of red deer fed two differing nutrition regimens during autumn before and after adjustment for dead material intake determined by pre- and post-grazing pasture composition.

		Nutrition			Genotype			
		Low	High	LSD (0.05)	NZ Red	Eastern European	Elk cross	LSD (0.05)
Unadjusted								
Forage intake	kg DM/d	2.27	1.65	0.29	2.03[1]	1.97	1.90	0.36
Digestibility	g/kg DM	777	715	27	753	730	755	33
Proportion of hay	%	36.1	15.3	12.1	9.1 c	43.3 a	23.9 b	14.9
Barley intake	kg DM/d	0.5	1	na	0.75	0.75	0.75	na
Metabolisable energy intake								
	MJME/d	32.9	30.7	3.8	32.7	31.3	31.3	4.6
	MJME/kg $BW^{0.75}$	1.49	1.37	0.16	1.51	1.50	1.27	0.21
Adjusted for dead intake								
Dead intake	kg DM/d	31	1	na				
Forage intake	kg DM/d	1.96	1.65	0.29	1.70	1.95	1.79	0.36
Digestibility	g/kg DM	732	715	31	717	716	740	38
Proportion of hay	%	23.1	15.3	13.4	5.9 b	36.5 a	14.4 b	16.5
Metabolisable energy intake								
	MJME/d	28.1	30.7	3.9	28.1	30.5	29.6	4.7
	MJME/kg $BW^{0.75}$	1.27	1.37	0.17	1.29	1.46	1.20	0.21
Average live weight	kg	62.4	63.6	3.0	60.6 b	57.2 b	72.5 a	3.7
Live weight gain	g/d	133	151	41	119	161	146	51

[1] Values with different letters are significantly different

Table 3 Forage intake, digestibility, and energy intake of three strains of red deer fed two differing nutrition regimens during winter.

		Nutrition			Genotype			
		Low	High	LSD (0.05)	NZ Red	Eastern European	Elk cross	LSD (0.05)
Forage intake	kg DM/d	1.9	1.3	0.27	1.37 b[1]	1.40 b	2.10 a	0.32
Digestibility	g/kg DM	619	617	37	598 b	603 b	653 a	45
Proportion of hay	%	26.9	4.4	7.9	8.6 b	16.4 ab	22.0 a	9.7
Barley intake	kg DM/d	0.5	1	na	0.75	0.75	0.75	na
Metabolisable energy intake								
	MJME/d	24.6	25.4	3	22.2 b	22.6 b	30.5 a	3.7
	MJME/kg $BW^{0.75}$	1.01	0.99	0.12	0.95	0.97	1.1	0.15
Average live weight	kg	69.5	74.9	2.6	67.7 b	64.9 b	84.0 a	3.2
Live weight gain	g/d	84	159	16	112 b	112 b	140 a	20

[1]Values with different letters are significantly different

Table 4 Forage intake, digestibility, and energy intake of three strains of red deer fed two differing nutrition regimens during spring.

		Nutrition			Genotype			
		Low	High	LSD (0.05)	NZ Red	Eastern European	Elk cross	LSD (0.05)
Forage intake	kg DM/d	2.61	2.86	0.36	2.52 b[1]	2.64 b	3.10 a	0.45
Digestibility	g/kg DM	617	736	26	688	654	691	32
Metabolisable energy intake								
	MJME/d	24.2	31.6	3.7	25.8 b	25.4 b	32.5 a	4.6
	MJME/kg $BW^{0.75}$	0.85	0.99	0.12	0.92	0.88	0.96	0.15
Average live weight	kg	81.9	93.1	3.7	80.2 b	81.8 b	102.6 a	4.56
Live weight gain	g/d	257	308	37	250 b	297 a	300 a	45

[1]Values with different letters are significantly different

to the original data, though this remained significantly greater than forage intake on the High regimen. Forage digestibility was also reduced by the recalculation and values were not significantly different between the nutrition regimens. The proportion of hay in the diets of the Low-nutrition regimen was reduced under this methodology, with similar reductions in the amount of hay eaten by the different genotypes (Table 2). The energy intake, once recalculated to reflect dead material content, of the Low regimen was numerically lower than that of the High regimen. Energy intakes of the three genotypes reflected their relative liveweight gains, with the eastern European deer having both the highest energy intake and highest liveweight gain, the elk-cross being intermediate and the NZ red deer having the lowest intake and liveweight gain (Table 2).

During winter forage intake was higher on the Low-nutrition treatment, while liveweight gain and average live weight were lower than the High-nutrition treatment (Table 3). The elk-cross deer had higher forage intake and digestibility than did the NZ red and eastern European deer in winter (Table 3). The elk-cross were the heaviest ($P<0.001$), had higher energy intake per day (Table 3) and significantly higher liveweight gain than the other genotypes. Concurrently, the intake of hay as a percentage of the diet was greater in the elk-cross deer compared with NZ red, with eastern European deer being intermediate (Table 3).

In spring, significant differences again occurred between the nutrition regimens (Table 4) with the High treatment having a higher digestibility, greater energy intake and higher liveweight gain. The eastern European deer had a liveweight gain similar to that of the elk-cross, while both grew faster than the NZ red deer. However, the intake of the eastern European deer was similar to the NZ red deer, and both were lower than the elk-cross (Table 4).

Interactions among nutrition regimen and genotype for liveweight gain occurred in winter and a trend towards interactions occurred in spring (Table 5). During winter the liveweight gain of all genotypes on the Low nutrition regimen was uniformly low. However, on the High regimen, the elk-cross deer grew faster than did either the NZ red or eastern European deer, which grew faster than their Low-nutrition cohort. The interaction term provided no

Table 5 Interactions among liveweight gain, feed intake and feed digestibility for NZ Red, Eastern European and elk cross weaner deer fed two nutrition regimens in winter and spring.

		Genotype				
Season	Nutrition	NZ Red	Eastern European	Elk cross	P values	LSD
Winter		Liveweight gain (g/d)				
	Low	92 c[1]	77 c	84 c	0.002[3]	28
	High	132 b	148 b	199 a		
		Total feed intake (kg DM/d)				
	Low	2.19	2.1	3.05	0.306	0.46
	High	2.08	2.22	2.67		
		Forage digestibility (%)				
	Low	60.4	59.5	65.7	0.789	6.4
	High	59.2	61.1	64.9		
		Energy intake (MJME/d)				
	Low	21.8	20.6	31.6	0.293	5.2
	High	22.5	24.4	29.5		
		Average liveweight (kg)				
	Low	65.8	61	81.5	0.42	4.5
	High	69.5	68.8	86.5		
Spring		Liveweight gain (g/d)				
	Low	251	259	260	0.07	45
	High	250	311	368		
		Total feed intake (kg DM/d)				
	Low	2.44 b	2.79 b	2.67 b	0.04	0.63
	High	2.59 b	2.47 b	3.57 a		
		Forage digestibility (%)				
	Low	64.9	58.1	62.6	0.089	4.6
	High	72.7	72.7	75.7		
		Energy intake (MJME/d)				
	Low	23.6 b	23.7 b	25.3 b	0.036	6.6
	High	28.1 b	27.2 b	40.2 a		
		Average liveweight (kg)				
	Low	75.3	76.3	95.7	0.709	6.5
	High	85	87	109.1		

[1]Values with different letters are significantly different

more explanation of difference in total feed intake, forage digestibility and energy intake during winter. During spring there was a trend towards a significant interaction between the nutrition regimens and the genotypes for liveweight gain (Table 5). While the NZ reds did not respond to the increased availability and quality of the pasture of the High-nutrition regimen, both the eastern European and elk-cross deer had a higher liveweight gain on the High-nutrition regimen compared with the Low regimen. This was reflected in significant interactions between nutrition regimen and genotype for total and metabolisable energy intake.

Discussion

The alkane technique to predict forage intake and diet composition has been used successfully in many situations. However, the key issues of alkane recovery and collecting a representative sample of the animals' diet remain challenging. Miller and Thompson (2005) compared botanical composition of the diet of grazing sheep and found that the alkane technique was more accurate than faecal cuticle analysis in a mixed native-grass community. However, this still requires an accurate collection of the diet components. Alkane concentrations vary among pasture species and the age and development of those species (Dove & Mayes 1991). Adjusting alkane concentrations to reflect the balance of the diet in Autumn was done in retrospect after examination of the original data. The subsequent results appear to represent the actual feed requirements of the animal reflected in the liveweight gains. However, this calculation needs to be treated with caution as it highlights the problems with the techniques without providing a definitive solution. Results from the winter and spring appear to be consistent with the feed requirements predicted by live weights and liveweight gains

The red deer genotypes currently being farmed in New Zealand have different forage use habits and exhibited different growth profiles in different seasons. Few differences were found in autumn. Overall the deer on the high-nutrition regimen had a lower digestibility of the forage eaten. High levels of grain in the diet may compromise the digestibility of forage (Van Soest 1994), though increasing forage intake can also result in lower digestibility through faster passage rate (Mertens & Ely 1979).

In winter, divergence in growth of the genotypes under the two nutrition regimens started to emerge. While the elk-cross genotype grew faster than the NZ red and eastern European genotype overall, the eastern European deer also began to exhibit greater growth than the NZ red deer when offered the high regimen. Forage intake of the elk-cross was greater, in part due to the greater live weight. The extra intake and the slightly higher liveweight gain would reflect the greater live weight of the elk-cross deer at this time of the year, similar to that measured by Stevens et al. (2003). Differences in intake between low and high regimens were small and forage digestibility appeared relatively unaffected by nutrition regimen. The two mechanisms that may influence potential liveweight gain are the capture of digestible energy as metabolisable energy, or the conversion of metabolisable energy to net energy. Evidence suggests the capture of digestible energy as metabolisable energy, as the red deer has exhibited the ability to reduce gut passage rate of feed in winter (Sibbald & Milne 1993). If this was the case on the low regimen, then more of the digested energy may be lost as heat and methane, lowering the yield of metabolisable energy, as has been measured in low-quality feeds in white-tailed deer (Ullrey et al. 1972).

The data also demonstrate a divergence in the performance of the genotypes when exposed to different nutrition regimens. Again the opportunity of the larger elk-cross deer to utilise the greater energy intake due to their size may explain some of this. However, the eastern European deer appeared to be beginning to exhibit some divergence from the NZ red deer, even though they were of approximately the same size.

In spring, the energy intake of the High-nutrition regimen was greater than that of the Low regimen as a consequence of slightly higher dry matter intake and significantly higher digestibility. This led to greater liveweight gains on average for the High treatment. However, the NZ red genotype did not respond to increasing feed availability, while the eastern European and elk-cross deer increased liveweight gain by approximately 53 to 108 g/d in response to increased feed availability. This was matched by increases in forage and metabolisable energy intake in all three genotypes, but no significantly greater liveweight gain in the NZ Red deer. These results are consistent with those of Judson and Nicol (1997) who found that an allowance of 8 kg DM/100 kg live weight was required to maximise liveweight gain in elk-cross deer while only 6 kg DM/100 kg live weight was needed to maximise the gain of NZ red deer, with both genotypes growing at similar rates when pasture allowance was low. This data suggests that the eastern European deer require similar allowances to elk-cross during spring to maximise their growth potential.

The liveweight gain in spring was approximately 100 g/d higher than during the winter and spring despite the energy intake on the Low nutrition treatment being similar in both seasons. This may reflect the added maintenance cost of the deer in winter (Simpson et al. 1978), though the translation of digestible energy to metabolisable energy may have been altered, due to greater losses during the digestion process.

The outcome of higher liveweight gain during each season for the High-nutrition regimen was a greater live weight in spring of 11.2 kg. This is valuable in financial terms as well as biological terms, as a greater proportion of the deer in the High-nutrition regimen were ready for slaughter (76% compared with 29% in the High and Low treatments, respectively, had an estimated carcase weight of

50 kg or greater) by mid-November. The efficiency of gain is reflected in the comparison of the feed intake, expressed as the ratio in metabolic live weight to liveweight gain. This demonstrated that the elk-cross genotype appeared to be more efficient in the winter, while the eastern European genotype was more efficient during the spring. Interestingly, these genotypes both had live weights of approximately 85-87 kg at their most efficient stage of growth.

Understanding these interactions provide the researcher and farmer with information that will enable tailored feeding systems to be developed to improve the efficiency of on-farm resources.

Acknowledgements

The authors thank DEEResearch for funding and AgResearch farm staff at Invermay and Winchmore for assistance.

References

Dillon P 1993. The use of n-alkanes as markers to determine intake, botanical composition of available or consumed herbage in studies of digesta kinetics with dairy cows. PhD thesis. National University of Ireland, Dublin.

Dove H, Mayes RW 1991. The use of plant wax alkanes as marker substances in studies of the nutrition of herbivore: a review. Australian Journal of Agricultural Research 42: 913-952.

Dove H, Mayes RW, Freer M 1996. Effects of species, plant part, and plant age on the n-alkane concentrations in the cuticular wax of pasture plants. Australian Journal of Agricultural Research 47: 1333-1347.

GenStat 2015. GenStat for Windows 18th Edition. VSN International Ltd, Oxford.

Judson HG, Nicol AM 1997. Effects of feeding level on the seasonal liveweight gain of young red deer and red/elk hybrid stags. Proceedings of the New Zealand Society of Animal Production 57: 139-143.

Mayes RW, Dove H, Chen XB, Guada JA 1995. Advances in the use of faecal and urinary markers for measuring diet composition, herbage intake and nutrient utilisation in herbivores. Recent developments in the nutrition of herbivores: Proceedings of the 4th International Symposium, Clermont-Ferrand, France. pp. 381-406.

Mertens DR, Ely LO 1979. A dynamic model of fiber digestion and passage in the ruminant for evaluating forage quality. Journal of Animal Science 49: 1085-1095. https://doi.org/10.2527/jas1979.4941085x.

Miller SM, Thompson RP 2005. Seasonal patterns of diet composition, herbage intake and digestibility identify limitations to performance of weaner sheep grazing native pasture in the Falkland Islands. Grass and Forage Science 60(4): 356-366. doi 10.1111/j.1365-2494.2005.00484.x.

Nicol AM, Barry TN 2003. Pastures and forages for deer growth. The nutrition and management of deer on grazing systems. Grassland Research and Practice series 9: 25-43.

Rhind SM, Archer ZA, Adam CL 2002. Seasonality of food intake in ruminants: recent developments of understanding. Nutrition Research Reviews 15: 43-65.

Rowe SJ, Clarke SM, Van Stijn TC, Hyndman DL, Ward JF, McEwan KM, Dodds KG, McEwan JC, Newman S-AN, Asher GW 2015. BRIEF COMMUNICATION: Developing genomic tools in the New Zealand Deer Industry. Proceedings of the New Zealand Society of Animal Production 75: 89-90.

Sibbald AM, Milne JA 1993. Physical characteristics of the alimentary tract in relation to seasonal changes in voluntary food intake by the red deer (*Cervus elaphus*). Journal of Agricultural Science, Cambridge 120: 99-102.

Simpson AM, Webster AJF, Smith JS, Simpson CA 1978. Energy and nitrogen metabolism of red deer (Cervus elaphus) in cold environments; a comparison with cattle and sheep. Comparative Biochemistry and Physiology 60: 251-256.

Stevens DR, Corson ID 2006. The feed intake and liveweight responses of hinds and calves grazing leaf turnip or pasture during late lactation. Proceedings of the New Zealand Grassland Association 68: 215-219.

Stevens DR, Corson ID, Littlejohn RP 2003. Preliminary findings of genotype variations in growth rate and feed intake of weaner deer. The nutrition and management of deer on grazing systems. Grassland Research and Practice series 9: 41-43.

Ullrey DE, Youatt WG, Johnson HE, Cown AB, Covert RL, Magee WT 1972. Digestibility and estimated metabolizability of aspen browse for white-tailed deer. Journal of Wildlife Management 36: 885-891.

Van Soest PJ 1994. Nutrition ecology of the ruminant. Cornell University Press, Ithica, NY. p476.

Evaluating anti-CarLA salivary IgA response in a deer progeny test

JF Ward[a*], M Wheeler[b], RJ Shaw[c] and GW Asher[a]

[a]*AgResearch Ltd, Invermay Agricultural Centre, Private Bag 50034, Mosgiel 9053, New Zealand;* [b]*AgResearch Ltd, Ruakura Agricultural Centre, Private Bag 3123, Hamilton 3240, New Zealand;* [c]*AgResearch Ltd, Hopkirk Research Institute, Private Bag 11008, Palmerston North 4442, New Zealand*

**Corresponding author.* Email: jamie.ward@agresearch.co.nz

Abstract

Farmed red deer (*Cervus elaphus spp*) are susceptible to infection by nematode parasites. A salivary antibody (IgA) that is naturally produced in response to exposure to a nematode parasite carbohydrate larval surface antigen (CarLA) can provide a protection against gastro-intestinal nematodes in sheep and rising-yearling farmed red deer. The concentrations of this CarLA-IgA were measured in saliva samples collected at 6 and 10 months of age, in 1531 rising-yearling progeny of 36 sires across three farms during a three-year progeny test. The CarLA-IgA concentrations differed across sires, farms and years, with 6-month levels being much lower than 10-month levels. Heritability estimates were low (h^2=0.10) for 6 months, but moderate and significant (h^2=0.37, $P<0.05$) for 10 months. These two traits were highly genetically correlated (r_g=0.86) and moderately phenotypically correlated (r_p=0.27). There were low (r_p 0.08-0.13) but significant ($P<0.05$) favourable phenotypic correlations with spring and pre-slaughter live weight, and with growth rate from 3 to 10 months of age and 6 to 10 months of age. Sire variation and heritability of 10-month response indicates that it may have utility as a selection criterion for improved ability of farmed deer to cope with nematode challenge.

Keywords: red deer; nematode parasite; carbohydrate larval antigen; immune; *Cervus elaphus*

Introduction

Pasture-based farmed red deer and red deer-wapiti crossbreds (*Cervus elaphus spp.*) in New Zealand are susceptible to clinical infection by parasitic nematodes (Mason 1994), especially as rising-yearlings (R1). The key nematodes are lungworm (*Dictocaulus eckerti*) and gastrointestinal nematodes (GIN): primarily, but not exclusively, abomasal parasites of the *Ostertagia* type (Mackintosh et al. 2014). Lungworm are the most pathogenic with deaths recorded on 5% of farms compared with 3% for GIN (Castillo-Alcala et al. 2007). Anthelmintic resistance is a risk, and New Zealand deer farmers are struggling to find fully effective anthelmintics (Pomroy et al. 2018), frequently utilising off-label preparations that incur a 91-day withholding period (WHP) for meat. Faecal-egg counting (FEC) has been shown to have limited effectiveness for quantifying GIN burden in R1 deer, especially after winter (Mackintosh et al. 2014). These factors all make management of parasites challenging and concerning for producers, presenting risks to animal welfare, productivity and market access, as well as threatening long-term sustainability of pastoral deer production.

One potential tool, which has been used in sheep to measure the immune response to parasitic nematode challenge, is the measurement of naturally-occurring IgA in the saliva that has been produced in response to a Carbohydrate Larval Antigen (CarLA) (Shaw et al. 2012). The antibody is produced in response to exposure to CarLA that has been presented to the animal from natural consumption of nematode parasites. The antigen is present in the complex glycolipid sheath which protects most infective third-stage (L3) common nematode parasites from the environment outside animal hosts. The sheath is normally shed by the parasite soon after entry to the host (Harrison et al. 2003a, b). In farmed sheep in New Zealand, the antibody responses have been shown to be correlated with resistance to challenges by mixed species of parasitic nematodes. The antibody concentration is very labile and reflective of the challenge environment (Shaw et al. 2012). The commercial CARLA® Saliva Test is currently available to farmers. Shaw et al. (2013) showed antibody levels increased over time for lambs grazing naturally infected pastures, and that the levels were moderately heritable and favourably genetically correlated with live weight. Mackintosh et al. (2014) used the CARLA® Saliva Test (CARLA) to demonstrate that for R1 deer concentrations peaked in late autumn and mid-spring, levels were lower for wapiti-crossbreds than for red deer, and that R1 deer with responses ≥2 units/ml had lower adult abomasal nematode burdens than did those with responses <2 units/ml.

A deer industry progeny test (DPT) (Ward et al. 2014), provided an opportunity to evaluate the antibody concentrations in saliva from offspring of multiple industry sires in different farm environments and to assess its suitability as a trait for genetic selection. The hypothesis was that the antibody concentrations would increase with natural exposure to nematodes in R1 deer as in lambs, and that the concentrations exhibit heritable variation.

Materials and methods

Animals

The animals in this trial were enrolled in the DPT over the period from March 2012 to June 2015 (Ward et al. 2014). All procedures involving animals were approved by the Invermay Animal Ethics Committee under the New Zealand Animal Welfare Act 1999. The progeny used were all bred by artificial insemination (AI), from 35 sires (n=

24 red deer and 11 wapiti-crossbred), out of red deer dams, and were born in late November or early December. A total of 1798 were weaned, 950 (all males and wapiti-crossbred females) were finished for slaughter at 11-12 months of age and 762 red deer females submitted for first mating as rising-two-year-olds (R2) at 15 months-of-age. The final, analysed dataset included 1531 individuals. Animals were run in either a single mixed-sex mob, or up to two mobs per sex, depending on farms and years (for more details on animals see Ward et al. (2014; 2019)).

Farms and animal management

The three farms were described in detail by Ward et al. (2014). Briefly, Haldon Station is a partly irrigated high-country sheep, beef, and deer station farm in the Mackenzie Basin, Invermay is an Otago hill-country sheep and deer research farm, and Whiterock Station is a Canterbury high-country beef and deer farm. Haldon and Whiterock actively integrate non-deer species (i.e., they graze or co-graze the same pastures) but Invermay did not integrate other livestock with the deer. Haldon and Whiterock Stations calved their hinds in hill blocks. After weaning, the calves were grazed on improved specialist pastures, including lucerne at Haldon and clover, chicory and plantain mixes at Whiterock. At Invermay the deer were grazed on improved ryegrass-dominant pastures before and after weaning. During the winter period R1 deer were on pasture and lucerne baleage at Haldon, brassica crops at Invermay and Whiterock, Whiterock supplemented with pea-vine and Invermay fed lucerne hay, both in racks. Winter feeding at Invermay was June-September, Haldon and Whiterock Jun-Oct. In 2014, both Whiterock and Haldon Stations experienced a summer drought during lactation and after weaning, restricting pasture availability, quality and reducing sward height and mass. Anthelmintic regimes differed between farms and years. Whiterock Station used an injectable moxidectin and oral benzimidazole at weaning then six- and 12-weeks after weaning, as did Invermay for the 2013 cohort. The 2011 Invermay birth cohort received pour-on moxidectin six-weekly after weaning until mid-winter, when injectable moxidectin was used, and Haldon alternated between oral benzimidazole and pour-on moxidectin, again six weekly after weaning. In spring, only the replacement (red deer) females were drenched. Any parasite challenges were natural and anthelmintic treatments were instigated to prevent any adverse effects on growth of the animals through parasitism.

Trait measurement

Live weights (LWT) were collected, as described by Ward et al. (2019), approximately every three months, from weaning at three-months of age at the start of March until just prior to transport to slaughter (i.e., pre-slaughter LWT) for all males and female wapiti-crossbreds, or pre-mating at 15-months for R2 red deer females. Growth rates (ADG (g/day)) were calculated between various LWT measurements. Carcass traits were collected after-slaughter at a licensed deer slaughter plant (DSP) (Alliance Group Limited DSP, Makarewa, Southland). Hot carcass weight (HCW) was measured after slaughter with the animal skinned, gutted, head removed and carcass trimmed by the meat inspector, hot dressing-out percentage was HCW/pre-slaughter LWT, and 24 h pH was the average of three pH measures along the striploin (*longissimus dorsi*) 24 hours after slaughter and after chilling at 4°C prior to carcass breakdown. Reproduction traits were determined by rectal ultrasonography (White et al. 1989) in R2 hinds in June at 18 months of age following joining with multiple stags for natural mating from late February until around May 10th.

Antibody concentration was measured after collecting saliva samples on cotton dental swabs held in forceps, as described for sheep by Shaw et al. (2012) and deer by Mackintosh et al. (2014). Animals were either free-standing in groups of five to eight in small pens or restrained in a hydraulic or mechanical crush during ultrasonic eye-muscle scanning (Ward et al. 2010). Samples were collected at the start of winter at six months of age (CARLA 6) and in spring at 10 months of age (CARLA 10) then stored frozen at –20°C until analysis in annual farm batches as per the method of Shaw et al. (2012).

Salivary antibody assay

Saliva samples were extracted from the cotton swabs by centrifugation at 2000 × g for 10 minutes, then stored frozen at –20°C. The CarLA-IgA ELISA was essentially the same as that described by Merlin et al. (2017), except that saliva samples were diluted to 1/20 in sample dilution buffer, then diluted in the assay to 1/33 and 1/50. Rabbit anti-sheep IgA conjugated with horseradish peroxidase (Bethyl Laboratories Inc., USA) diluted at 1/5000 with sample dilution buffer was used to detect CarLA specific deer IgA. Samples with very high CarLA-IgA responses (>40 units/ml) were re-assayed at 1/100 or 1/200 dilution. The intra-assay coefficient of variation (CV = (SD/mean) × 100) was 7.6% while the inter-assay CV was 21.0.

Statistical analysis

All zero antibody concentrations were assigned a value of 0.1 units/ml, which was the smallest reliable response measurable by the assay. Prior to analysis, CarLA-IgA data were transformed to natural logarithms. Statistical analyses were as described by Ward et al. (2019). Briefly, all traits were analysed using ASREML (Gilmour et al. 2009) using a first univariate, then a bivariate model. All models fitted Animal as a random effect with fixed effects of herd by year, sex, weaning mob, and breed type covariate (Ward et al. 2019). All twins and any animals with contradictory mob information or missing trait data were excluded from analysis. Significance testing assumed normal distribution of data after accounting for fixed effects in the model; CARLA 10 was normally distributed CARLA 6 was not: it was biased as many individuals expressed zero response.

Results

Collection of the saliva samples was straightforward

Table 1 Percentage and number (in parentheses) of antibody concentrations measured from saliva samples of singleton rising-yearling red deer and wapiti-crossbreds from three progeny test farms, across three birth years (2011-2013) at about 6 (CARLA 6) and 10-months of age (CARLA 10), for five response classifications. Responses classified as none detected (<0.10), trace (0.10-0.49), low (0.50-0.99), medium (1.00-4.99), high (≥5.00).

CARLA trait	Birth Year	Farm	None	Trace	Low	Medium	High	Total n
CARLA 6	2011	Invermay	30 (72)	40 (94)	14 (34)	12 (29)	3 (8)	237
	2011	Whiterock	85 (212)	13 (31)	2 (4)	0.4 (1)	0 (0)	248
	2012	Haldon	29 (73)	61 (156)	9 (22)	2 (5)	0 (0)	256
	2012	Whiterock	4 (10)	31 (88)	37 (106)	24 (69)	4 (11)	284
	2013	Haldon	53 (138)	3 (7)	19 (50)	20 (51)	5 (12)	258
	2013	Invermay	90 (222)	2 (4)	3 (8)	5 (12)	1 (2)	248
CARLA 10	2011	Invermay	0 (0)	10 (23)	8 (20)	50 (120)	32 (75)	238
	2011	Whiterock	30 (73)	50 (121)	13 (31)	7 (18)	0.4 (1)	244
	2012	Haldon	0 (0)	0.4 (1)	4 (11)	57 (146)	38 (97)	255
	2012	Whiterock	1 (4)	11 (30)	26 (71)	53 (145)	9 (24)	274
	2013	Haldon	6 (14)	1 (2)	6 (14)	40 (102)	48 (122)	254
	2013	Invermay	4 (11)	1 (3)	11 (28)	42 (104)	41 (100)	246

Table 2 Genetic and phenotypic correlations (±SE) between CarLA-IgA response traits (CARLA) at 6- and 10-months of age, in rising-yearling red deer and wapiti-crossbreds, and production traits of live weight (LWT), growth rate (ADG) (3, 6, and 10 months-of-age), pre-slaughter live weight and carcass traits at 10-12 months-of-age, and rising-two-year-old female live weight and reproduction traits (at 15 and 18 months of age). Bold type and * indicates significant correlation at P<0.05.

	Genetic correlation (r_g)		Phenotypic correlation (r_p)	
	CARLA 6	CARLA 10	CARLA 6	CARLA 10
LWT 3	-0.28 ± 0.31	0.02 ± 0.20	-0.03 ± 0.04	0.04 ± 0.04
LWT 6	0.26 ± 0.33	0.14 ± 0.19	0.02 ± 0.04	0.04 ± 0.03
LWT 10	0.15 ± 0.31	0.06 ± 0.18	0.08 ± 0.04	**0.09 ± 0.03***
LWT pre-slaughter	0.14 ± 0.34	0.22 ± 0.20	0.09 ± 0.04	**0.13 ± 0.04***
ADG 3-6	0.82 ± 0.23	0.23 ± 0.22	0.08 ± 0.03	0.01 ± 0.03
ADG 3-10	0.47 ± 0.27	0.04 ± 0.20	0.12 ± 0.03	**0.08 ± 0.03***
ADG 6-10	-0.02 ± 0.33	-0.08 ± 0.19	0.10 ± 0.04	**0.10 ± 0.03***
Eye-muscle area	-0.50 ± 0.27	0.01 ± 0.18	-0.03 ± 0.03	-0.02 ± 0.03
Hot carcass weight	-0.07 ± 0.35	0.08 ± 0.21	0.05 ± 0.04	**0.10 ± 0.04***
Carcass dress-out	-0.54 ± 0.28	**-0.43 ± 0.16***	-0.13 ± 0.04	**-0.12 ± 0.04***
Primal meat yield	-0.45 ± 0.30	0.13 ± 0.21	-0.05 ± 0.05	0.05 ± 0.04
Striploin 24hr pH	-0.60 ± 0.42	-0.45 ± 0.25	-0.04 ± 0.04	**-0.12 ± 0.04***
LWT 15	-0.05 ± 0.37	**-0.41 ± 0.21***	0.05 ± 0.05	-0.01 ± 0.05
Conception date	0.31 ± 0.52	0.43 ± 0.35	-0.04 ± 0.05	-0.02 ± 0.05
Pregnancy status	0.19 ± 0.47	0.09 ± 0.33	-0.02 ± 0.05	0.06 ± 0.05
CARLA 6	1.00	0.86 ± 0.22	1.00	0.27 ± 0.03
CARLA 10	0.86 ± 0.22	1.00	0.27 ± 0.03	1.00

as most animals were not aversive to the procedure and very few had to be physically restrained for sampling when free-standing in a pen. The restrained individuals generally became non-aversive once the cotton swab was in their mouths. The saliva swabs received in the laboratory contained consistently more saliva than those collected from lambs. The R1 CARLA 6 and CARLA 10 means varied across farms, sampling periods and years (Table 1). Means for CARLA 6 were much lower than CARLA 10 and the extent of "no detectable response" decreased from 48% to 7% across farms and birth years (Table 1). The CARLA 6 non-detected response was highly variable across birth years within farms; the most extreme example was Whiterock Station with 4% and 85% not detected in 2012 and 2011 respectively (Table 1). The spring response at 10 months of age was much more normally distributed and repeatable within farms and birth years, except for Whiterock Station 2011 (Table 1). Extreme values for CARLA 6 or 10 were considerably higher than comparable measurements that had been observed in lambs. There was no significant (P<0.05) difference between the regressions of antibody concentration on breed fraction of Eastern European and English red deer compared to wapiti, with regression coefficients for CARLA 6 –0.33 ± 0.26 and –0.27 ± 0.25, and for CARLA 10 of –0.59 ± 0.33 and 0.04 ± 0.32, for Eastern European and English red deer, relative to wapiti.

Heritability estimates for CARLA 6 were low (h^2= 0.10 ± 0.07), but moderate and significant for CARLA 10 (h^2= 0.37 ± 0.09). The two traits were highly genetically correlated (r_g =0.86 ± 0.22) and moderately phenotypically correlated (r_p =0.27 ± 0.03) (Table 2), and the phenotypic standard deviations were 0.92 and 1.07 for CARLA 6 and 10, respectively. There were three notable genetic correlations with the other production traits: a high positive correlation between CARLA 6 and growth from weaning to start-winter (ADG 3-6), and moderate negative correlations between CARLA 10 and hot-carcass dress-out percentage, and female 15-month live weight (Table 2.) Many of the genetic correlations had a large standard error often combined with a low genetic correlation (Table 2). Phenotypic correlations all were low. Correlations with the growth-rate traits and with spring or pre-slaughter live weights and carcass weight were mostly positive (Table 2). The three exceptions were negative: CARLA 6 and 10 with hot-carcass dressing-out percentage and CARLA 10 with striploin pH 24-hours after slaughter (Table 2).

Discussion

Heritability of CARLA 10 in R1 deer was moderate and significant during spring (10-11 months of age), but low and non-significant at the start of winter (6 months of age). This study did not agree with the hypothesis of Mackintosh et al. (2014) that late autumn would be the optimal single time point to measure the antibody concentration in R1 deer. In the current study, spring would appear to be more suitable for genetic evaluation purposes as >90% of individuals produced a detectable concentration, compared with 48% producing nothing detectable at the start of winter.

The antibody concentration response in R1 deer increased within a mob with increasing age, as reported by Mackintosh et al. (2014), and has been observed in lambs and cattle (Shaw et al. 2013, Merlin et al. 2017). The response in R1 deer also does appear to require an environmental challenge of nematode parasites to elicit detectable measures, as indicated by Mackintosh et al. (2014). The environmental challenge was variable among farms and years, especially during the autumn. At Whiterock Station in 2012, the 2011 birth cohort produced low responses when weaned and grazed on clean (conserved) pastures, and after spending an extended time grazing winter brassica crop, having only grazed pasture for 10 days prior to CARLA 10 sampling (Table 1). Conversely, the 2012 Whiterock birth cohort produced much higher responses especially at CARLA 6 (Table 1) during a drought, where the deer grazed pasture at low covers that had been grazed previously by other deer. The low number of individuals producing a measurable antibody concentration before winter is likely a combination of the development of general immunity and environmental parasite challenge present, and interactions between these two factors.

The response is present in individuals under differing anthelmintic regimens, meaning that animal health does not need to be compromised to measure CARLA as long as the deer are still ingesting and responding to the L3 larvae. The moderate heritability estimate for CARLA 10 (h^2= 0.37 ± 0.09) was similar and correlation between CARLA traits was the same (r_g = 0.86) as the values observed in lambs (Shaw et al. 2013). In contrast to the observations reported by Mackintosh et al. (2014), this study found no significant effect of breed type (red deer or wapiti) on CARLA 6 or 10.

There was little evidence of unfavourable genetic or phenotypic correlations between the other production traits analysed and CARLA 6 or 10. There were favourable phenotypic correlations with growth and liveweight traits and striploin pH. The unfavourable genetic and phenotypic correlations with carcass dressing percentage are likely of no concern; as the hot carcass weight phenotypic correlation was favourable, the dressing percentage may simply relate to rumen digesta weight and associated inaccuracies of determining ruminant live weight (Wilson et al. 2015).

Summary

In this progeny test, the proportion of R1 deer producing an antibody response to a nematode antigen increased with age, but the response was variable across farms and years, during regular anthelmintic treatment. In pasture-grazed R1deer in spring at 10 or 11 months of age, between 70 and 100% (mean 93%) of animals produced a measurable response, providing suitable variation for genetic evaluation. This spring, CARLA 10 was moderately heritable and suitable to use for quantitative genetic selection, with little evidence of negative impacts on other production traits. The data suggests that stud breeders could use high levels of the CARLA 10 trait to select deer with elevated immune response to ingestion of parasitic nematodes.

Acknowledgements

We are grateful to the owners and staff of Whiterock and Haldon Stations, AgResearch Invermay deer farm, and the partner-herd breeders who contributed sire genetics. The DPT project was funded by DEEResearch Limited, AgResearch Core Funding, PAMU and Alliance Group Limited.

References

Castillo-Alcala F, Wilson PR, Pomroy WE, Hoskin SO 2007. A survey of anthelmintic use and internal parasite control in farmed deer in New Zealand, New Zealand Veterinary Journal 55 (2): 87-93.

Gilmour A, Gogel B, Culls B, Thompson R 2009. ASReml User Guide Release 3.0. Hemel Hempstead: VSN International Ltd.

Harrison GBL, Pulford HD, Hein WR, Barber TK, Shaw RJ, McNeill M, Wakefield J, Shoemaker CB 2003a. Immune rejection of Trichostrongylus colubriformis in sheep: a possible role for intestinal mucus antibody against an L3-specific surface antigen. Parasite Immunology 25: 45-53.

Harrison GBL, Pulford HD, Hein WR, Severn WB, Shoemaker CB 2003b. Characterization of a 35-kDa carbohydrate larval antigen (CarLA) from Trichostrongylus colubriformis: a potential target for host immunity. Parasite Immunology 25: 79-86.

Mackintosh CG, Johnstone P, Shaw RJ 2014. Observations on the phenotypic relationship between anti-CarLA salivary IgA antibody response, nematode infection levels and growth rates in farmed red deer (Cervus elaphus) and wapiti hybrid deer (Cervus elaphus canadensis). Veterinary Pathology 203: 160-166.

Mason PC 1994. Parasites of deer in New Zealand. The New Zealand Journal of Zoology 21(1): 39-47.

Merlin A, Shaw R, Chauvin A, Bareille N, Chartier C 2017. Significance of anti-CarLA salivary IgA antibody in first grazing season cattle naturally infected with gastrointestinal nematodes. Veterinary Parasitology 243: 36-41.

Pomroy WW 2018. Anthelmintic resistance: a perspective on our current understanding and ability to control this problem. New Zealand Journal of Animal Science and Production 78: 105-108.

Shaw RJ, Morris CA, Wheeler M, Tate M, Sutherland IA 2012. Salivary IgA: a suitable measure of immunity to gastrointestinal nematodes in sheep. Veterinary Parasitology 186: 109-117.

Shaw RJ, Morris CA, Wheeler M 2013. Genetic and phenotypic relationships between carbohydrate larval antigen (CarLA) IgA, parasite resistance and productivity in serial samples taken from lambs after weaning. International Journal for Parasitology 43: 661-667.

Ward JF, Archer JA, Asher GW, Farmer RJ, Sweetman MF, Nicoll GB, Yuan JV 2010. BRIEF COMMUNICATION: Can ultrasound eye muscle area scanning be used in the New Zealand deer industry? Proceedings of the New Zealand Society of Animal Production 70: 275-277.

Ward JF, Archer JA, Asher GW, Everett-Hincks JM, Mathias-Davis HM 2014. Design and implementation of the Deer Progeny Test (DPT). Proceedings of the New Zealand Society of Animal Production 74: 220-225.

Ward JF, Schütz KE, Wheeler M, Asher GW 2019. Relationships between deer temperament and production traits. New Zealand Journal of Animal Science and Production 79: 32-36.

White IR, McKelvey WA 1989. Diagnosis of pregnancy and prediction of fetal age in red deer by real-time ultrasonic scanning. Veterinary Record 124: 395-397.

Wilson RF, Hardwick-Smith JA, Logan CM, Corner-Thomas RA, Bywater AC, Greer AW 2015. BRIEF COMMUNICATION: Optimising a fasting protocol to assess live weight of sheep. Proceedings of the New Zealand Society of Animal Production 75: 223-224.

Deer Industry Advance Parties: farmer groups lead practice change for improved profit

I Moffat[a] and GW Asher[b*]

[a]*P2P Manager, Deer Industry New Zealand, Wellington;* [b]*Agresearch Ltd, Invermay Agricultural Centre, Mosgiel*

**Corresponding author.* Email: geoff.asher@agresearch.co.nz

Abstract

The NZ deer industry's 'Passion2Profit' productivity improvement programme, launched in 2013, established 'Advance Parties' (APs) to improve profitability among New Zealand deer farmers. Animal performance on farms was highly variable, and sometimes well below potential productivity, despite a large body of knowledge from prior research investments aimed at optimising animal performance. APs are small groups of like-minded farmers focussed on helping each other implement changes in their businesses. The benefits of these changes are disseminated to the wider deer farming community through various industry communications and regional workshops. As of December 2018, there are 27 APs, with the aim for 30 on an ongoing basis, which would involve approximately 350 deer farms. This paper describes the history, functioning and measured outcomes of APs within the New Zealand deer industry.

Keywords: Deer Industry New Zealand; Passion2Profit; deer-farming practice change

Introduction

Deer Industry New Zealand (DINZ) identified that deer farming required a transformational change to improve productivity and gain the confidence of the entire industry that its profitability was at least competitive with alternative land uses. The national deer herd had fallen from a peak of 1.7 million in the early 2000s to under 1 million in 2015 (Statistics New Zealand National Agriculture Survey 2015). Without change, the New Zealand deer industry would likely continue to decline and miss the opportunity to derive full market value from farmed-deer products.

A minority of leading farmers had shown that integrating the best scientific knowledge on deer feeding, animal health, and genetics into farm systems resulted in delivery of favourable returns from deer farming. Those practices had not, however, been packaged into forms or systems that the majority of farmers choose to use or were capable of deploying.

New Zealand's five major venison marketing companies and the New Zealand Deer Farmers' Association (NZDFA) agreed a programme of work that endeavours to create transformational change in the New Zealand venison industry, which is being delivered by their industry-good organisation, Deer Industry New Zealand (DINZ). This programme is called Passion2Profit (P2P). Central to the P2P is the Advance Party project; a means of providing deer farmers confidence, skills and motivation to make changes to their management to improve the profitability of their deer farming operations.

Passion2Profit: The P2P is made up of two groups of interlinked projects: **Project 1 - Marketing premium venison:** aims to increase the amount of venison sold year-round in chilled form at higher prices, through collaborative branding and positioning of New Zealand venison in new markets or new market niches, and **Project 2 - Market led production:** aims to develop the systems that will "power up" farmers' ability to respond to current and future value drivers. Project 2 is employing a two-pronged approach; firstly, packaging the new farming knowledge, technologies and guides into forms and systems easily usable by farmers, including those around feeding, genetics, animal health and environmental management knowledge. Secondly P2P has created new opportunities for farmers to work with each other to apply improved farm management practices.

Barriers to adoption: A report into deer farmers' attitudes to change (Hudson & Hawksley 2011) highlighted that the four main incentives to change were improving the productivity, profitability and sustainability of farmers and improving animal welfare. What had been missing were consistent commercial signals to describe and encourage the required changes, and the structures to break down the barriers of change. A recent notable enabler of producer change was individual electronic identification of deer. Producers need to be able to capture the benefits of adopting new technologies. These benefits may include labour and time saving, management simplification, or user reassurance. Simply describing an increase in outputs or potential increase in profit was seldom enough to motivate change if the outcome was uncertain, or the practice difficult to adopt.

Achieving 'Practice Change' is a critical element of the P2P and will primarily determine whether the P2P is successful or not. If knowledge of how to implement farming systems that deliver market requirements exist, the critical challenge becomes engagement with farmers to drive adoption of those systems.

Deer Industry New Zealand have developed the philosophy that personal attitude to change is based on several factors, including motivation (e.g., profit, altruism, peer recognition, legacy, and competing priorities), confidence (e.g., self-belief, past success or failures, peer, advisor, or family support) and ability (e.g., skills, knowledge, experience, debt levels). Tactical practice change initiatives are operational, on-the-ground tools, which drive behaviour change (G.Sheath pers.comm.). The Deer Industry has an array of traditional practice change engagement strategies in place (e.g., Focus Farms) which have had success, but with limited reach. P2P has developed, and is trialling, some innovative new practice-change engagement strategies. A central means of encouraging the adoption of the new technology and implementing change in the P2P programme is the Advance Party project.

Materials and Methods

An Advance Party (AP) was designed as a well-supported group of motivated deer farmers who identify opportunities for, and implement, changes to lift profit on their individual farms. There are generally some elements of farming practice that are common to all APs. Change is facilitated by group learning; trialling different changes as part of a supportive group to see their effect on profit and sharing the results with the wider deer farming community to encourage wider adoption of successful changes. Figure 1 shows the process in a simplified way.

Each AP has about 10 farming businesses. Importantly, all key decision makers from each farming business, especially the spouses in farming families, are encouraged to participate in the AP. Advance Parties provide a supportive environment that encourages producers to learn from others' experiences and implement new management technology

Figure 1 Diagramatic model of the DINZ Advance Party (AP) process. Individual APs (top layer) are voluntary groupings of localised farmers with shared improved-productivity aspirations across one or more themes. The APs are self-mentoring (second layer) but link into DINZ resources (bottom two layers) for support and to ensure their experiences are shared across the entire industry (reproduced from Deer Industry Advance Party Guidelines for Facilitators v 1.2).

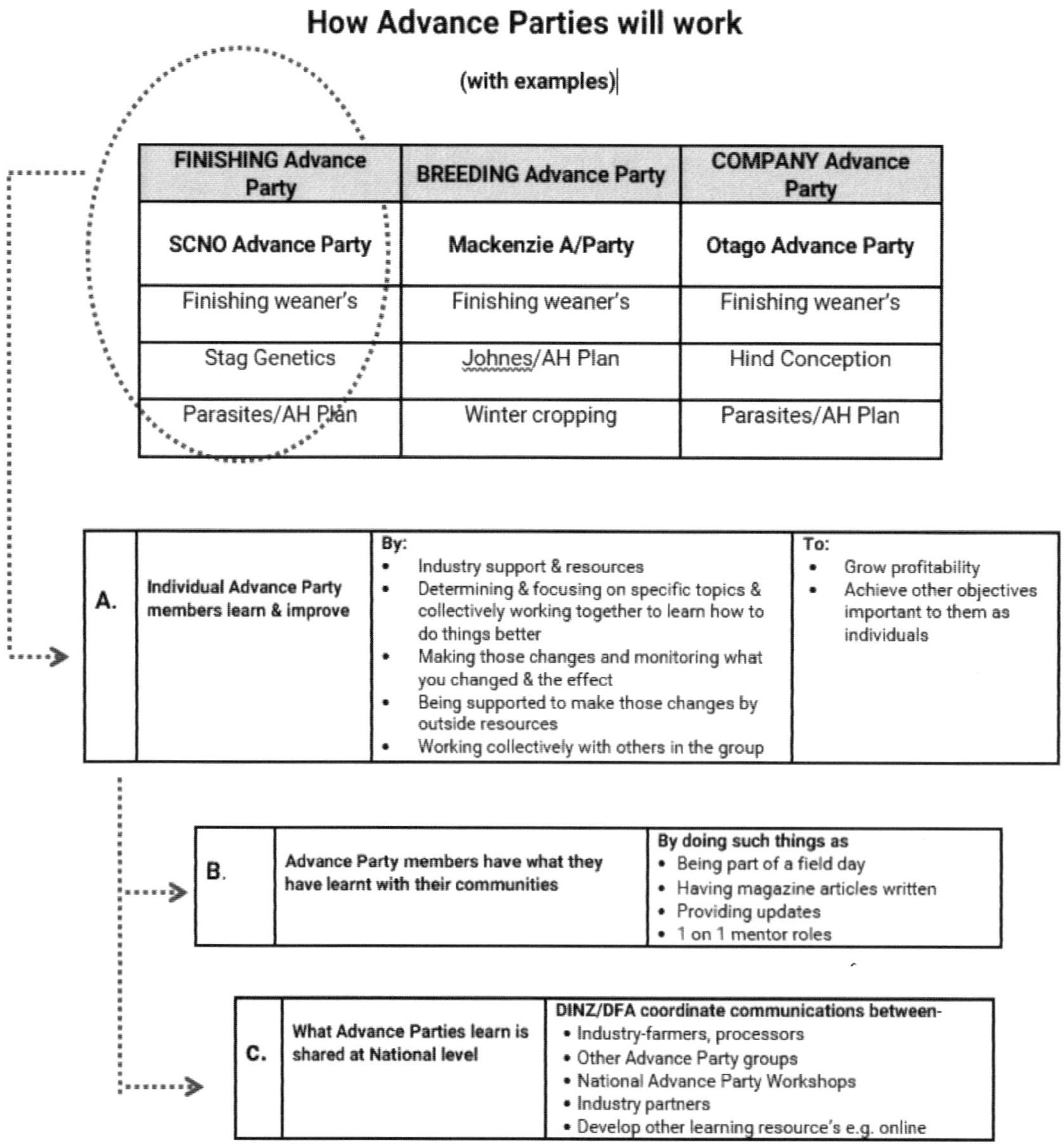

or practices that improve their deer-farming enjoyment and profitability. Results of these farmer-led changes are disseminated through the wider deer-farming community, using traditional engagement approaches, helping to lift the prevalence of the most-effective management techniques until they become common practice.

APs are not traditional farm discussion groups, which are facilitator-led and tend to focus on historic outcomes of management decisions on a single farm, with limited input from other farmers. Successful APs are farmer-led and in which members mentor each other through change. A commissioned email survey of AP members found that most were motivated to make a change when they are advised to do something by their peers, and they see successful examples being used on other's properties (Hudson &, Hawksley 2016). APs must be facilitated in order to ensure good group function, but the most successful ideas come from the farmers, not the outside experts. Group members must be committed to share personal and farm business development that includes sharing their data, methods, plans, results, problems and successes. They are not for the group alone but are a means to test and refine opportunities for profit, and to demonstrate those methods (and their limitations) to the wider deer farming community. APs are supported by DINZ and run collaboratively by a chair nominated from within the group members and an independent facilitator. Their roles are defined below:

The DINZ role: DINZ provides financial resources and support for the management of APs. DINZ project manager(s) provide oversight and monitoring of the Advance Party initiative. They are the first point of contact for the AP facilitators and chairs who are seeking guidance.

The Chair's role: Each AP appoints a chair from within their members to lead their group. The chair leads meetings and works with the facilitator to organise meetings and resources. The chair is also an active member of the AP working to implement improvements on their own farm.

The Facilitator's role: The facilitator coordinates the group by following a well-structured process and aims to instil confidence in the members so that they build trust between each other. Facilitators do not advise a group where their focus should be, or answer questions, but rather create the atmosphere where the group members collectively develop and brainstorm potential issues and solutions themselves. All successful rural programmes have a key individual who maintains the drive or focus within a group. The AP facilitator is there to act as the motivator for the group. The facilitator keeps a record of key objectives, issues and statements made within each AP meeting to ensure that records of agreed actions are kept to ensure that progress to be monitored. This is also kept as a record of the AP day at DINZ and circulated to group members after the meeting.

DINZ has a goal of operating up to 30 APs at any one time. The AP programme was launched with assistance from the Ministry for Primary Industries (MPI) Sustainable Farming Fund. Once proof of concept was established, funding has come from DINZ and the Primary Growth Partnership. DINZ used the NZ Deer Farmers Association branch network to form the first round of APs.

Results

Recruitment and early outcomes

The first advance party was formed in early 2014 in the MacKenzie Country (central region within the South Canterbury province). Managers and owners of six properties were invited to attend early meetings by a leading farmer from the district. A common characteristic of all these properties was that deer comprised the third class of livestock (i.e., merino sheep, cattle and deer) on these extensive high-country runs, often the lesser component in terms of overall stock numbers. Only one of the group weighed their deer, and no one undertook body condition scoring, or collected production data suitable to produce productivity metrics (e.g., kg venison produced per kg live hind mated). Most were questioning the role deer had on their properties. Anecdotal evidence suggests that after two years, deer numbers had expanded on the Mackenzie Country properties. All the AP members had weigh scales and were monitoring deer performance and all the AP members expressed excitement about the potential for deer on their properties. The members of the group observed that one unexpected benefit they got from involvement in the AP was that during the 2014/15 drought they were able to discuss their personal situation with others in a supportive atmosphere, which helped them take the steps needed to manage through a stressful time. Members of this group continue to enjoy working together to focus on the long-term profit of their deer farms. A similar transformation in attitude toward deer and farm management has been noted by facilitators in other Advance Party groups.

Monitoring: change from "data driven" to "documenting change"

Initially, APs were to be project focussed and data driven. Individual farmers were to regularly collect data on their operations and provide updates to monitor progress against targets, and comparisons could be made across groups to observe the rate of change. However, differences in farm-management systems and recording made meaningful between-farm comparisons difficult, and DINZ acknowledged the practical difficulties and resistance to data collection and production recording among deer farmers. In practice, few of the deer farmers in Advance Parties undertook performance monitoring of venison production. But all were keen to make changes that they felt would improve their deer-farming operation. AP facilitators are now tasked with collecting records of the actions that individual farmers take and what changes they make. What was the initial issue/opportunity, what did the farmers do, what was the outcome, and would they do it again? This process of documenting change, taken from the farmer's perspective, is expected to provide a record of the 'real world' experiences of producers which farmers may find more relevant than a data-centric report.

An initial report was undertaken by AgResearch (Peoples 2014) on the attitudes to change among AP participants. A total of 25 telephone interviews were completed over two months in early 2014. Broadly, the report indicated that farmers who had recently joined APs were keen to advance the production and profitability of their deer-farming operations but were not assessed as innovative or industry leaders, therefore, were less likely to change than were producers who were rated as 'innovators' (Hudson & Hawksley 2011).

An important component of the programme is monitoring changes among members. Advance Parties are monitored for member engagement, meeting frequency, member satisfaction with facilitator, and forward planning. A successful AP is one that has a high level of regular attendance, has a plan for future events and results in farmers feeling more empowered to manage their deer operations. An email survey to 177 AP members in 2016, that had a 51% response rate (Hudson & Hawksley 2016), found that 57% were planning to expand the deer component of their farming operation over the next five years, 73% attributed their motivation for change as a result of being a member of an AP, and 70% gained confidence to seek more information and make practice changes as a result of being an AP member. Farmers report that, due to their involvement with an AP, the most useful change (36% of respondents) was to the quantity and quality of deer feed.

This survey also recorded that:

(1) Those who have been an AP member for 1 to 2 years are significantly more likely than those who have been with an AP for less than a year to say they are more likely to try out new methods and products overall;
(2) The advice and information from other AP members is considered to be more useful than that of a veterinarian or other sources overall;
(3) More AP members say that assurance that the change will lift productivity or profitability would make farming practice changes easier overall than any other support in general; and
(4) Members are most likely to attribute motivation for change, information seeking, and confidence in making changes as being influenced by being part of an Advance Party.

The common elements of successful APs to date have included:

(1) A strong leader in the group. This is someone who proactively works with the facilitator to agree group priorities, someone who will provide feedback on facilitator performance and who encourages farmers to participate in the group. This could be the facilitator, the chair or one of the farmers. A motivator to encourage involvement and participation is the most important factor contributing to a vibrant group.
(2) An open and trusting environment. A culture is established in which people will willingly offer opinions, make suggestions and ask questions without fearing a negative response from individuals within the group.
(3) Some information for action. Groups are initially reluctant to collect and analyse data; resisting the demand to collect numbers for the sake of it. But, once the group settle upon making changes that can be measured, the conversations, and the sense of friendly competition for everyone's benefit, become established. Examples of this include; foetal scanning (to allow comparison of pregnancy rates and compare management practices that arrive at higher rates), feed budgeting (often not undertaken on winter crops in some areas that have traditionally relied on grass wintering systems), and weighing finishing animals (provides group members with points of reference to consider their own operations and discuss actions that can be taken to improve profit).

Next steps

DINZ understands that APs need to evolve so that they remain relevant. At the outset it was planned that an AP should have a finite life of about three years. If project based, the AP should have a defined end point so that members knew that they were working toward a goal. The APs have evolved since their inception and it was found that it is only after the group has been meeting for at least a year that the members move on from the easy wins to the more strategic questions about farm-management monitoring. The first round of visits often identified the obvious improvements that farmers probably know they should do, but need the motivation of some scrutiny of their peers to make the changes that will improve efficiency. In many instances we are observing that these obvious fixes occupy farmers' pragmatic problem-solving approach, but the members eventually move on to consider broader issues of farm systems analysis and management for group action.

Examples of the day-to-day fixes have included application of nitrogen on hill country, realignment of deer yards, extension of reticulated water supply and better netting on fences to prevent fawn deaths. Examples of more strategic projects that whole groups have moved on to have included leptospirosis monitoring and management, group winter-feed options and budgeting, appropriate financial analysis of deer performance, proactive health management and environmental management (e.g., monitoring stream health and water quality).

Outcomes to date

Membership of an Advance Party motivates farmers to improve their deer farming operation. Another email survey of AP members in 2018 (Hudson & Hawksley 2018) reported that after joining an AP the members were more confident in changing their farming practices and introducing new technologies. Examples include pregnancy scanning, weighing finishing deer, feed budgeting, recording deaths, using estimated breeding values for stag selection, using body condition scoring of hinds, introducing new technology such as weigh scales or EID readers, undertaking annual reviews of production with a vet, completing animal health plans with help from a vet, increased production recording, and receiving annual production summaries from their deer processor.

The practice changes implemented by AP membership after joining, in descending order of popularity were:

(1) 55% found improving the quality/quantity of the deer feed very useful, quite useful or somewhat useful;
(2) 35% found undertaking regular body conditioning very useful, quite useful or somewhat useful (38% were doing this before joining an AP);
(3) 33% found increased production recording very useful, quite useful or somewhat useful (52% were doing this before joining an AP);
(4) 24% found carrying out a proactive animal health plan very useful, quite useful or somewhat useful (64% were doing this before joining an AP); and
(5) 21% found introducing new technology such as scales or EID readers very useful, quite useful or somewhat useful (60% were doing this before joining an AP).

The challenge for the deer industry remains how to extend this level of adoption of new practices to non-AP members.

Conclusions

The APs are proving to be popular with the participants and are resulting in changes being made on individual properties. The benefits of belonging to an AP have been improved animal performance, increased confidence among deer farmers to tackle changes, and improved social interaction between members. APs need a strong central leader, and a genuine commitment to participate among the members to be successful. The role of the facilitator is important to the functioning of the group; they must allow the participants to own the decisions being made. Deer Industry New Zealand looks forward to expanding the number of APs being operated to reach a goal of 30 operational APs at any one time.

Acknowledgements

The authors are thankful for the support from the Ministry for Primary Industries Sustainable Farming Fund for co-funding the trial phase of this project and MPIs Primary Growth Partnership for co-funding the expansion of the programme.

References

Hudson F, Hawksley R 2011. Deer Industry New Zealand Achieving Practice Change. Report prepared for Deer Industry New Zealand, January 2011. Cinta Agri Research.

Peoples S 2014. Advanced Parties Practice Change Project Report. Report Prepared For Deer Industry New Zealand.

Hudson F, Hawksley R 2016. Advance Party Survey. Report prepared for Deer Industry New Zealand, January 2016. Cinta Agri Research.

Hudson F, Hawksley R 2018. Deer Industry New Zealand Achieving Practice Change Report # 2. Report prepared for Deer Industry New Zealand, January 2018. Cinta Agri Research.

AUTHOR INDEX